D1595192

Python Programming and Visualization for Scientists

2nd Edition

Alex J. DeCaria

Grant W. Petty

Sundog Publishing LLC
Madison, Wisconsin

© 2016 by Alex J. DeCaria, © 2020 by Alex J. DeCaria and Grant W. Petty

Manufactured in the United States of America.

All rights reserved.

No part of this book may be reproduced or transmitted in any form or by any means, electronic or mechanical, including photocopying, recording, or by an information storage and retrieval system — with the exception of a reviewer who may quote brief passages in a review to be printed in a newspaper or magazine — without written permission. For permission to reuse copyrighted content from this work, please contact the publisher via the contact page at *www.sundogpublishing.com*.

Ordering information: Instructors and students should visit *www.sundogpublishing.com* to take advantage of discounts available to students who order directly from the publisher. Free examination copies may be requested by qualifying instructors.

Online resources: Electronic files, errata, and other materials relevant to this book can be found at *www.sundogpublishing.com*.

Sundog Publishing LLC, Madison, Wisconsin

Names: DeCaria, Alex J., author. | Petty, Grant W., author.
Title: Python programming and visualization for scientists , 2nd edition / Alex J. DeCaria ; Grant W. Petty.
Description: Madison, WI: Sundog Publishing, 2020.
Identifiers: LCCN: 2020950960 | ISBN: 978-0-9729033-5-6
Subjects: LCSH Python (Computer program language) | Object-oriented programming (Computer science) | Python (Computer language). | BISAC: COMPUTERS / Programming Languages / Python | GSAFD: Instructional.
Classification: LCC QA76.73.P98 .D43 2020 | DDC 005.133--dc23

10 9 8 7 6 5 4 3

Anaconda is a registered trademark of Continuum Analytics, Inc.
Canopy is a registered trademark of Enthought, Inc.
IDL is a registered trademark of Exelis Inc., a subsidiary of Harris Corporation.
Macintosh and macOS are registered trademarks of Apple Inc.
Mathematica is a registered trademark of Wolfram Research, Inc.
MATLAB is a registered trademark of The MathWorks.
Windows is a registered trademark of Microsoft Corporation
Other trademarks and registered trademarks are the property of the respective trademark holders.

Cover design by Linda J. Weidemann.

For Victor and LaVera DeCaria, without whom
I would not be here—literally.

– AD

Acknowledgments

Foremost, I thank my wife, Marcia, for her constant support, and for proofreading. I am especially grateful to George Young for providing very useful feedback, suggestions, and much needed encouragement during moments when my enthusiasm for writing the first edition waned. Thanks also go to the numerous students in my classes through the years, who have allowed me to experiment with teaching styles and hone my craft.

Thank you to my sons, Victor and Michael, who have both developed into career mathematicians, scientists, and programmers, and who have provided hours of kitchen-table discussions on the philosophy of computer languages and programming. Sharing such interests with my children has been a blessing beyond description. Thanks also to my colleagues in the Department of Earth Sciences at Millersville University for providing encouragement and support, and to the university administration for granting me a sabbatical leave to finish this project.   *– AD*

There are far too many individuals who have contributed to the vast Python ecosystem to mention by name, even if I knew most of those names. But Guido van Rossum (Python), the late John D. Hunter (Matplotlib), Travis Oliphant (Numpy), and Wes McKinney (Pandas) stand out among those whose contributions to my computational productivity—and thus my scientific and academic productivity—have been monumental. I am especially grateful to live in a time when extensive language and library documentation, as well as diverse real-world examples, are instantly available via an internet search, in contrast to my first thirty years of programming experience. And so I must also acknowledge and thank the community of Python experts who freely share their time and knowledge via insightful blog posts and answers to questions in the Stack Overflow forums. Without them, I would still be a Python novice.   *– GP*

CONTENTS

LIST OF TABLES

PREFACE TO THE SECOND EDITION

Writing a second edition was not anticipated so soon after the first was published. However, in the past few years the Python ecosystem has evolved considerably, with the not-fully-backwards-compatible Python 3 becoming more robust and extensively used in the scientific community, and Python 2 no longer being developed. New means of creating, communicating, and executing code have been widely adopted, most notably Jupyter notebooks. Writing a second edition also presented the opportunity to add a co-author, allowing us to augment each other's strengths and expand the topics covered.

Major differences between this edition and the first include the appearance of two completely new chapters. One is on Cartopy, the replacement for the Basemap library for plotting georeferenced data onto map backgrounds. The original chapter on Basemap has been omitted, since it is no longer being developed or supported. The second new chapter is a brief introduction to the Pandas library for analysis of data sets.

In addition, a section on linear algebra operations from the first edition has been given its own chapter, and the chapter on Time has been extensively revised. Some individual sections have been expanded or reorganized, and a new section has been added on using physical dimensions and units in Python programs. Another difference between the two editions is more subtle—we have included more functions and methods throughout the various chapters and better explanations of some items. This new edition also adds devotes appendices to explain the use of Jupyter notebooks and to introduce the LaTeX markup language which is used for rendering mathematical formulas and symbols in plots and Jupyter notebooks. Finally, we have greatly expanded our use of color throughout the text. In particular, we now use syntax highlighting in all code and program output samples so that less effort is needed to visually identify the functional elements.

In short, this new edition is not simply a ruse to get you purchase another book. The first edition remains a solid and useful transition to Python from other languages, and with few exceptions, works in both Python 2 and Python 3. However, the second edition contains significantly more information than the original, and, even for some topics that are not new, we have taken the opportunity to improve the exposition. It is our hope that this edition will remain relevant and useful at least until the next major revision of the Python language.

Alex DeCaria
Lancaster, Pennsylvania
2020

Grant Petty
Madison, Wisconsin
2020

PREFACE TO THE FIRST EDITION

In the scientific community, Python has rapidly become the preeminent language for analyzing and visualizing data. The reasons are manifold but are primarily due to its concise, intuitive syntax and its free availability without purchase of an expensive license. In my own field of specialty, atmospheric science, the popularity of Python is particularly evident. One senior faculty member at a research university recently remarked to me, "I still use MATLAB, but our graduate students all use Python."

I adopted Python for my own use in 2011, migrating from Fortran and IDL. I was first attracted to its object-oriented nature but quickly became sold on the intuitive simplicity of its syntax. Learning how to plot and visualize data was less easy, since the resources for learning how to use the matplotlib plotting library are spread across the Internet. You can usually eventually find what you need, but it may take a lot of searching and sifting through posts on Stack Exchange. Hence, the idea for this book.

In 2012 I adopted Python as the language for the scientific programming and visualization course that I teach annually at Millersville University, having previously taught the course using IDL. Finding no suitable textbook for the course, I chose to write my own. However, this book is not just a textbook. I wrote it from the perspective of, "What book would I want to have had when I was transitioning to Python?"

I hope the book will not only be useful as a classroom text, but also as a guide and reference for those students, teachers, and researchers who have some programming experience already and want to start creating plots and analyzing data using Python. This book is not meant for the person who is completely new to programming, nor is it an introductory computer science textbook. My assumption is that the reader has some experience programming, though not necessarily with Python.

Although the new Python programmer may wish to read the book cover to cover, the book is organized such that the experienced Python programmer who wants to start in with plotting data can readily jump to the appropriate chapter. The last few chapters include topics that are more advanced, such as using regular expressions for matching text patterns, performing spectral analysis of data, and solving systems of linear equations.

I sincerely hope that this book will find a home on the desk of many students, teachers, scientists, and researchers and will in some ways make their lives easier. If not, then perhaps it will find use under the desk, propping up a short leg.

Alex DeCaria
Lancaster, Pennsylvania
2015

Part I

Basic Python Programming

ONE

GETTING STARTED

1.1   Purpose of This Book

This book is written for those who want to use Python to perform scientific data analysis and create visually pleasing, publication-quality plots of their data. It assumes familiarity with computer programming, though not necessarily with Python. The introductory chapters provide a quick start of Python syntax, data types, and control structures, while the later chapters focus on data analysis and plotting, primarily with the Matplotlib, Numerical Python (Numpy), and Scientific Python (Scipy) libraries.

1.2   Why Python?

There are many computer languages that can be used for scientific data analysis and visualization. These include proprietary languages such as MATLAB, Mathematica, and IDL, for which a license must be purchased, as well as open-source languages such as Perl, Fortran, and C++, which are free for use. With enough ingenuity and patience, virtually any language can be used to perform a specific data analysis and visualization task. However, Python has certain advantages over other languages (in the authors' opinion). These are:

- It is open source and does not require the purchase of a license for use. Anyone can download Python and the libraries that are used in this book. You can develop your own applications and code, without fear that if you move to a different job or school you will no longer be able to use your programs.

- Python syntax is intuitive and easy to learn. There are no cumbersome braces or semicolons cluttering up the code. Python also forces the user to indent code blocks, making for clean-looking, easy-to-read programs.

- Python is an *interpreted* language, rather than a *compiled* language. In a compiled language the entire source code text file is read and then converted into executable code (in machine language) that can be directly executed by the operating system. This executable code is often optimized for the operating system. In an interpreted language the source code text file is read line-by-line and each statement converted into machine language and executed before the next line is read, or the text file is read completely and converted into an intermediate code that is then further converted into machine language for execution by the operating system.

  Compiled languages are generally more efficient and faster than interpreted languages, since the conversion to machine language only occurs once creating a machine language code that can be executed whenever the program needs to be run. However, interpreted languages such as Python are often more flexible and changes can be easily made to the program at runtime, without going through the extra step of compilation after every minor change to the code.

- Python is widely used and supported, and its use is growing rapidly. It is neither a fad nor a flash in the pan.

1.3   Python 3 versus Python 2

Python,[1] developed by Guido van Rossum, began in 1991 with version 0.9 and has transformed via dozens of subversions since. Python 2.0 appeared in 2001, with the latest version, 2.7, appearing in 2010. Python 3 first appeared in 2008, and is *not* backward-compatible with older versions of Python. Notable differences are: 1) the use of the `print()` function rather than the `print` statement; 2) how formatted strings are created; 3) an important new distinction between `str` and `bytes` objects; 4) handling of integer division; and 5) objects returned from the `range()` function.

Because so many scientific libraries have been developed using the Python 2 paradigm, transition and acceptance of Python 3 in the scientific community has been slower than it might have been; however, Python 2 ceased to be maintained after January 1, 2020 making transition to Python 3 imperative. All code examples in this book are Python 3 compatible. Significant differences in syntax between Python 3 and Python 2 are pointed out as they are encountered, so that those working with legacy code written in Python 2 should still find this book useful. Sections where differences between Python 3 and Python 2 are discussed may be located by referring to the index entry "Python 3 vs Python 2". Important differences are also boxed where they appear in the text.

---

[1]Python is named after the British comedy troupe Monty Python.

Table 1.1: Syntax highlighting conventions used in this book.

Function	Examples
Built-in keywords	`for, import, Class, pass`
Strings	`'This is a string'`
General identifiers	`x, radius, numpy, plt.plot`
Comments	`# This is a comment`
Shell command	`pip install numpy`
External text and program output	`This is some text output`

1.4   A Few More Things About Python

Python is dynamically-typed. Most variables do not need to be declared as a specific data type (real, string, integer, etc.) before assigning values to them. This feature is known as *dynamic typing*, because the type of variable is determined completely by the type of data assigned. The type of a variable can be changed at any time simply by assigning a different value of a different type to it.

Python is case sensitive. Python syntax, commands, and variable names are all case sensitive. Thus, three variables named `Pressure`, `pressure`, and `PRESSURE` are three completely different variables. Likewise, the `print()` function is a valid Python statement, while `Print()` would throw an error.

Python is object-oriented. Python was built from the ground up as an object-oriented language, though it can also be readily used for both procedural programming and functional programming. Much of what we discuss in this book can be learned without dwelling on the fact that Python is object oriented. Relevant object-oriented concepts will be explained as they appear.[2]

1.5   Notation and Syntax Highlighting

In general, we will identify Python statements, object names, code, string literals, user-typed input, and output written by a program using a typewriter typeface; for example, `print(a, b)`. When placeholder names are used for function arguments or in assignment statements, these will be italicized: `fig, ax = plt.subplots(rows, cols)`. Optional arguments for functions and methods are indicated with italicized square brackets: `contour([x, y,] z)`. The greater-than symbol '>' is used to indicate input from an interactive terminal. Finally, for code samples and commands

---

[2]Those interested in quickly and effectively learning what object-oriented programming is all about are encouraged to read the excellent book, *The Object Oriented Thought Process*, by Matt Weisfeld, published by Addison-Wesley.

appearing in separate blocks, we further use color-coded syntax highlighting to facilitate visual identification of the major language elements, as shown in Table 1.1

1.6   Installing Python

Python is open source and can be downloaded for and installed on any of the three main operating systems—Windows, Linux, and macOS.[3] The individual components can be downloaded separately. There are also several pre-built packages assembled by various organizations and groups that install Python and a myriad of associated libraries. Some of these pre-built packages are open source, while others charge a fee. Keep in mind that you can *always* download and use Python and most libraries free of charge. Also, many Linux and macOS operating systems come with Python preinstalled.

1.6.1   Pre-built packages

The easiest way to obtain and install Python and many of the analysis and plotting libraries useful for scientists is to download a pre-built package such as Anaconda (*www.anaconda.com*) or Enthought's Canopy (*www.enthought.com*). The big advantage of pre-built packages is that when you install libraries with these packages the dependencies are automatically reconciled. Anaconda and Canopy may also be installed concurrently on the same computer without interfering with one another (although you should always be aware of which one is the default Python installation).

1.6.2   Installing individual libraries

As an alternative to installing one of the above distributions, one can download basic Python via *www.python.org*. Additional libraries can be downloaded individually as needed. For the examples used in this book, Scipy, Numpy, Matplotlib, Pandas, and Cartopy may be downloaded from the following sites:

- **Numpy:** *www.numpy.org*
- **Scipy:** *www.scipy.org*
- **Matplotlib:** *www.matplotlib.org*
- **Pandas:** *pandas.pydata.org*
- **Cartopy:** *scitools.org.uk/cartopy*

---

[3]The operating system for Apple's Mac computers was previously known as Mac OS X, or OS X.

When downloading and installing individual components, it is very important to ensure that the version of the library is compatible with the version of Python being used. Also, there are certain dependencies that may need to be met. For example, installing Matplotlib requires that Numpy already be installed. Careful reading of the documentation is imperative.

A website of great usefulness for Windows users is maintained by Chris Gohlke at *http://www.lfd.uci.edu/~gohlke/pythonlibs/*. This site is a treasure trove of Python extension installers tailored for Windows.

1.6.3   Package managers

Conda

Conda is an open-source package manager that is in common use for installing and updating Python libraries. Its reference page can be found at *https://docs.conda.io/en/latest*. Conda has many commands that are executed in a terminal window, with relatively easy syntax. Conda comes installed as part of the Anaconda Python installation.

If Conda is installed, then Python libraries may be easily installed with the command

```
conda -install newlibrary
```

where `newlibrary` is the name of the library to be installed. If you wish to install a community-supplied package available from the `conda-forge` repository, then you would use

```
conda -install newlibrary -c conda-forge
```

Some users wish to permanently configure Conda so that it always automatically includes the `conda-forge` repository when searching for a library to be installed. This is accomplished as follows:

```
conda config --add channels conda-forge
```

Also, when working with multiple channels, it is now recommended that the following command be executed once to reduce the likelihood of package incompatibility problems. Beginning with Conda 5.0, this will be the default setting. Note, however, that this command can cause problems with updates to existing environments.

```
conda config --set channel_priority strict
```

Existing libraries may be updated using the command

```
conda -update library
```

What is particularly nice about Conda is that it will find and attempt to resolve any dependencies among the various libraries.

Conda may be used to update Python to the latest version[4] using

```
conda update python
```

And Conda itself may be updated using the command

```
conda update conda
```

Multiple, independent Python environments may be created with Conda. Each virtual environment can have a different set of libraries. Environments can also be created that use different versions of Python itself. It is highly recommended that you use virtual environments as a matter of habit rather than the default (root) environment, especially when installing packages outside of Conda. See additional comments under "Mixing package managers," below.

To create a new Python virtual environment, type

```
conda create -n newenv library1 library2
```

where *newenv* is the name of the new environment, and *libary1*, *library2*, etc. are the names of any libraries to be installed in the new environment. If a different version of Python is desired, then include python=*x.x* in the command, where *x.x* is the version number desired (e.g., 2.7, 3.5).

Switching between environments is accomplished in Linux or macOS by

```
conda activate environment
```

and in Windows by

```
activate environment
```

where *environment* is the name of the environment to be activated.

pip

A generic package manager that comes with most Python installations is pip, which is a recursive play on words standing for 'pip installs Python'. The reference page for pip is at *https://pip.pypa.io/en/stable*.

To install a library from the command line using pip, type

```
pip install library
```

and to uninstall a library use

```
pip uninstall library
```

Mixing package managers

Occasionally it is necessary to use pip to install a specialized package that isn't available from the Conda or Enthought package managers. While this is

---

[4]This cannot be used to upgrade from Python 2.x to Python 3.x.

possible, it should be done with care, because the default package manager will not be aware of the changes, and it can break dependencies and lead to a broken environment. Before using pip to add a new package, use your regular package manager first to satisfy as many dependencies as possible for that package. Also, it is important that you do all of this in a virtual environment, rather than your root environment, so that if anything does break, the damage is limited to that virtual environment, and you can easily recover by deleting the affected environment and starting fresh with a new one.[5]

1.7 Alternate Python Implementations

Because Python is open source, there is no monopoly on interpreters for Python code. Besides the standard implementation of CPython[6] (available from *https://www.python.org*), several other interpreters and implementation are available:

- **IPython** (*http://ipython.org*) is a version of Python for interactive computing from a command shell.
- **Jython** (*http://www.jython.org*) is a version of Python using a Java-based interpreter and running on the Java Virtual Machine.
- **PyPy** (*http://pypy.org*) is an implementation optimized for speed and efficiency of computational resources.
- **StacklessPython** (*http://www.stackless.com*) is based on CPython but is built for thread-based programming.

1.8 Set-up and Testing

If you are using Anaconda or Canopy, you can skip this section. If you installed Python yourself, you may want to read on.

1.8.1 Path settings

A standard Python installation creates a directory structure where the python interpreter and libraries are stored. On Windows, this is usually \python36.[7] For Linux and macOS installations, the directory is usually /usr/bin/python, /usr/local/bin/python, or /usr/local/python. Other Python installations

---

[5]For more about safely using pip with Conda, see *https://www.anaconda.com/blog/using-pip-in-a-conda-environment*.

[6]The name CPython comes from the fact that the Python interpreter itself is written in the C programming language.

[7]The "36" refers to the version number, in this case Python 3.6.

may have a different directory name and structure. It is important to have the `PATH` environment variable set to include the path to the desired Python installation.

1.8.2   Testing the Python installation

Testing from the command prompt

To test a standard Python installation, open a terminal window and type `python` at the prompt. This should bring up an interactive shell. If nothing happens, or an error appears, it is likely that the `PATH` environment variable is not set to include the proper directory (see previous section). If Python is installed properly and the correct path is set, you will see text similar to

```
Python 3.7.3 (default, Mar 27 2019, 16:54:48)
[Clang 4.0.1 (tags/RELEASE_401/final)] ::
Anaconda, Inc. on darwin
```

If IPython is installed then it may be opened by typing `ipython` from the terminal window.

1.8.3   Testing libraries

Most of the examples in this book use the Scipy, Numpy, and matplotlib libraries. To ensure that these libraries are properly installed, from an open terminal window running Python or IPython type `import numpy` and hit the enter or return key.[8] If nothing happens other than a new prompt appearing, it means that Numpy is installed and available. If error messages appear, it means that either Numpy is not installed or that the version of Numpy is not compatible with the version of Python installed. Likewise, typing `import scipy` and `import matplotlib` will show whether these libraries are properly installed.

1.9   Executing Python Code

Python code can be executed interactively either by typing a statement directly into the Python shell or via one of the interactive development environments. Python code can also be saved to a file for later execution. The file can then be executed by running it within one of the interactive development environments. The file can also be executed directly from the terminal window command line.

---

[8]Python is case sensitive, so this command must be all lower case.

Under Windows, Python files are saved using either the *.py* or *.pyw* extension.[9] The difference between the two extensions is solely whether or not a new terminal window is opened during execution of the code.

- When a file having a *.py* extension is selected to run, the Python interpreter is opened using the executable file `python`. This opens a new terminal window, and all standard input/output is then accomplished via this terminal window. Any error messages will also be displayed to the open terminal window.

- When a file having a *.pyw* extension is selected, the Python interpreter is opened using the executable file `pythonw`. In this case a terminal window is not opened. This is appropriate if the program does not need to display or print information to the computer screen, and does not require user input.

Once a Python program file has been saved with either the *.py* or *.pyw* extension, it can be executed via several different means:

Execution within a terminal window: Stored Python programs can be executed from a terminal window prompt by typing `python` *progname* where *progname* is the name of the stored program file. As long as the `PATH` environment variable includes the directory containing the Python interpreter executable files, the system will locate these files, run the interpreter, and execute your program.

Typically the user need not worry about the location of the python executable files, as the appropriate directory is normally added to the user's path variable when Python is installed. These files normally reside in a directory named Python*XX*, where *XX* is the version number of the Python installation. However, they may be located in other directories for nonstandard installations. To find the location of the Python executable files, first open the Python interpreter window and import the `sys` module by typing `import sys`. Then type `sys.prefix`, which will return the path to the Python installation. The executable files will either be in this directory, or one of its subdirectories, likely the *scripts* or *bin* subdirectory. The specific location will depend on Python installation and the operating system.

Execution within an interactive development environment: You can open and edit programs within an interactive development environment such as Canopy, Spyder, Scite, IPython, etc. The development environment will either have a play button or a 'Run' menu heading that can be selected to run the program.

---

[9]Under macOS and Linux, only the *.py* suffix is normally used.

Execution from a desktop icon: It is also possible to execute stored Python code by directly clicking on the desktop icon for the program file. In this case, the program icon must be associated with either the `python` or `pythonw` files. Clicking on the file will then load the Python interpreter and execute the commands within the program file.

Execution as a Jupyter notebook: Another means of executing Python code is as a Jupyter notebook, which allows text, mathematical symbols, and Python code to be combined in a single document. This makes for ease of sharing computations and results, and is also very useful for classroom instruction. Jupyter notebook files have a *.ipynb* file extension. Many Python installations, including Anaconda and Canopy, support Jupyter notebooks. Jupyter Lab is the latest, browser-based interface for running Jupyter notebooks. Appendix A contains a very basic primer on Jupyter notebooks. More detailed information about using notebooks can be found at *https://jupyter.org*.

1.10 Additional Resources

There is considerable online documentation for Python and of the libraries discussed in this book, if one is patient enough to track it down. Much of the information is spread across a variety of unrelated sites, and explanations are often spotty. One purpose of this book is to bring the more essential information together into a coherent tutorial and reference. However, this book certainly is not a complete reference manual for Python or its libraries, and other resources can be indispensable, including those listed below.

Books. An exhaustive bibliography is not presented here; however, a few particularly notable books relevant to new scientific users of Python are worth mentioning.

- An outstanding overall reference book for the Python language itself is the *Python Essential Reference* by David Beazley.

- A beginning book for those working mainly in the atmospheric and oceanic sciences is *A Hands-On Introduction to Using Python in the Atmospheric and Oceanic Sciences* by Johnny Wei-Bing Lin. Scientific users outside of these fields may also find this text useful.

- *High Performance Python* by Micha Gorelick and Ian Ozsvald emphasizes techniques for using Python for numerically intensive computations.

- *Effective Computation in Physics* by Anthony Scopatz and Kathryn D. Huff discusses Python as one of several software tools for general purpose computing in the physical sciences.

- Though not a Python-specific book, the aforementioned *The Object-oriented Thought Process* by Matt Weisfeld is an excellent resource for those wanting to understand the essence of object-oriented programming in any language.

Documentation web sites. Python and most libraries each have their own documentation web sites, some of which are listed here.

- **Python:** *https://docs.python.org/3*
- **NumPy:** *http://docs.scipy.org/doc/numpy/reference*
- **SciPy:** *http://docs.scipy.org/doc/scipy/reference*
- **matplotlib:** *http://matplotlib.org*
- **Jupyter Notebook:** *https://jupyter.org*

Documentation web sites for other libraries can easily be found using a web search.

User forums. There are several user forums for Python and its libraries. These can be found using a web search.

SYNTAX AND DATA TYPES

2.1 General Syntax

Python syntax is clean and fairly intuitive. This section discusses the major features.

2.1.1 Python is case-sensitive

Care must be exercised to ensure proper use of capitalization in Python syntax, in both Python statements and in names for variables, modules, and functions. A variable named `Pressure` is not the same as a variable named `pressure`. Likewise, the proper call to the `print()` function is all lower case. Use of `Print()` would result in an error, unless a user-defined function of this name is created.

2.1.2 Functions

Functions are called by giving the name of the function, followed by the arguments list contained within parentheses and separated by commas. If a function does not require any arguments, the parentheses must still be present. Functions are discussed in more detail in Chapter 8.

2.1.3 Writing output to terminal

One of the simplest Python functions is `print(args)`, which prints the arguments *args* to the *standard output*, which is usually the terminal. The `print()` function is discussed in more detail in Sec. 5.9.

> In Python 2 print is a *statement*, not a function, and hence is called not using parentheses but with a space before the first item to be printed.

2.1.4   Code blocks and indentation

Although Python is a free-form language in the sense that there is no requirement to begin a statement at any particular column of a record, it is structured in the sense that indentation plays a key role in delineating blocks of code. As an example, a simple for-loop in Python has the form

```
for i in range(0,5):
    x = i**2
    print(x)
```

The colon : indicates that a code block follows. Any statements after this that are indented by the exact same amount are part of the code block. The code block ends when a statement is no longer indented. The amount of initial indentation is arbitrary, but most Python programmers prefer an indentation of between two and four spaces.

In other languages, code blocks are not required to be indented, though proper programming style suggest they should be. One of Python's many strengths is that it requires code blocks to be indented.

2.1.5   Continuation of lines

There is no limit to how long a line in a Python program can be. However, it is best to break long lines for easier reading. The \ symbol is used at the end of a line of code to signify that the next line is a continuation. When using a continuation line symbol the normal rules of indentation are suspended, so the code can be formatted for readability using as many spaces as are desired. For example, the three lines of code below all produce the same result when printing the string variable y.

```
y = 'The quick brown fox jumped over the lazy dog.'
y = 'The quick brown fox jumped \
over the lazy dog.'
y = 'The quick brown fox jumped' \
    ' over the lazy dog.'
```

In certain circumstances a line can be continued without the use of the \ character. Comma-separated items contained within parentheses (), square brackets [], or curly braces {} can be continued on multiple lines without the use of \.

2.1.6   Comments

Comments in Python are indicated by use of the # symbol. Any code between this symbol and a new line is ignored. Comments can begin at the beginning or in the middle of a line of code.

Python syntax does not officially support commenting out entire blocks of code; however some programmers use the **docstring** mechanism of Python to do this by enclosing the block in triple single-quotes (''''). It should be kept in mind, however, that the intended purpose of docstrings is specifically to document the programming interface to functions. Thus, docstrings are not actually ignored by the compiler, unlike true comments.

Many code editors do allow a block of code to be selected and then commented or uncommented out using context menus. In Jupyter, for example, block commenting is accomplished by highlighting the code to be commented and then pressing $\boxed{\text{control}}$ + / at the same time, which will prepend # to all lines in the block. This same key sequence will also uncomment a highlighted block of code.

2.2 Variable Names and Assignment

2.2.1 Valid names

Any letter, number, or the underscore (_) character may be used when naming a variable, function, module, or object. However, there are a few rules to keep in mind.

- A name cannot begin with a number as the first character.
- Although an underscore may be used as the leading or trailing character, avoid doing so unless you know what you are doing since there are special rules for how the interpreter handles leading and trailing underscore characters. Details may be found in the Python documentation.
- Remember that Python is case sensitive, so that a variable named Pressure and one named pressure are two distinct variables!

2.2.2 Reserved words

There are 32 reserved words in Python that should never be used as variable or function names. These are: and, as, assert, break, class, continue, def, del, elif, else, except, exec, finally, for, from, global, if, import, in, is, lambda, nonlocal, not, or, pass, print, raise, return, try, while, with, and yield.

2.2.3 Variable assignment

Assigning a value or reference to a variable is done using the assignment operator =. For example,

```
a = 6.7
```

assigns the floating-point value 6.7 to a variable named a. Python also supports *parallel assignment*, whereby multiple variables can receive assigned values on a single line of code. For example, instead of using three lines of code,

```
a = 6.7
b = 'hello'
c = 8
```

we could use a single line of code:

```
a, b, c = 6.7, 'hello', 8
```

2.3 Numeric Data Types

2.3.1 Boolean

The Boolean data type has two possible values, `True` and `False` (note the capitalization.) The value of `True` is also numerically equivalent to the integer value 1 or the floating-point value 1.0. The value of `False` is numerically equivalent to the integer value 0 or floating-point value 0.0.

Integers, floating-point values, and some other data types can be converted to Boolean values using the `bool()` function. There are important rules to keep in mind when converting to Boolean.

- Any zero value or empty object will convert to `False`.
- All other values or objects will convert to `True`.

For example:[1]

```
> bool(3)
True
> bool(0)
False
> bool(-3)
True
> bool(None)
False
> bool([]) # An empty list
False
> bool([3, 5, 'hi'])
True
```

2.3.2 Integer

The integer data type is used to hold integers (no decimals). The number of digits is limited only by memory constraints.

---

[1]The notation > indicates that this line is being input using an interactive Python terminal.

> In Python 2 there were two integer data types: integer, and long-integer. Long integers had an 'L' or 'l' after the number. Python 3 has consolidated these into a single integer data type.

2.3.3 Floating-point

All floating-point numbers are stored as 64 bits, which is the equivalent of double-precision in other programming languages. Scientific notation is achieved by using either an upper or lower case E or e between the mantissa and the exponent, such as 4.6e9, -7.3e3, .0065E-64, etc.

2.3.4 Complex

Python has a built-in data type for storing and manipulating complex numbers. A complex number is represented in the form of 3.5+9.7j, where the first number is the real part and the second number, followed by the j, is the imaginary part. Complex numbers can be created by either directly typing the numbers in complex-number format, or by using the built-in complex(*real*, *imag*) function, where *real* and *imag* are the real and imaginary components. Examples are shown here.

```
> a = 4.9 - 8.3j
> a
(4.9-8.3j)
> b = complex(2.3, 4.6)
> b
(2.3+4.6j)
```

The direct-typing means of creating a complex number only accepts actual numbers (integer or floating-point), not variables representing numbers. The complex() function accepts either. This feature is illustrated below.

```
> c = 3
> d = -4.5
> e = c+dj
Traceback (most recent call last):
  File "<stdin>", line 1, in <module>
NameError: name 'dj' is not defined
> e = complex(c, d)
> e
(3-4.5j)
```

The complex data type contains two *attributes* for returning the real and imaginary components of the number, and one *method* for returning the conjugate of the complex number. These attributes and methods are accessed as shown here.

```
> a.real
4.9
> a.imag
-8.3
> a.conjugate()
(4.9+8.3j)
```

Note that the attributes `real` and `imag` are accessed without parentheses, while the method `conjugate` has parentheses. Attributes and methods are more fully explained in Sec. 2.4.

2.3.5 Conversion between numeric types

Integers are converted to floating-point values by using the `float()` function. A floating-point number is converted to an integer via the `int()` function.[2]

```
> float(4)
4.0
> int(4.6)
4
```

Note that the `int()` function results in truncation of the floating-point number. If rounding is desired, use the `round()` function. For numbers that are equally distant between two integers, such as 4.5, the `round()` function rounds to the *even* multiple, 4. The `round()` function is described further in Sec. 4.5.

```
> round(4.4)
4
> round(4.5)
4
> round(4.6)
5
> round(5.5))
6
```

> Rounding of numbers that are equally distant between two integers is very different in Python 3 vs. Python 2. In Python 3 such numbers are always rounded to the *even* multiple, while in Python 2 they are always rounded *away from zero*.

2.4   Objects, Attributes, and Methods

The complex data type provides us an opportunity to discuss the object-oriented nature of Python. In Python, nearly all entities are *objects*. An object

---

[2]Python 2 has a `long()` function for converting to the long-integer data type.

is a member of a *class* which can be thought of as a template or blueprint that defines the characteristics of the object. When an object is created from the class it is said to be *instantiated*. For example, a complex variable defined as c = 4.5-3.2j is a complex object, meaning it is an *instantiation* of the complex class.

2.4.1 Data types as classes

In previous sections we have been referring to data types such as *integer*, *floating-point*, *Boolean*, *complex*, etc. Actual variables that are of these data types are really instantiations of the objects defined by the respective classes int, float, bool, and complex. We will continue to refer to data types, but really they are classes. So when we say something is of the integer data type we really mean that it is of the int class. Likewise, when we talk about a complex number, we really mean an object of the complex class.

2.4.2 Attributes

Objects may have *attributes* associated with them, which are really nothing more than data that belongs to or is associated with the particular object. Complex numbers (complex objects) have two attributes. One attribute is named real and contains the real part of the complex number. The other attribute is named imag and contains the imaginary part of the number.

Attributes are accessed by giving the object's name, a period, and then the name of the attribute.

```
> c = 4.5 - 3.2j
> c.imag
-3.2
```

Note that there are no parentheses associated with attributes.

2.4.3 Methods

Objects may also have *methods* associated with them. A method can simply be thought of as a *function* that belongs to an object, and operates on the object's attributes. Complex numbers have one method called conjugate(). This method operates on the two attributes, real and imag, and returns the complex conjugate of the number.

Methods are invoked by giving the object's name, a dot, and then the name of the method with arguments contained in parentheses. Many methods require no arguments, such as the conjugate() method of complex numbers, but these still require the parentheses.

```
> c = 4.5 - 3.2j
> c.conjugate()
(4.5+3.2j)
```

If the parentheses are not provided, Python will not give an error. Instead, it will simply return a *bound method*, which is then primed to return values once arguments are provided.

```
> d = c.conjugate
> d
<function complex.conjugate>
> d()
(4.5+3.2j)
```

Though using bound methods is sometimes desired, neglecting to provide parentheses to a no-argument method such as `c.conjugate()` can cause many debugging headaches, so care should be taken to provide parentheses to method calls.

2.4.4   Inspecting objects

Objects can be inspected using the built-in `dir(obj)` function, where *obj* is the object to be inspected. This returns a list of an object's attributes and methods.

Many objects also contain a *documentation string*, which contains information about the object. The documentation string can be accessed by calling the `__doc__()` method of the object (note the two leading and trailing underscores.)

The `inspect` module is another powerful tool for inspecting objects. Though only covered very briefly in Sec. 8.1.9, the interested reader may consult the online Python documentation for more information.

2.5   The None Data Type

If a variable is created but not explicitly assigned a value or an object, then it has the `None` data type. The `None` data type is essentially the null value or empty value. It is not the same as the value 0. The `None` data type can be assigned to a variable by simply typing `a = None`.

2.6   Strings

Strings are defined by including text within single, double, or triple quotes. Chapter 3 contains a thorough discussion on defining and manipulating strings.

2.7   Lists and Tuples

Lists and tuples are both collections of values or objects. The major difference between them is that lists are *mutable*, meaning that their contents can be changed after creation, while tuples are *immutable*. Other than this difference, most operations on lists and tuples are identical. The values or objects contained within a list or tuple do not have to all be of the same type. The collection can be a mixture of any data types or objects, and can even contain other lists or tuples.

Lists are denoted by enclosing a comma-separated collection of objects within square brackets, while tuples are enclosed within parentheses.

```
> l = [4.5, -7.8, 'pickle', True, None, 5] # List
> t = (4.5, -7.8, 'pickle', True, None, 5) # Tuple
```

2.7.1 Accessing elements of a collection

Lists and tuples are both examples of *collections*, which are objects that contain multiple elements. In this section we describe how elements of collections, including lists and tuples, are accessed. We will use lists and tuples in the following examples, but the indexing scheme can be applied to other collections as well.

The elements of a collection are accessed by specifying the integer index of the element's position enclosed within square brackets after the name of the collection. The first element always has index 0. Negative indexes are referenced backwards from the end of the collection, with -1 representing the last element. Some examples:

```
> mylist = [0, -5, 8, 'hi', (1,3,5), False]
> mylist[0]
0
> mylist[1]
-5
> mylist[4]
(1, 3, 5)
> mylist[5]
False
> mylist[-1]
False
> mylist[-3]
'hi'
```

Notice that `mylist[5]` and `mylist[-1]` both return the last element.

2.7.2 Nested elements

Since lists and tuples may contain other lists and tuples, we need to know how to access nested elements. This is accomplished by using a series of indexes, each contained within its own brackets. This is best shown with an example of a nested list with two levels of nesting.

```
> mylist = [[3,4,8],[6,2], [8,-8,1], [-3, 5, 2, 7]]
> mylist[0]
[3, 4, 8]
> mylist[0][1]
4
> mylist[2][-1]
1
> mylist[0][0]
3
> mylist[-1][-1]
7
```

2.7.3   Using ranges of indexes

Multiple, consecutive elements can be accessed at once using ranges of indexes. The syntax for this is b:e, where b is the beginning index and e is *one integer greater* than the ending index to be accessed. The range specified in this manner will access indexes beginning with b and ending with e-1. For example, `mylist[2:8]` would only return elements with indexes from 2 through 7. For those not familiar with this indexing system, this is unintuitive and can be a headache when trying to debug Python programs. It is perhaps less confusing if you think of the numerical indices as referring to *boundaries* between elements of a collection, as illustrated here:

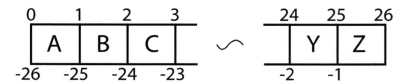

In this example, the ranges 0:3, -26:3, 0:-23 and -26:-23 all refer to the same elements A, B, and C. The range 24:26 is the same as the range -2: and refers to elements Y and Z.

If the leading integer b is left out then all elements from 0 to e-1 will be returned, while if the trailing e is omitted then all elements from b to the end of the collection are returned. If : is used without either b or e, then every element is returned.

```
> mylist = [0, 1, 2, 3, 4, 5, 6, 7, 8]
> mylist[3:7]
[3, 4, 5, 6]
> mylist[:]
[0, 1, 2, 3, 4, 5, 6, 7, 8]
```

```
> mylist[:4]
[0, 1, 2, 3]
> mylist[3:]
[3, 4, 5, 6, 7, 8]
> mylist[-5:]
[4, 5, 6, 7, 8]
```

2.7.4 Striding and reversing

Using ranges of indexes provides a powerful means of skipping over indexes or even reversing the contents of a list or tuple. Striding is accomplished by including a third integer s in the range construct, $b\!:\!e\!:\!s$, which defines the striding interval. For example:

```
> mylist = [0, 1, 2, 3, 4, 5, 6, 7, 8]
> mylist[0:-1:2]
[0, 2, 4, 6]
```

Striding can even be performed backwards by using a negative interval.

```
> mylist[::-1]
[8, 7, 6, 5, 4, 3, 2, 1, 0]
> mylist[-1:0:-2]
[8, 6, 4, 2]
> mylist[::-2]
[8, 6, 4, 2, 0]
```

2.7.5 Reassigning values

Once a tuple is created it may not be altered, since it is immutable. Lists, however, may have their values reassigned, as shown in these examples.

```
> p = ['cat', 'dog', 'ferret', 'llama']
> p[2] = 'squirrel'
> p
['cat', 'dog', 'squirrel', 'llama']
> p[0:2] = ['zebra', 'monkey']
> p
['zebra', 'monkey', 'squirrel', 'llama']
```

2.7.6 The range() function

The built-in `range()` function generates a `range` object. A `range` object behaves somewhat like a list containing a sequence of integers. However, it is not an actual list, but is instead an *iterator* that generates the next integer in the sequence on demand as needed (see Sec. 5.4). The syntax is `range(b, e, s)` where b is the beginning integer, e is one greater than the last integer to be generated, and s is the stride.

Two important things to note about the `range` object are:

- It is *not* an actual list!

- It does not generate the integer representing the ending integer in the arguments list, *e*.

A `range` object can be converted to a list by using the `list()` function, or to a tuple by using the `tuple()` function. Some examples:

```
> range(0,10)
range(0, 10)
> list(range(0,10))
[0, 1, 2, 3, 4, 5, 6, 7, 8, 9]
> list(range(0,10,2))
[0, 2, 4, 6, 8]
> list(range(10,0,-1))
[10, 9, 8, 7, 6, 5, 4, 3, 2, 1]
> tuple(range(10,-1,-3))
(10, 7, 4, 1)
```

> The behavior of the `range()` function differs significantly between Python 3 and Python 2. In Python 2 the function returns a `list` object, not a `range` object. To return a `range` object in Python 2 you would use the now-deprecated `xrange()` function.

2.7.7   Functions and methods for lists

There are several built-in function and methods for manipulating lists, and for returning information about lists and tuples. Some of these are explained here using *ls* to indicate the name of a list.

- `len(`*ls*`)` returns the number of items in the list.

- `del` *ls*`[`*i*`:`*j*`]`[3] deletes items at indexes *i* through *j-1*.

- *ls*`.append(`*elem*`)` adds element *elem* to the end of the list.

- *ls*`.extend(`*elems*`)` adds multiple elements given by another list or tuple, *elems*, to the end of the list.

- *ls*`.count(`*target*`)` returns the number of instances of *target* contained in the list.

- *ls*`.index(`*target*`)` returns the first index of the list that contains *target*. If optional *i* and *j* are given, it returns first index of occurrence in the range *i* through *j-1*.

- *ls*`.insert(`*i*`, `*elem*`)` inserts *elem* at index *i*.

---

[3]`del` is actually a statement, not a function.

- *ls*.remove(*target*) removes first occurrence of *target* from the list.

- *ls*.reverse() reverses the list in place.

- *ls*.sort() sorts the list in place. If the keyword **reverse** is set to **True**, then it also reverses the results of the sort.

Note that the **reverse**() and **sort**() methods both change (mutate) the original list. They do not merely return a copy.

2.7.8 Zippering and unzippering lists

The **zip**() function allows you to combine two or more separate lists or tuples like a zipper. The result is a **zip** object, which is an iterator (see Sec. 5.4). The **zip** object can be turned into a list using the **list**() function.

```
> a = [1, 2, 3]
> b = [4, 5, 6]
> c = list(zip(a, b))
> print(c)
[(1, 4), (2, 5), (3, 6)]
```

If the original lists each have N elements, the result is a list of N tuples. If one list is longer than the other the extra elements are simply lost.

The **zip**() function does especially interesting things when combined with the asterisk * operator (see Sec. 2.13), as in the following example.

```
> c = [(1, 4), (2, 5), (3, 6)]
> d = list(zip(*c))
> print(d)
[(1, 2, 3), (4, 5, 6)]
> e = list(zip(*d))
> print(e)
[(1, 4), (2, 5), (3, 6)]
```

Note that the list *e* is the same as the original list *c*. In other words, **zip**() is the inverse of itself when applied to an asterisked list! In essence, it becomes an *unzippering* function.

> Like the range() function, the behavior of the zip() function differs significantly between Python 3 and Python 2. In Python 2 the function returns a list object, while in Python 3 it returns a zip object.

2.7.9   List comprehension

A shorthand means of looping through the elements in a list or tuple and creating a new list is known as *list comprehension*. Although a full understanding of list comprehensions requires knowledge of loops, which are not covered until Sec. 5.5, a brief example is provided here.

Suppose we have a list comprised of numbers represented as strings, `ls = ['2.3', '-4.5', '7.8', '12.3']`, and we want to convert it into a list of floating-point values. We cannot simply use `fls = float(ls)`, since the `float()` function cannot take a list as the argument. A list comprehension would look like `fls = [float(s) for s in ls]`, which would create the new list named `fls` holding the floating-point values. See Sec. 5.8 for details.

2.8   Dictionaries

Dictionaries are similar to lists, except that instead of being indexed using integers, the values are each tied to a *key* that may be a number, a string, or another object. In other languages dictionaries are referred to as *hashes* or *associated arrays*.

2.8.1   Creating and accessing

There are several ways to create dictionaries. One is to use a series of key/value pairs within curly braces, with the keys separated from the values by colons.

```
d = {'first':'John', 'last':'Doe', 'age':34}
```

In this example, the keys are `'first'`, `'last'`, and `'age'` while the values are `'John'`, `'Doe'`, and 34.

Dictionaries can also be created using the `dict()` function and providing the key/value pairs as arguments, either as a series with the keys and values separated by an equals sign or as a nested list of key value pairs.

```
d = dict(first='John', last='Doe', age=34)
d = dict([['first','John'], ['last', 'Doe'],
          ['age', 34]])
```

The values in a dictionary are accessed by giving the name of the dictionary followed by a key in square brackets.

```
> d['first']
'John'
> d['age']
34
```

Dictionaries are mutable, so values can be reassigned.

2.8.2 Adding elements

Entries can be added to an existing dictionary by using the assignment operator and providing a new key and value. For example, the code

```
> d
'age': 34, 'last': 'Doe', 'first': 'John'
> d['weight'] = 187
> d
'age': 34, 'last': 'Doe', 'weight': 187, 'first': 'John'
```

shows how to add a new entry with a key named `'weight'` to an existing dictionary.

2.8.3 Functions and methods for dictionaries

Some useful built-in functions and methods for dictionaries are listed here.

- `len(d)` returns the number of key/value pairs in *d*.
- `del d[k]` removes the item from *d* whose key is *k*.
- *k* `in` *d*   checks to see whether *d* contains an item with key given by *k*. It returns either `True` or `False`.
- *d*`.clear()` deletes all items in the dictionary.
- *d*`.copy()` returns a copy of the dictionary.
- *d*`.keys()` returns a list of all the keys in the dictionary.
- *d*`.items()` returns a list containing tuples of all the key/value pairs in the dictionary.
- *d*`.values()` returns a list of all the values in the dictionary.

2.9   Sets

Sets are a collection of objects that are unordered. They are created by including the members within curly braces, such as `s = {4, 9, 2, 'cat'}`, or by using the `set()` function with a list or tuple as the argument. Sets cannot contain duplicate members, so if a tuple or list is converted to a set, duplicates are eliminated. This property of sets is handy for eliminating duplicate entries from categorical data. For example, suppose we had a list containing automobile makes, and we wanted to know how many unique makes the list contains. The following shows how this is done.

```
> make = ['Ford', 'Chrysler', 'Chevrolet', 'Toyota',
          'Ford', 'Toyota','Honda', 'Subaru']
> mset = set(make)
> mset
'Chevrolet', 'Chrysler', 'Ford', 'Honda',
          'Subaru', 'Toyota'
> len(mset)
6
```

Sets have operators that can return the union, intersection, difference, and symmetric difference between two sets. These are illustrated for the two sets s and t.

```
> s = {-5, -4, -3, -2, -1, 0, 1, 2, 3, 4}
> t = {0, 1, 2, 3, 4, 5, 6, 7, 8, 9}
```

Union: The operator | returns all the elements that appear in either set.

```
> s | t
-5, -4, -3, -2, -1, 0, 1, 2, 3, 4, 5, 6, 7, 8, 9
```

Intersection: The operator & returns all elements that are common to both sets.

```
> s & t
0, 1, 2, 3, 4
```

Difference: The operator - returns the items that are unique to the set on the left side.

```
> s - t
-5, -4, -3, -2, -1
> t - s
5, 6, 7, 8, 9
```

Symmetric difference: The operator ^ returns items that are unique to one or the other of the sets.

```
> s^t
-5, -4, -3, -2, -1, 5, 6, 7, 8, 9
```

A single item can be added to a set using the add(*item*) method. Multiple items can be added using the update(*items*) method, where *items* is a list or tuple containing the items to be added. An item can be removed from a set using the remove(*item*) method.

2.10   Arrays

Python does have a built-in module for defining and manipulating arrays. These are very similar to lists, with the exception that they can only hold a single type of data. For scientific computing it is much more efficient to use the arrays defined in the Numerical Python (Numpy) module, which are the subject of Chapter 7. Therefore, we will not discuss the built-in arrays further.

2.11   Finding an Object's Type

The built in type() function allows an object's type to be determined.

```
> a = 4
> type(a)
int
> b = 4.5
> type(b)
float
> c = 'Hello'
> type(c)
str
> d = 4+7j
> type(d)
complex
```

2.12 Copying Objects

Copying objects in Python must be done with care, as there are different levels of copying. *Shallow copies* are not actual separate copies of an object, but are merely pointers or references to the original object. *Deep copies* are truly separate but identical clones of an object. When the equals sign (=) is used to copy an object in Python, the copy may be either deep or shallow depending on the original type of the object. For simple objects such as integers or floating-point numbers, the equals sign will return a completely new, or deep, copy. But for *compound objects* such as lists, tuples, or dictionaries, Python creates only a shallow copy. The following code demonstrates this behavior.

```
> a = ['cat', 'dog', 'mouse']
> b = a
> a, b
(['cat', 'dog', 'mouse'], ['cat', 'dog', 'mouse'])
> a[1] = 'frog'
> a, b
(['cat', 'frog', 'mouse'], ['cat', 'frog', 'mouse'])
```

Note that in this example, *a* and *b* are the exact same object! When an element of *a* is changed, the corresponding element of *b* also changes.

To create a deep copy of an object you must first import the **copy** module, and then use the **deepcopy()** function, as illustrated here:

```
> import copy
> a = ['cat', 'dog', 'mouse']
> b = copy.deepcopy(a)
> a, b
(['cat', 'dog', 'mouse'], ['cat', 'dog', 'mouse'])
> a[1] = 'frog'
> a, b
(['cat', 'frog', 'mouse'], ['cat', 'dog', 'mouse'])
```

2.13   Unpacking Lists and Tuples

The unpacking operator, *, can be used to unpack lists, tuples, or other sequence-like objects. One use for this is illustrated here,

```
> my_list = [0, -5, 8, 'hi', 'brown', False]
> a, b, *c = my_list
```

In this syntax the first element of `my_list` is assigned to variable a, the second element is assigned to variable b, and all of the rest of the elements, regardless of how many are left, are assigned to variable c as a list, yielding

```
> a, b, c
(0, -5, [8, 'hi', 'brown', False])
```

The variable preceded by the * does not have to be the last variable in the list. For instance,

```
a, *b, c, d = my_list
```

distributes the contents of `my_list` among the four variables as follows

```
> a, b, c, d
(0, [-5, 8, 'hi'], 'brown', False)
```

Two important points to note:

- In any such unpacking there may only be one variable that is preceded by the * operator.
- If there are not enough elements left for the asterisked variable then it will contain an empty list.

The unpacking operator is particularly useful is when passing a tuple or a list containing arguments to a function. For example, say we had the list a = [-2, 11, 2] and we wanted to send it to the `range()` function to be used as the beginning, ending, and striding values. However, the range function does not accept a list as its argument, but needs the three values separated. By using the unpacking operator we can send our list to the function as follows

```
> range(*a)
range(-2, 11, 2)
```

The previous code is much simpler than the following alternative:

```
> range(a[0], a[1], a[2])
```

STRINGS

3.1 Defining Strings

Strings are denoted by enclosing them in single, double, or triple quotation marks (either tripled single quotes or tripled double quotes). The type of quotes used at the beginning and ending of the string must match. Additional quotes used within a string are treated as literals with no special meaning. However, these interior quotes cannot be of the same type used at the beginning or end of the string. This ability to use interior quotes is handy for storing strings that contain apostrophes or quoted material, such as

```
> s = 'Dad said, "Do it now!"'
> print(s)
Dad said, "Do it now!"
```

A backslash can be used to escape from quotes within a string itself.

```
> s = 'An apostrophe looks like \'.'
> print(s)
An apostrophe looks like '.
```

3.1.1 Special characters

Special characters such as the newline (\n), return (\r), and tab (\t) can be included in strings, and are used to control the printing of the string. These special characters are holdovers from the days of teletype. As the teletype printer reached the end of a line, the code \n directed the printer to advance to the next line, keeping the print head in place horizontally, while the code \r directed the print head to return to the beginning (left side) of the page. The combination \r\n was needed to direct the teletype print head to advance to the beginning of a new line. Modern computers still use these special characters to indicate the end of a line in a file, though the exact usage is software- and operating system-dependent. In most modern applications, \n is assumed to indicate both a new line and a return to the left side, and so \r is not necessary. However, other applications still require both characters, \r\n, to accomplish this.

This block of code illustrates the use of special characters.

```
> s = 'This string prints\nacross three lines\n\tand
    contains a tab.'
> print(s)
This string prints
across three lines
        and contains a tab.
```

The backslash character is used to escape from special characters. For example, if a string is supposed to contain a literal \n that is not meant to be a new line, then adding an extra \ prior to it will cause it to be treated as a literal character and not as a special character.

```
> print('Hello \\n there.')
Hello \n there.
```

3.1.2 Triple-quoted strings

Triple-quoted strings have the special property that the text within them maintains its formatting, including tabs and line breaks. The new line character, \n, and the tab character, \t, are automatically inserted within triple-quoted strings in locations where the text is broken across lines, or is tabbed. The triple quotes can be either triple single quotes or triple double quotes. This example illustrates triple-quoted string assignment and behavior.

```
> s = '''This sentence runs
over a
few lines.'''
> s
'This sentence runs\n over a\n few lines.'
> print(s)
This sentence runs
 over a
 few lines.
```

3.1.3 Raw strings

raw string is a type of string in which there are no special characters, and all backslashes are treated as literals. A raw string is defined by preceding the leading quote with a lowercase **r**. An example of raw string usage is shown here.

```
> s = r'Hello \n there\'.'
> print(s)
Hello \n there\'.
```

If you look at the contents of a raw string without printing you find that all single backslashes have been converted to double backslashes,

```
> s
"Hello \\n there\\'."
```

Note also that in this example the single quotes defining the string have been automatically converted to double quotes to avoid conflict with the single, literal quote appearing in the middle of the string.

3.2 Formatting Strings

Strings have a `format()` method that allows variables to be inserted into the string with a specified format, including specifying the width and number of decimal places to be displayed. This block of code illustrates the syntax for formatting strings.

```
> x = 654.589342982
> s =  'The value is {0:7.2f}'.format(x)
> print(s)
The value is 654.59
```

In this example the value of x was inserted into the string at the position of the curly braces and formatted to be 7 characters wide with two decimal places. Within the curly braces the syntax is $\{n:fs\}$ where n refers to the nth variable in the argument to the `format()` method, and fs is the format specifier detailing how the value is to appear in the returned string.[1]

Multiple arguments can be inserted into a formatted string, as shown in the following code block.

```
> name, age = 'John', 47
> s =  'His name is {0:s} and his age is {1:d}
    years.'.format(name, age)
> print(s)
His name is John and his age is 47 years.
```

There are six format specifiers in Python.

- d, indicating integer data;

- f, indicating floating-point data;

- e, indicating floating-point data in scientific notation;

- g, indicating floating-point data using scientific notation for exponents less than -4 or greater than $+5$, and regular floating-point notation otherwise;

---

[1]The use of format specifiers is actually optional. They need only be used if greater control over the formatting is desired.

- %, indicating floating-point data converted to percentages; and

- s, indicating string data.

The format specifiers often take additional parameters to specify the field width, number of decimal places, whether or not the results are padded with zeros, and whether to force the printing of a + sign for positive numbers. The format specifiers used in Python are shown in Table 3.1, along with some examples of their use.

> Python 2 had a different means of string formatting that is also supported in Python 3 and still utilized in certain contexts, such as contour label formatting. This consists of a percent sign, %, within the string at the locations where values are to be inserted followed by a format specifier. The entire string is then followed by another percent sign and the values to be inserted within the string in the same order. The values are represented in tuple form, unless there is only a single value. This is very similar to the sprintf() function found in the C programming language. The format specifiers are those listed in Table 3.1. As an example, the formatted string
>
> ```
> s = 'The radius is %07.2f centimeters.'% 56.3410
> ```
>
> would print as
>
> ```
> The radius is 0056.34 centimeters.
> ```

3.3   Indexing and Iterating

The characters within a string are each assigned a unique index, beginning with 0 at the first character. Individual characters and substrings can be accessed by specifying their indices or range of indices within square brackets.

```
> s = 'Halleluiah'
> s[0]
'H'
> s[3:6]
'lel'
> s[-1]
'h'
> s[4:]
'eluiah'
```

Strings can also be used to create iterators,

```
> s = iter('Halleluiah')
> s.__next__()
'H'
> s.__next__()
'a'
```

and can therefore be used as the basis of a for loop. The code

```
for c in 'Fun':
    print(c)
```

yields the following result.

Table 3.1: Python format specifiers. The parameter w indicates the total field width, while d indicates the number of decimal places displayed.

Specifier	Explanation	Example	Result
d	integer	`'{0:d}'.format(45)`	`'45'`
wd	field of width w	`'{0:5d}'.format(45)`	`'   45'`
+wd	force + sign to be printed	`'{0:+5d}'.format(45)`	`'  +45'`
0wd	pads with zeros	`'{0:05d}'.format(45)`	`'00045'`
f	floating point	`'{0:f}'.format(-3.5)`	`'-3.500000'`
w.df	field width w and d decimal places	`'{0:6.2f}'.format(-3.5)`	`' -3.50'`
0w.df	pad with zeros	`'{0:06.2f}'.format(-3.5)`	`'-03.50'`
+w.df	forces + sign to be printed	`'{0:+6.2f}'.format(4.3)`	`' +4.30'`
e	scientific notation	`'{0:e}'.format(0.654)`	`'6.540000e-01'`
w.de	field width w and d decimal places	`'{0:9.2e}'.format(0.654)`	`' 6.54e-01'`
+w.de	forces + sign to be printed	`'{0:+9.2e}'.format(0.654)`	`'+6.54e-01'`
g	uses floating point notation for exponents from -4 to $+5$; otherwise uses scientific notation.	`'{0:g}'.format(45679.3)` `'{0:g}'.format(0.00346)` `'{0:g}'.format(0.0000346)`	`'45679.3'` `'0.00346'` `'3.46e-05'`
%	converts decimal to percent	`'{0:%}'.format(0.4567)`	`'45.670000%'`
w.d%	field width w and d decimal places	`'{0:8.2%}'.format(0.4567)`	`'  45.67%'`
0w.d%	pad with zeros	`'{0:08.2%}'.format(0.4567)`	`'0045.67%'`
s	string	`'{0:s}'.format('Hello')`	`'Hello'`
ws	field width of w	`'{0:9s}'.format('Hello')`	`'Hello    '`

```
F
u
n
```

Iterators and loops are explained more fully in Sec. 5.4 and Sec. 5.5.

3.4 Concatenation

Strings can be concatenated (combined) by use of the + operator.

```
> 'hot' + 'dog'
'hotdog'
> 'Do-' + 'Re-' + 'Mi'
'Do-Re-Mi'
```

Strings can also be concatenated using the `join()` method, which joins its arguments each separated by the string itself.

```
> ', '.join(['cat', 'dog'])
'cat, dog'
> ' '.join(['cat', 'dog'])
'cat dog'
> ' + '.join(['cat', 'dog'])
'cat + dog'
> ' and '.join(['cat', 'dog'])
'cat and dog'
```

Note that the argument must be a tuple or list.

3.5   Multiplication

Strings may also be multiplied.

```
> 'rabbit '*5
'rabbit rabbit rabbit rabbit rabbit '
```

Although this feature seems rather esoteric, it can be very useful for generating strings consisting of a given number of dashes, spaces, or other characters.

3.6   More String Functions and Methods

3.6.1   Retrieving information about a string

The following functions and methods return information about a string *s*.

- `len(s)` returns the length of the string.
- `s.count(sub)` returns the number of times that the substring *sub* occurs in the string.
- `s.endswith(sfx)` returns True if the string *s* ends with the substring *sfx*.
- `s.isalnum()` returns True if the string *s* contains only numbers and letters.
- `s.isalpha()` returns True if the string *s* contains only letters.
- `s.isdigit()` returns True if the string *s* contains only numbers.
- `s.islower()` returns True if the string *s* contains only lower-case characters.
- `s.isspace()` returns True if the string *s* contains only whitespace characters.
- `s.istitle()` returns True if the first letter of every word in string *s* is capitalized.
- `s.isupper()` returns True if the string *s* contains only upper-case characters.

- `s.startswith(pfx)` returns True if the string *s* starts with the substring *pfx*.

3.6.2 Searching a string

Strings can be searched for characters and substrings using either the `find()` or `index()` methods.

- `s.find(target [, i, j])` returns an integer representing the value of the index in *s* at which the target substring *target* begins. If *target* is not contained within *s* then a value of −1 is returned. If the optional values *i* and *j* are included, only that portion of the string between indices *i* and *j* is searched. Otherwise, the search commences from the beginning of the string. Regardless of whether the entire string is searched, or only the portion between *i* and *j*, the returned index value is always relative to the beginning of the entire string.

- `s.index(target [, i, j])` is similar to `s.find(target)`, except that if *target* is not located, then an error is thrown.

Both `find()` and `index()` begin from left to right, and only return the index of the first instance of *target*. To search backward from the end of the string, use `rfind()` or `rindex()`.

3.6.3 Editing, stripping, and justifying strings

The following functions and methods are used to edit, strip, and justify strings.

Replacing text

- `s.replace(target, new)` replaces all occurrences of *target* with the new text, *new*. The original string *s* is not changed. Instead, a modified copy of *s* is returned.

Stripping

- `s.strip()` removes any leading or trailing whitespace and newline characters, returning a modified copy of the string.

- `s.lstrip()` behaves the same as `s.strip()` except it only removes leading whitespace and newline characters.

- `s.rstrip()` behaves the same as `s.strip()` except it only removes trailing whitespace and newline characters.

Justification

- `s.center(w [, pad])` returns a copy of *s* centered in a field of width *w*. If the optional character *pad* is provided, then the leading and trailing blank spaces are padded with this character.

- *s*.ljust(*w* [, *pad*]) returns a copy of *s* with left justification in a field of width *w*. If the optional character *pad* is provided, then the trailing blank spaces are padded with this character.

- *s*.rjust(*w* [, *pad*]) returns a copy of *s* with right justification in a field of width *w*. If the optional character *pad* is provided, then the leading blank spaces are padded with this character.

3.6.4   Converting cases

There are string methods for changing the cases (upper and lower) of characters within a string.

- *s*.lower() returns a copy of the string *s* with all characters converted to lower case.

- *s*.upper() returns a copy of the string *s* with all characters converted to upper case.

- *s*.title() returns a copy of the string *s* with the first character of each word converted to upper case.

- *s*.swapcase() returns a copy of the string *s* with all lower-case characters converted to upper case, and all upper-case characters converted to lower case.

3.6.5   Splitting strings

The *s*.split(*del*) method splits a string *s* on a specified delimiter, *del*, and returns a list containing the substrings. The delimiter may be a single character, or multiple characters.

```
> s = 'cat, dog, mouse, bird'
> s.split(',')
['cat', ' dog', ' mouse', ' bird']
> s.split('o')
['cat, d', 'g, m', 'use, bird']
> s.split(' ')
['cat,', 'dog,', 'mouse,', 'bird']
```

If there are multiple white spaces, then splitting using the white space as a delimiter will return elements containing empty strings in the list.

```
> s = '  This string    has extra   white spaces.   '
> s.split(' ')
['', '', 'This', 'string', '', '', '', 'has', 'extra', '',
    'white', 'spaces.', '', '', '']
```

However, if no argument is provided then the string is split on white spaces, and consecutive white spaces are ignored.

```
> s = '   This string   has extra   white spaces.   '
> s.split()
['This', 'string', 'has', 'extra', 'white', 'spaces.']
```

The need for splitting strings often arises when reading in lines of comma-delimited or space-delimited data from a data file. An efficient way of handling such data is described in Section 6.5.

3.7   Byte Strings

Text may also be stored and represented in binary form as *byte strings*. These are denoted by including the letter b prior to the quotes, such as

```
> bstring = b'Alex DeCaria'
> type(bstring)
bytes
> print(bstring)
b'Alex DeCaria'
```

The characters in a byte string are encoded into bytes using using a specified encoding scheme. The type of encoding may be ASCII, UTF-8, UTF-16, ISO 8859-1 (Latin-1 encoding), or any of a myriad of different encodings. The default encoding for your particular system may be found by importing the sys module and calling the sys.getdefaultencoding() function. For example, on our systems the result is

```
> import sys
> sys.getdefaultencoding()
'utf-8'
```

showing that the UTF-8 encoding is the default.

Byte strings may also be created from a text string by using the encode() method of the string, the argument of which is the encoding to be used. For example, to turn a regular string into a UTF-8 encoded byte string we would do

```
> s = 'cat'   # a regular string
> sb = s.encode('utf-8')   # UTF-8 byte string
```

A byte string may be converted back to a text string by using the byte string's decode() method. Unfortunately, the encoding scheme used to create a byte string is not an attribute of the byte object. So, in order to correctly decode a byte string back to a text string you need to know in advance how it was encoded in the first place. Here is an example showing how a UTF-8- encoding byte string becomes garbled if it is decoded using UTF-16 encoding.

```
sb = 'Alex DeCaria'.encode('utf-8')
print(sb)
print(sb.decode('utf-8'))
print(sb.decode('utf-16'))
```

```
b'Alex DeCaria'
Alex DeCaria
汁碻腉鏖牡憪
```

In Python 2 certain operations such as concatenation between text strings and byte strings were allowed. In Python 3 there is a more rigid separation between the two types of strings.

CHAPTER

FOUR

MATHEMATICAL OPERATORS AND FUNCTIONS

4.1 Numerical Operators

Python has the standard numerical operators of addition (+), subtraction
(-), multiplication (*), and division (/). Raising a quantity to a power is
accomplished using the double asterisk (**), so that a^b would be typed as
a**b.

4.1.1 Division

One of the major differences between Python 3 and Python 2 is the way that division
of integers is handled. In Python 2, as in most programming languages, division of
two integers returns a truncated integer result. This trend is broken by Python 3, which
always returns a floating-point result, regardless of whether either the numerator or
denominator are integer or floating-point. This can result in issues with legacy code, if
the older, integer division is assumed.

4.1.2 Truncating division

Python also has a *truncating division* operator denoted with two forward slash
characters, //. Truncating division returns an value with the fractional part
dropped. If either numerator or denominator are floating-point, the returned
value is floating-point. If both numerator and denominator are integer, an
integer value is returned.

```
> 16.3//5.2
3.0
> 16//5.2
3.0
> 16//5
3
> -8.9//2.2
-5.0
```

4.1.3 Modulo operator

The *modulo* operator (%) returns the remainder of the division between two numbers. It is useful for determining whether one number is an integer multiple of another, as the remainder would be zero in such cases.

```
> 5 % 3
2
> 27 % 3
0
```

Although the modulo operator also works with floating-point numbers, the Python documentation recommends using the fmod() function found in the math or numpy modules for floating-point input (see Sec. 4.7.8).

4.2   Augmented Assignment

The equals sign (=) is used as the assignment operator in Python. There are also *augmented assignment* operators that are used as shorthand for replacing the contents of a variable with some operation on the original variable.

x += y is equivalent to x = x + y

x -= y is equivalent to x = x - y

x *= y is equivalent to x = x*y

x /= y is equivalent to x = x/y

x //= y is equivalent to x = x//y

x **= y is equivalent to x = x**y

4.3   Boolean Operators

There are three *Boolean* operators in Python. These are and, or, and not. These return Boolean values of True or False.

```
> x, y, z = True, False, True
> x or y
True
> x or z
True
> x and y
False
> x and z
True
> not y
True
> not z
False
```

4.4   Comparison Operators

Comparison of objects is achieved using the *comparison operators*, also known as *relational operators*:

- Equal to: == [1]
- Not equal to: !=
- Less than: <
- Greater than: >
- Greater than or equal to: >=
- Less than or equal to: <=

Use of a comparison operator returns a Boolean value of `True` or `False`.

Comparisons may only be made between objects that have a distinct ordering. Obvious examples are integers or floating-point values. Strings also have a defined ordering and may be compared, as may many other objects. An example of objects that do not support comparison are complex numbers.

4.4.1   Simple comparison

The comparison operators can be used to compare two objects.

```
> 5.0 == 6.7
False
> 4.5 == 4.5
True
```

---

[1]A common programming error is to inadvertently use the assignment operator = in place of the equivalence operator ==. Try to avoid this!

```
> -3 <= 0
True
> 2.3 != 3.4
True
> -4.3 != -4.3
False
```

4.4.2   Chained comparison

Multiple objects can be compared with one another using a chained comparison, which has the form

```
a comp1 b comp2 c comp3 d
```

where *comp1*, *comp2*, and *comp3* are comparison operators. The chained comparison expression is evaluated as

```
(a comp1 b) and (b comp2 c) and (c comp3 d)
```

As examples, the expression 4 == 2*2 < 9 returns `True`, and the expression 5 < 2 < 9 returns `False`.

4.5   Built-in Math Functions

There are few built-in mathematical functions in Python. Some are:

- `abs(x)` returns the absolute value of real value *x*.
- `divmod(x,y)` returns the tuple containing the truncated division *x//y* as the first element and the modulo *x%y* as the second element.
- `max(x,y[, z, ...])` returns the maximum value of the input. The input consists of 2 or more values separated by commas.
- `min(x,y[, z, ...])` returns the minimum value of the input. The input consists of 2 or more values separated by commas.
- `pow(x,y)` is the same as *x***y*. It also behaves similarly to the `numpy.power()` function (see Sec. 4.7.2).
- `round(x [, m])` returns *x* rounded to the nearest integer value if *m* is not given. If *m* is given, then it rounds to the nearest multiple of 10^{-m}.

A few additional notes about the `round(x [, m]])` function:

- If *m* is not given, the result of `round(x)` will be an integer.

```
> round(4.6)
5
```

- If *m* is given, the result will be a floating-point value, even if *m* = 0.

```
> round(4.6, 0)
5.0
```

- It is permissible for *m* to be a negative number.

```
> round(16.6, 0)
17.0
> round(16.6, -1)
20.0
> round(16.6, -2)
0.0
```

- If the number to be rounded lies equally between two multiples, the number is rounded to the even multiple.

```
> round(4.4, 0)
4.0
> round(4.5, 0)
4.0
> round(4.6, 0)
5.0
> round(5.5, 0)
6.0
```

Rounding of numbers that are equally distant between two integers is very different in Python 3 vs. Python 2. In Python 3 such numbers are always rounded to the *even* multiple, while in Python 2 they are always rounded *away from zero*.

- Some unexpected and seemingly strange behavior may occur, as shown in this example:

Command	Result
round(6.05, 1)	6.0
round(6.15, 1)	6.2
round(6.25, 1)	6.2
round(6.35, 1)	6.3
round(6.45, 1)	6.5
round(6.55, 1)	6.5
round(6.65, 1)	6.7
round(6.75, 1)	6.8
round(6.85, 1)	6.8
round(6.95, 1)	7.0

Though we would expect all of these values to round to the even multiple, several of them do not. This is due to the limitations of the computer to give an exact representation of floating-point values. For example, when the number 6.45 was placed in the computer's memory it was represented as a number ever-so-slightly greater than 6.45, and so it rounded to 6.5

4.6   The math Module

Besides the built-in math functions, Python has a `math` module that comes with every Python installation. The `math` module contains many more functions and is imported via the command `import math`. Once the module is imported, its associated functions and constants are accessed by prefacing them with the name of the module, followed by a period, and then the name of the function or constant, e.g. `math.cos(.25)`.

4.7   The numpy Module

Many Python installations also include the Numerical Python (`numpy`) module that includes the same functions as the `math` module, as well as additional functions and features. The `numpy` library is usually imported using the command `import numpy as np`, which imports the `numpy` module aliased as `np`. Its functions are then accessed by prefacing them with `np.` (see Sec. 4.8).

```
> import numpy as np
> np.sin(1.0)
0.8414709848078965
> np.exp(-1.5)
0.22313016014842982
```

For the remainder of this book we will be using the mathematical functions and constants in the `numpy` module, as these are the most prevalently used in the scientific community. The basic functions and their usage are generally the same in both the `math` and `numpy` modules. The `numpy` module contains many more features and functions that are not found in the `math` module.

4.7.1   Constants

The `numpy` module contain two constants: `pi` returns the value of π, and `e` returns the value of e.

```
> np.pi
3.141592653589793
> np.e
2.718281828459045
```

4.7.2   Powers and roots

Square roots

The square root is accomplished via the `np.sqrt()` function.

```
> np.sqrt(4)
2.0
```

The np.sqrt() function will return an error if given a negative argument. If the square root of a negative number is needed then the np.lib.scimath.sqrt() function can be used. It returns a floating-point value if given a positive argument, and a complex value if given a negative argument.

```
> np.lib.scimath.sqrt(4)
2.0
> np.lib.scimath.sqrt(-4)
2j
```

Of course, it is also valid to simply raise a number to the 1/2 power in order to obtain a square root,

```
> 4**(1/2)
2.0
```

and this also works for negative numbers,

```
> (-4)**(1/2)
(1.2246467991473532e-16+2j)
```

However, at least for the negative case the np.lib.scimath.sqrt() function seems to do a better job.

If performance is a concern, benchmarking tests on our system using the timeit() function described in Sec. 21.9.6 show that 4**(1/2) executes an order of magnitude faster than does np.sqrt(4).

Powers and roots

Powers can always be taken by simply using the power operator ** as discussed in Sec. 4.1, or using the built-in pow() function introduced in Sec. 4.5. Numpy also has two other functions for taking powers, these being np.power() and np.float_power(). These two functions differ in that np.float_power() always returns a floating-point value, whereas np.power() returns either an integer or a floating-point value depending on whether both argument are integer, or at least one is a floating-point value.

Roots can be found by using fractional powers, such as 1/3 for the cube root. The choice as to whether to use 3**(1/3), pow(3, 1/3), np.power(3, 1/3), or np.float_power(3, 1/3) to find the cube root of 3 is mostly a matter of personal preference. However, if speed is important, benchmarking tests on our system using the timeit() function described in Sec. 21.9.6 show that 3**(1/3) is by far the fastest, being a full order of maginitude faster than pow(3, 1/3), and two orders of magnitude faster than np.float_power(3, 1/3) or np.power(3, 1/3).

If you need to take an even root of a negative number, such as $\sqrt[4]{-3}$ then the only options are to use (-3)**(1/4), pow(-3, 1/4), or the `np.lib.scimath.power(-3, 1/4)` function, as these will return a complex number as the result. Using `np.power()` or `np.float_power()` for the even roots of negative numbers will result in 'not-a-number' (NaN) values.

4.7.3   Trigonometry functions

The trigonometry functions in the numpy module require their arguments to be in units of radians. In order to facilitate conversion between degrees and radians, there are two conversion functions:

- `np.radians(angle)` converts *angle* from degrees to radians.[2]

- `np.degrees(angle)` converts *angle* from radians to degrees.

There are three trig functions, all of which expect *angle* to be a value in radians:

- `np.cos(angle)` returns the cosine of *angle*.

- `np.sin(angle)` returns the sine of *angle*.

- `np.tan(angle)` returns the tangent *angle*.

There are no specific functions for secant, cosecant, or cotangent. These can be obtained by simply taking the reciprocals of the appropriate trig functions.

4.7.4   Hyperbolic functions

- `np.cosh(x)` returns the hyperbolic cosine of *x*.

- `np.sinh(x)` returns the hyperbolic sine of *x*.

- `np.tanh(x)` returns the hyperbolic tangent of *x*.

4.7.5   Inverse trig and hyperbolic functions

The inverse trig and hyperbolic functions are just the trig functions prefaced with the letters arc[3]. Any angles returned will be in radians.

- `np.arccos(x)` returns the inverse cosine of *x*.

- `np.arccosh(x)` returns the inverse hyperbolic cosine of *x*.

- `np.arcsin(x)` returns the inverse sine of the angle *x*.

---

[2]An alternative convention that is useful to reduce ambiguity and the potential for errors is to simply define a constant factor `DEG = np.pi/180` and utilize that factor whenever an angular value in degrees in introduced. One can then write, for example, `right_angle = 90*DEG`. That way, all variables representing angles are known *a priori* to have values expressed in radians. The value in degrees can always be obtained by dividing by `DEG`.

[3]This is different than the math module, in which the inverse trig functions are `asin()`, `acosh()`, etc.

- np.arcsinh(x) returns the inverse hyperbolic sine of x.
- np.arctan(x) returns the inverse tangent of x. The resulting angle, θ, will be in the range $\pi/2 \geq \theta \geq -\pi/2$.
- np.arctan2(y,x) returns the inverse tangent of y/x. The resulting angle will be placed in the proper quadrant based on the signs of y and x.
- np.arctanh(x) returns the inverse hyperbolic tangent of x.

4.7.6 Exponentials and logarithms

- np.exp(x) returns the value of e^x.
- np.expm1(x) returns the value of $e^x - 1$. For small values of x this function is more accurate than using np.exp(x)-1.
- np.log(x) returns the natural logarithm of x, $\ln x$.
- np.log10(x) returns the base 10 logarithm of x.
- np.log1p(x) returns $\ln(x + 1)$ and is more accurate than using np.log(x+1) for small values of x.

4.7.7 Numeric functions

There are several numeric functions in the numpy module, used for rounding or otherwise manipulating numbers.

- np.ceil(x) returns the smallest integer that is greater than or equal to x.
- np.floor(x) returns the largest integer that is less than or equal to x.
- np.fabs(x) returns the absolute value of real value, x.
- np.absolute(x) returns the absolute value of complex value, x.
- np.trunc(x) returns the value of x truncated to the nearest integer. The returned value will be of integer type, not a floating-point value.
- np.copysign(x,y) returns the value of x with the same sign as y.

4.7.8 Modulo arithmetic

Although there is a built-in modulo operator, %, the Python documentation recommends only using it for purely integer input. If one of the input values is floating-point it is recommended to use the numpy module's np.fmod(x,y) function, which behaves like x%y.

A related function is np.modf(x), which breaks the floating-point value x into a tuple containing its decimal and integer parts.

```
> np.modf(45.342)
(0.34199999999999875, 45.0)
```

4.7.9   Special mathematical functions

The submodule `numpy.math` contains some special functions, a few of which are discussed below. Note that to use these functions they must be prefaced with `np.math`.

- `np.math.erf(x)` returns the error function, defined as

$$\text{erf}(x) = \frac{2}{\sqrt{\pi}} \int_0^x e^{-t^2} \, dt.$$

- `np.math.erfc(x)` returns the complementary error function, defined as

$$\text{erfc}(x) = 1 - \text{erf}(x).$$

- `np.math.factorial(x)` returns $x!$.
- `np.math.gamma(x)` returns the Γ function, defined as

$$\Gamma(x) = \int_0^\infty t^{x-1} e^{-t} dt.$$

- `np.math.lgamma(x)` returns the natural logarithm of the Gamma function, $\ln \Gamma(x)$.

4.7.10   Functions for infinity or NaN

The `numpy` module contains functions for checking whether a floating-point value x is infinite or undefined ('not a number', or NaN):

- `np.isinf(x)` returns a value of `True` if x is either positively or negatively infinite.
- `np.isposinf(x)` returns a value of `True` if x is positively infinite.
- `np.isneginf(x)` returns a value of `True` if x is negatively infinite.
- `np.isnan(x)` returns a value of `True` if x is an undefined floating-point value NaN.
- `np.isfinite(x)` returns `True` if the floating-point value x is not infinite or NaN.

The `numpy` constant, `np.nan`, can be used to set a floating-point value of NaN.

```
> a = np.nan
> np.isnan(a)
True
```

If an element in a list or array is set to `np.nan`, either deliberately or due to an illegal mathematical operation, such as division by zero, then it will be excluded from plots of that array. It is also to possible to exclude it from certain calculations on the array; e.g., using the `np.nanmean()` function.

4.8   Aliasing Modules and Functions

We have seen that modules are imported using the `import` command and that once imported, in order to use the functions and constants in the module, we must preface the function or constant with the module name. In formal terms, the name under which a module is imported is known as its *namespace*. When we import numpy, its submodules and functions belong to the *numpy namespace*. If we import math, then its function belong to the *math namespace*.

We have also made use of the concept of *aliasing*, which is importing a module and assigning it a different, usually shorter, namespace. For instance, it is common practice to alias `numpy` using simply two letters, np, with the command

```
import numpy as np
```

It is also possible to import and alias individual functions from a module.

```
from numpy import cos as npcos
```

imports the `numpy.cos()` function and renames is as `npcos()`.

```
> from numpy import cos as npcos
> npcos(1)
0.54030230586813977
```

And finally, it is possible to import every function from a module and use them without having to type the module name. This is done by the command

```
from numpy import *
```

However, **it is strongly recommended that you never do this!** There may be functions or constants of the same name in two different modules, and, if you import all the functions from each module using `import *`, then you may not be using the correct function when you call it in your program. For example, the `numpy.cos()` function is different than the `math.cos()` function.

```
> import numpy
> import math
> numpy.cos(1)
0.54030230586813977
> math.cos(1)
0.5403023058681398
```

If you used both `from numpy import *` and `from math import *`, then when you used `cos()` in your program you would not necessarily know whether you were using the `numpy` or the `math` version of the function. Such a conflict between modules is referred to as *clobbering* a module's namespace.

STRUCTURE AND CONTROL

5.1   Introduction

In this chapter we discuss the basic control structures used in a Python program. We will learn how to get interactive input from a terminal, and the use of conditional statements and loops. Error handling is also discussed.

5.2   Interactive Input from Terminal

Many programs require the user to interactively input data from the terminal window. Although discussion of this topic may be more appropriately discussed in a chapter on input/output, we include it here so that our example programs may make use of user input.

Interactive user input in Python is accomplished using the `input()` function. The syntax is

```
s = input(prompt)
```

where *s* is a string variable that will hold the input, and *prompt* is a string that contains a message that will be displayed to the user in the terminal window, prompting them to enter the data.

```
> s = input('Enter data: ')
Enter data: 4.57
> s
'4.57'
```

In Python 2 the function for interactive user input is `raw_input()`.

Note the following important aspects of `input()`:

- The returned value, *s*, is *always* a string, even if a numerical value is entered. If the program needs the input to be a floating-point or integer, the string variable *s* will need to be converted using the `float()` or `int()` functions.

```
> s = input('Enter data: ')
Enter data: 4.57
> s = float(s)
> s
4.57
```

- Multiple values may be input on the same line, but the variable *s* will still be a single string.

```
> s = input('Enter name, age, and gender: ')
Enter name, age, and gender: Alex, 51, Male
> s
'Alex, 51, Male'
```

The individual values can then be parsed from the string using the `split()` method of strings.

```
> name, age, gender = s.split(',')
> name, age, gender
('Alex', ' 51', ' Male')
```

Note that age is still a string and would have to be further converted to integer if needed.

- As a purely cosmetic issue, it is a good idea to have the prompt end in a blank space. This way the cursor for the user entry is not pressed up against the end of the prompt string.

5.3   Conditional Statements

5.3.1   The if-elif-else construct

The `if` statement defines a block of code that will only be executed if a specified condition is `True`.

```
if condition:
    [code block]
```

When there are multiple conditions, an `if` statement is used for the first condition, and `elif` (shorthand for else-if) is used for each additional condition.

```
if condition 1:
    [code block 1]
elif condition 2:
    [code block 2]
elif condition 3:
    [code block 3]
```

There is no limit on how many `elif` statements may be used.

An `else` statement may be included at the end of the `if-elif` construct, and the code block associated with the `else` statement will be executed if none of the prior conditions are met,

```
if condition 1:
    [code block 1]
elif condition 2:
    [code block 2]
elif condition 3:
    [code block 3]
else:
    [default code block]
```

5.3.2 The single-line conditional statement

For a simple, binary choice a short-hand, single-line conditional statement of the form

```
[expression 1] if condition else [expression 2]
```

may be employed. In this construct, *[expression 1]* will be executed if *condition* is true. Otherwise, *[expression 2]* will be executed. As an example, the code

```
a = float(input('Enter number: '))
x = a**2 if a >= 0 else a**3
print(x)
```

would produce the following input/output when executed.

```
Enter number: 4
16.0
Enter number: -4
-64.0
```

As a further example, the same code could be written as

```
a = float(input('Enter number: '))
print(a**2) if a >= 0 else a**3
```

and would produce the same output as before.

For the single-line conditional statement, *[expression 1]* must be in the form of an assignment or a function, and *[expression 2]* is the alternate right-hand side of the assignment or the alternate argument to the function.

Use of the single-line conditional statement is optional. The same results as the examples could be accomplished using the more traditional `if-else` construct.

5.3.3 Using single objects or values as conditions

In Section 2.3.1 we noted that empty or numerically zero objects convert to a Boolean value of `False`, while all non-empty or non-zero objects convert to `True`. Because of this, we can use a single number or object as a condition in a conditional statement. Python automatically converts the object to Boolean in such constructs. For example, the code

```python
mylist = ['hi', 'bye']
if mylist:
    print('The list has {0:d} \
                elements.'.format(len(mylist)))
else:
    print('The list is empty.')
```

would print

```
The list has 2 elements.
```

because if `mylist` were converted to Boolean it would have a value of `True`. However, if we substituted `mylist = []` and reran the code, it would print

```
The list is empty.
```

5.4 Iteration

Certain objects in Python are *iterable*, meaning that they have a method named `__iter__()` that returns an `iterator` object. Note that the leading and trailing underscores are both doubled! An `iterator` object has a method named `__next__()` that returns the next item in the iterator.

```python
> a = ['Apple', 'Pear', 'Peach']
> b = a.__iter__()
> b.__next__()
'Apple'
> b.__next__()
'Pear'
```

Calling `__next__()` after the last item has already been returned will invoke a `StopIteration` error. Once the last item of an iterator has been returned, the iterator is expended. There is no way to rewind to the beginning. Instead, a new iterator must be created.

Using the `enumerate()` function with an iterable object as the argument returns an iterator whose items are a tuple that contains both the index values and items in the object.

```python
> c = enumerate(a)
> c.__next__()
(0, 'Apple')
```

```
> c.__next__()
(1, 'Pear')
> c.__next__()
(2, 'Peach')
```

Examples of iterable objects are lists, tuples, NumPy arrays, and even strings. Iterators form the basis for constructing most loops in Python, as shown in the next section.

In addition to creating an `iterator` via an object's `__iter__()` method, it is also possible to create an `iterator` using the built-in `iter(obj)` function, which takes an iterable object, *obj*, as the argument.

> The `__next__()` method is another significant difference between Python 3 and Python 2. In Python 2 the method name does not include the leading and trailing underscores, and is simply `next()`.

5.5 Loops

There are two types of loops in Python, these being *for* loops and *while* loops.

5.5.1 For loops

Basic loops

A basic for loop requires an iterable object such as a list, tuple, string, etc. The general syntax is

```
for var in itobj:
    [code block]
```

In this syntax, *itobj* represents the iterable object that is being looped over,[1] and *var* holds the value of the current element of *itobj*. The Python statements within the code block will be executed as long as there are remaining elements in the iterable object. The number of times the code block is executed will be equal to the total number of elements in *itobj*.

As a concrete example, suppose we have a list containing five items

```
data = [4, 9, -8, 'cat', 'mouse']
```

We can loop over the list and print the contents with the following code:

---

[1]Within the `for` statement the iterable object is automatically converted into an `iterator` object. An `iterator` object itself could also be used directly in place of the iterable object. For the relationships between `iterator` objects and iterable objects see Section 5.4.

```
for d in data:
    print(d)
```

When this code is run, each iteration of the loop places the next element of the list into the variable d and prints it to the screen.

If you need a loop that will execute a set number of iterations you can simply use the range() function to generate a range object to be used as the iterable object. For example, to create a loop that will perform 10 iterations, we would use

```
for i in range(0, 10):
```

Using enumerate()

Sometimes we want to keep track of which iteration we are on within the loop. This is accomplished by using the enumerate(*iterobj*) function with the iterable object, *iterobj*, as the argument. This return two values, the index and the contents of the next element of the iterable object. The general syntax is as follows.

```
for i, val in enumerate(iterobj):
    [code block]
```

As an example,

```
for i,val in enumerate(range(-10, -4)):
    print(i, val)
```

produces the following output.

```
0 -10
1 -9
...
5 -5
```

5.5.2   While loops

The other looping construct in Python is a while loop, which executes as long as a specified condition is met. The syntax is

```
while condition:
    [code block]
```

The loop will continue to execute as long as the condition evaluates as True. For example:

```
a = 0
while a < 5:
    print(a)
    a += 1
```

produces

```
0
1
2
3
4
```

5.5.3 Skipping to top of a loop

Sometimes we may want to skip back to the top of a loop if a certain condition is met. This is handled with the `continue` statement. Any statements within the code block that appear after the `continue` statement is encountered are ignored for that particular iteration of the loop. Instead, control is sent back to the top of the loop. As an example,

```
for val in range(0, 10):
    if val % 2 == 0:
        continue
    print(val)
```

only prints the odd-numbered values from 1 to 9. The `continue` statement works with either for or while loops.

5.5.4 Breaking out of a loop

To exit a loop prematurely we use the `break` statement. Any statements after the `break` statement are disregarded, and execution proceeds with the first statement outside of the code block. For example:

```
for val in range(0,10):
    if val > 5:
        break
    print(val)
```

will only print the values 0 through 5, and then the loop will stop, even though the `range` object contains integers up through 9. The `break` statement can be used with both for and while loops.

5.6 Verifying User Input

One very useful application of a while loop is in verifying that a user enters valid input into a program. For example, let's say we want the user to enter a valid atmospheric pressure in millibars (mb). We would not accept negative values of pressure, nor pressures that are absurdly large, say, greater than 1100 mb. If a user enters such values we want them to be queried again, until a valid value is entered. This is accomplished with the following code,

```
p = -99.0
while p <= 0 or p > 1100:
    p = float(input('Enter pressure (mb): '))
```

If the user enters negative values or values greater than 1100, then the prompt keeps appearing. The while loop is not exited until the user enters a positive value that is 1100 or less.

Notice that we had to assign an invalid value to the pressure variable p before entering the while loop. If we didn't assign any value we would have received an undefined value error. If we had assigned a positive value, then the loop would not have been executed.

5.7　The pass Statement

There are occasions where we may want to have an empty, or do-nothing code block. This often occurs when testing or debugging incomplete code, but there are other scenarios. To create a do-nothing code block we use the **pass** statement. For example, the code

```
a = int(input('Enter integer: '))
if a < 0:
    print(a)
elif a == 0:
    pass
else:
    print(a**2)
```

produces

```
Enter integer: -4
-4
Enter integer: 0
Enter integer: 4
16
```

Note that the number 0 was not printed.

5.8　List Comprehension

A useful mechanism for creating a new list from an iterable object is *list comprehension*, which was briefly introduced with a simple example in Sec. 2.7.9. The basic construct for a list comprehension is

```
newlist = [{operation on elem} for elem in iterobj ]
```

where *elem* is an element of the iterable object *iterobj*, and *{operation on elem}* is the result from some operation acting on the element. The *operation* is often a function that takes the element as an argument, or is a method of the element. But, it could be any Python statement or action which acts on the element.

The list comprehension syntax is essentially shorthand for

```
newlist = [] # Create empty list
for elem in iterobj:
    newlist.append({operation on elem})
```

In the example from Sec. 2.7.9, *operation* was the `float()` function. As another example, suppose we have a list of file names

```
> fnames = ['good.txt', 'bad.txt', 'ugly.txt']
```

and we want to create a new list that has the base name without the file extension. We can do this with the code

```
> bases = [f[0:-4] for f in fnames]
> bases
['good', 'bad', 'ugly']
```

In this example *operation* was not a function or a method, but was the act of using indexing to retrieve all but the last four characters of the element (which was a string in this case).

5.9   The print() Function Revisited

The `print()` function was briefly introduced in Sec. 2.1.3. This sections describes some options for the `print()` function, as well as considerations for buffered output.

5.9.1   Options

By default, multiple arguments to the `print()` function are printed with a single white space separating them. The `sep` keyword can be set to specify the separator.

```
> print('hello', 'goodbye')
hello goodbye
> print('hello', 'goodbye', sep=',')
hello,goodbye
> print('hello', 'goodbye', sep=':')
hello:goodbye
> print('hello', 'goodbye', sep='')
hellogoodbye
```

Also by default, the hidden newline character \n is printed at the end of every call to the `print()` function, resulting in a newline being printed at every call. This can be overridden by specifying the **end** keyword. For example, the code

```
for i in range(1,5):
    print(i, end='')
```

prints the result

```
1234
```

while the code

```
for i in range(1,5):
    print(i, end=':')
```

prints

```
1:2:3:4:
```

5.9.2   Flushing the buffer

Sometimes it happens that a `print()` function will be executed, but the output will not immediately appear in the terminal. This is because the output is *buffered*, and the data not written until the buffer is full. If this occurs, the buffer can be made to flush by importing the `sys` module and calling the `flush()` method of the `sys.stdout` object,

```
import sys
sys.stdout.flush()
```

5.10   Error Handling

If the Python interpreter encounters an exception while a program is running, it will either deliver a warning message or, if serious enough, it will terminate the program execution. In certain applications we may not want the program to quit running, even if it encounters an error. In Python this is accomplished using the *try-except* construct, which has the general syntax

```
try:
    [code block]
except:
    [alternate code block]
```

In this construct, if an error is encountered in the code block associated with the `try` statement, then instead of exiting the program, the alternate code block associated with the `except` statement will be executed. The code in the alternate code block will attempt to mitigate the error and keep the program running.

In the previous example, the alternate code block will be invoked regardless of the type of error encountered. The try-except construct can be tailored to handle specific errors that may occur. There are a few dozen different specific errors recognized by the Python interpreter. Some of the specific errors recognized by the Python interpreter are listed here.[2]

- `ArithmeticError`: Raised on any arithmetic exceptions. Includes the subclasses of `FloatingPointError`, `OverflowError`, and `ZeroDivisionError`.

- `EOFError`: Raised when an end of a file is reached during input.

- `IOError`: Raised on a failed input-output operation.

- `ImportError`: Raised when a module that is being imported either does not exist or cannot otherwise be imported.

As an example, imagine we are writing some code that needs the trigonometric function for cosine. We would like to use the Numpy `cos()` function, but want our code to also work in an environment where Numpy might not be installed. Because both the `numpy` and `math` modules have a `cos()` function we could use the following code,

```
try:
    import numpy as np
except ImportError:
    print('Unable to import numpy! Importing math
    instead.')
    import math as np
print(np.cos(np.pi/4))
```

If the `numpy` module imports without error, then the statements in the `except` block will be ignored. But if there is an error in loading the `numpy` module, instead of exiting, the program will simply import the `math` module aliased as `np`.

The error can also be saved into a variable and printed to the screen or a file for debugging. Modifying the prior example,

```
try:
    import numpy as np
except ImportError as e:
    print(e)
    print('Unable to import numpy! Importing math
    instead.')
    import math as np
print(np.cos(np.pi/4))
```

---

[2]For a complete list of all the built-in exceptions refer to the Python documentation.

This will also print the specific text of the error to the screen.

Multiple `except` statements and their associated code blocks may be used with a single `try` statement to handle different specific errors that arise. This would have the syntax

```
try:
    [code block]
except IOError:
    [alternate code block to handle input-output errors]
except EOFError:
    [alternate code block to handle end of file errors]
except OverflowError:
    [alternate code block to handle arithmetic overflow
    errors]
```

An `else` statement and block can also be used after the final `except` statement. The code in the `else` block will be executed if there are still remaining errors that were not specifically handled by the prior `except` blocks.

There is also a `finally` statement and associated code block that can be used at the very end of the try-except construct, as shown here:

```
try:
    [code block]
except IOError:
    [alternate code block to handle input-output errors]
except EOFError:
    [alternate code block to handle end of file errors]
except OverflowError:
    [alternate code block to handle arithmetic overflow
    errors]
finally:
    [code to be executed no matter what.]
```

The code in the `finally` block will be executed regardless of whether or not an error occurred in the `try` statement. It is used for housekeeping chores, such as ensuring that open files are closed prior to exiting the program.

There is far more to Python's ability to handle exceptions than has been presented here, including the ability for the user to define and raise their own exceptions within the code. Readers desiring an advanced understanding of exception handling are encouraged to consult the Python documentation or more advanced books.[3]

---

[3]The book *Python Essential Reference* by David Beazley is an invaluable resource for such information.

FILE I/O

6.1 Opening and Closing Files

6.1.1 Opening files

A file is opened using the **open()** function, which has the syntax

```
f = open(filename, mode)
```

in which *filename* is a string or string variable denoting the pathname of the file, and *mode* is a string indicating the mode in which the file is to be opened. The variable *f* will contain a reference to the file.[1] The different modes are:

- `'r'`: Text file is opened as read only.
- `'w'`: Text file is opened for write only. Output will overwrite existing file.
- `'r+'` or `'w+'`: Text file is opened for both reading and writing. Output will overwrite existing file.
- `'a'`: Text file is opened for writing in append mode. Output will be appended to the end of an existing file.

If the character `'b'` is included at the end of the mode, then the file is opened as a binary file. For example, `'rb'` indicates a read-only binary file, and `'rb+'` would indicate a read and write enabled binary file.

---

[1]The variable *f* is really a reference to an object of the `_io.TextIOWrapper` class. For convenience we will simply call it a file.

6.1.2   Closing files

A file is closed by using its `close()` method, `f.close()`. Files should always be closed prior to ending program execution.

6.1.3   Automatically closing files

A shorthand method for ensuring that files are closed after use is to use the `with` statement as shown here,

```
with open(file_name, mode) as f:
    [code statements within code block]
```

This opens the file as `f`, executes the statements within the code block, and then automatically closes the file when the code block is finished.

6.2   Interactive File and Directory Selection

Standard Python installations contain a module called `tkinter` which provides a Python interface to the Tcl/Tk graphical user interface (GUI) library. Although we will not discuss GUI programming in this book, this section will show a convenient way to interactively select a file or directory using a GUI interface.

Note! The interactive file and directory selection code described in this section can be somewhat 'buggy' depending on the operating system or Python installation, and may not work, or even cause unexpected termination of programs. This is a rare instance of a feature that worked nearly flawlessly in Python 2 being rendered almost useless in Python 3. One thing to consider if problems occur is substituting `window.update()` in place of `window.withdraw()`. This sometimes (but not always) fixes the issue and, even worse, has been known to completely crash Macintosh computers, so use with caution! If a reader experiences difficulty with the code in this section, the best advice that can be offered is to perform an internet search. Hopefully, someone else has had the same difficulty as you, and has found a solution.

> In Python 2 the `Tkinter` module is capitalized, and the usage of the functions for interactive file and directory selection is different. We do not cover them in this book.

6.2.1   File selection

The basic code shown below should open a GUI window for interactive file selection, and then will store the path to the selected file in the variable `filename`.

```
import tkinter as tk
from tkinter.filedialog import askopenfilename
window = tk.Tk()
window.withdraw()
filename = askopenfilename(multiple=False)
window.destroy()
```

These commands do the following:

1. `import tkinter as tk` imports the `tkinter` library aliased as `tk`.

2. `from tkinter.filedialog import askopenfilename` imports the `askopenfilename()` function from the `tkinter.filedialog` submodule.

3. `window = tk.Tk()` creates a *master* or *root* window.

4. `window.withdraw()` removes the master window from view. This line is optional.

5. `filename = askopenfilename(multiple=False)` calls the `askopenfilename()` function and opens a file selection window that allows the user to interactively navigate to and select the file. The selected file name is stored in the `filename` variable.
   - The Boolean keyword `multiple` either allows or denies the selection of multiple files.
   - If a single file is chosen the file name is returned as a string.
   - If multiple files are selected they may be returned as a list of strings, or as a delimited string.[2]

6. `window.destroy()` destroys the master window once it is no longer needed.

There is some additional customization possible using keywords in the `askopenfilename()` function.

   - The initial directory for the interactive selection can be set using the `initialdir` keyword.

   - The title for the GUI window can be set using the `title` keyword.

   - Specific file types can be specified using the `filetypes` keyword. The desired file types are contained in a list. As an example, to use the `askopenfilename()` function for selecting only files with *.jpg* or *.gif* extensions, the syntax we would use is

---

[2]This seems somewhat operating-system-dependent, with Python on differing operating systems not necessarily being uniform as to how multiple file names are returned. The user should inspect the returned object to ascertain the exact type and format of the returned object.

```
ft = [('GIF Files (*.gif)', '*.gif'),
      ('JPG Files (*.jpg)', '*.jpg')]
filename = askopenfilename(multiple=False,
                           filetypes=ft)
```

6.2.2   Directory selection

A directory name can also be interactively selected using slightly different code shown here:

```
import tkinter as tk
from tkinter.filedialog import askdirectory
window = tk.Tk()
window.withdraw()
dirname = askdirectory(mustexist=True)
window.destroy()
```

Setting the `mustexist` keyword equal to `True` will only allow the selection of directories that exist. If it is `False`, then the user can type in the name of a directory.

6.3   Reading Text from Files

In this section we illustrate how to read text from a file using the `readline()` and `readlines()` methods of a file. The returned values from these methods are either a string or a list of strings. If the data read from the file is supposed to represent numerical values then the strings must be converted to integer or floating-point values after they are read.

6.3.1   Reading individual lines

The `open()` function returns a reference to the file. Files are iterable,[3] and each call to their `__next__()` method returns the next line from the file. As an example, suppose we have a file named *datafile.txt* that contains the following text:

```
The quick brown
fox jumped over
the
lazy
dog.
```

If we opened the file using

---

[3]See Sec. 5.4.

```
> f = open('datafile.txt', 'r')
```

and then called the __next__() method, we would get the following output:

```
> f.__next__()
'The quick brown\n'
> f.__next__()
'fox jumped over\n'
```

Files also have a `readline()` method that behaves just like the __next__() method, returning the next line from the file each time it is called. Although the __next__() and `readline()` methods behave identically, their usage cannot be mixed.

6.3.2 Looping over file

Since files are iterable they can be used in a loop construction. For example, the code

```
with open('datafile.txt', 'r') as f:
    for line in f:
        print(line)
```

would open the file named *datafile.txt* and print each of its lines to the screen.

6.3.3 Reading an entire file into a list

Files also have a `readlines()` method (note the plural), which returns the contents of a file as a list, with each line as an element of the list. For example, using our previous data file, the code

```
with open('datafile.txt', 'r') as f:
    data = f.readlines()
print(data)
```

returns

```
['The quick brown\n', 'fox jumped over\n', 'the\n',
    'lazy\n', 'dog.']
```

6.4 Writing Text to Files

6.4.1 Writing individual lines of text

Individual lines of text can be written to a file using either the file's `write()` method, or the `print()` function. One advantage of the `print()` function is that it automatically places a newline character at the end of the printed items, whereas the `write()` method requires the newline character to be explicitly included.

write() method

Files have a `write()` method that writes a single string to a file. The newline character, \n, is not automatically inserted at the end of the string and must be explicitly included. For example, to create a text file named *myfile.txt* containing the following text

```
Now is the time
for all good men
to come to the aid
of their country.
```

we could use the following code,

```
with open('myfile.txt', 'w') as f:
    f.write('Now is the time\n')
    f.write('for all good men\n')
    f.write('to come to the aid\n')
    f.write('of their country.')
```

print() function

It is also possible to use the `print()` function to write text to a file. This is accomplished by specifying the `file` keyword, setting it equal to an already opened file. For example, the following code achieves the same result as the previous code.

```
with open('myfile.txt', 'w') as f:
    print('Now is the time', file=f)
    print('for all good men', file=f)
    print('to come to the aid', file=f)
    print('of their country.', file=f)
```

Note that since the newline character is written by default when using the `print()` function it did not have to be included explicitly in the output strings.

6.4.2   Writing a list of strings

Using the `writelines()` method (note plural) we can write a list of strings to a file, with each element written to a separate line. The following code will do the same thing as the previous example:

```
s = ['Now is the time\n','for all good men\n', \
     'to come to the aid\n','of their country.']
with open('myfile.txt', 'w') as f:
    f.writelines(s)
```

Again, note that the newline character, \n, is not automatically inserted at the end of each element and must be included explicitly in order to write on a new line.

6.4.3   Buffered output

It may happen that a file's `write()` or `writelines()` method may be called, but the data are not immediately written to the file. This can occur if the output is *buffered*, and the output stream is not written until the buffer is full. The contents of the buffer can be forced to *flush* by calling the `flush()` method of the file. Files are not the only objects that have a `flush()` method. All *file-like objects* such as `sys.stdout` have a `flush()` method.

6.5   Reading and Writing Delimited Files Using the csv Module

In many instances, the data files in which we are interested are text files that contain a regular number of data values separated by commas, colons, whitespace, or some other delimiter. Standard Python installations include a module called `csv`, which has functions and classes defined for easily reading and writing such files.

6.5.1   Reading delimited files

For illustration, let's say that we have a comma-delimited file named *datafile.csv* with a single header row and five data columns:

```
Name, City, Age, Height (in), Weight(lbs)
Alex, Layton, 51, 72, 195
Francis, Ogden, 34, 68, 177
Megan, Las Vegas, 23, 65, 120
Lois, St.~George, 56, 60, 130
```

We first import the `csv` module and open the data file for reading.

```
> import csv
> f = open('datafile.csv', 'r')
```

> When using the `csv` module in Python 2, even text files should be opened in binary mode using the specifier 'rb' or 'wb'. Failure to do so may cause unexpected results in how the newline character is treated. These issues were fixed in Python 3.

We then create a `csv.reader` object by calling the `reader()` function of the csv module.[4]

```
> r = csv.reader(f, delimiter=',')
```

---

[4]The object created is actually of the class `_csv.reader`, but for convenience we will omit the leading underscore in the class name.

A `csv.reader` object is an iterable object whose `__next__()` method returns the next line of the file as a list of strings whose elements are the words or phrases contained between the delimiters.

Since the `csv.reader` object is iterable, it is very easy to incorporate it into a loop structure. For example, suppose we wanted to read the data and calculate the body-mass index (BMI) for each person in the data file using the formula $bmi = 703 \times lbs/in^2$. One way to accomplish this is with the code

```python
import csv
with open('datafile.csv', 'r') as f:
    r = csv.reader(f, delimiter=',')
    for i, data in enumerate(r):
        if i == 0:   # Skips header row
            pass
        else:
            lbs = float(data[4])
            inches = float(data[3])
            bmi = 703.0*lbs/inches**2
            print(data[0], round(bmi,1))
```

which, when executed, prints the following.

```
('Alex', 26.4)
('Francis', 26.9)
('Megan', 20.0)
('Lois', 25.4)
```

In this example, we also showed how to skip a header row of text. Notice that the data elements returned from the `csv.reader` are strings, and had to be converted to floating-point values before using them in calculations.

6.5.2 Writing delimited files

Delimited files can be written by first creating a `csv.writer` object.[5] This is accomplished by calling the `csv` module's `writer()` function. The `csv.writer` object has two methods for writing data to the file, which are described as follows:

- `writerow(ls)` writes the 1-D list, *ls*, to a single row of the file, with each element separated by the delimiter.

- `writerows(ls)` writes the 2-D list, *ls*, to the file, with each element of the list on a row and with the subelements separated by the delimiter.

---

[5]The object created is actually of the class `_csv.writer`, but we omit the leading underscore for convenience.

Their usage is illustrated in the example below, in which we have a single list containing headings, and a nested list containing some data.

```
head = ['City', 'County', 'Population']
data = [['Layton', 'Davis', 77303],
        ['Ogden', 'Weber', 88825],
        ['Toole', 'Toole', 31605]]
import csv
filename = 'cities.txt'
with open(filename, 'w') as fout:
    w = csv.writer(fout, delimiter=';')
    w.writerow(head)
    w.writerows(data)
```

This results in the creation of a semicolon-separated file named *cities.txt*, the contents of which are

```
City;County;Population
Layton;Davis;77303
Ogden;Weber;88825
Toole;Toole;31605
```

6.5.3 Additional notes regarding the csv module

- The default delimiter when creating `csv.reader` and `csv.writer` objects is the comma. Any other single character may also be used as a delimiter, by setting the `delimiter` keyword.

- If the delimiter appears anywhere within quoted text being read, then it is not treated as a true delimiter. Instead, it is escaped and treated as part of the text. For example, if the comma is used as the delimiter, and a line of the text file were

```
"Simson, Jon", Layton, 51, 72, 195
```

then, after splitting, the list for that line would be

```
['Simson, Jon', ' Layton', ' 51', ' 72', ' 195']
```

Notice that the first element contains the comma and was not split. This behavior can be modified (see online `csv` documentation for details).

- If the keyword `skipinitialspace=True` is used then whitespace immediately following the delimiter is ignored.

6.6 Reading/Writing Numpy Arrays from/to Files

Numerical Python (Numpy) arrays can be read from and written to files using built-in Numpy functions and methods. These are covered later in Sec. 7.21.

6.7   The os.path Module: Working with Path and File Names

Standard Python installations include a module named `os.path` that includes functions for working with file and path names and for checking for the existence of specific files and directories. This module is imported and aliased using

```
> import os.path as pth
```

To illustrate some of the features of `os.path`, we use the following command to define a path name:

```
> p = '/Users/Smith/data/temperature/june11.dat'
```

(Note: For Windows users we would need to use double backslashes, \\, as separators for the subdirectories.)

The following functions provided by `os.path` can then be applied as follows:

- `abspath()` simply returns the full, absolute path.
- `basename()` returns the base name of the path.

```
> pth.basename(p)
'june11.dat'
```

- `dirname()` returns the directory name of the path.

```
> pth.dirname(p)
'/Users/Smith/data/temperature'
```

- `split()` returns a tuple with the directory and the base path as its two elements.
- `splitdrive()` returns a tuple with the drive and the remainder of the path without the drive as its two elements.
- `splitext()` returns a tuple with the path minus the file extension, and the file extension itself, as its two elements.

The `os.path` module also contains functions for testing for the existence of files and directories:

- `exists(`*p*`)` returns True if *p* exists as an actual path.
- `isfile(`*p*`)` returns True if *p* is an existing file.
- `isdir(`*p*`)` returns True if *p* is an existing directory.

6.8   Internet File Access

Files from the internet may be accessed using the `urllib.request` module. The `urlretrieve(`*url, newfile*`)` function saves the webpage located at the URL given by *url* to a local file named *newfile*. The syntax for this is

```
from urllib.request import urlretrieve
urlretrieve(url, newfile)
```

The URL needs to include the full path to the remote file, such as `"https://www.aviationweather.gov/docs/metar/stations.txt"` The saved file can then be opened and read just like any other file.

If you do not want to physically download a copy of a file but, but simply want to read a remote document online, then use the `urlopen(url)` function, which returns a `HTTPResponse` object. The `HTTPResponse` object behaves very much like a file object. It may be used as the basis of a for loop, returning each line of the file. It also has a `readline()` method and a `readlines()` method. The `readline()` method reads a single line of text from the file as a byte string, while the `readlines()` method reads the entire contents of the file into a list of byte strings. An example syntax for reading the contents of a web page would be

```
from urllib.request import urlopen
page = urlopen(url)
data = page.readlines() # Save contents as a list
page.close()
```

The connection to the web page should be closed using the `close()` method, just as for a file.

The `with` statement may also be used to automatically close the connection to the web page,

```
with urlopen(url) as page:
    data = page.readlines()
```

NUMPY ARRAYS

7.1   Introduction

Unlike lists or tuples, Numerical Python (Numpy) arrays cannot hold elements having different data types. The data type of the array is either determined automatically, or it can be specified when the array is created. Numpy arrays are much more efficient than lists or tuples when performing calculations on large sets of data.

Numpy arrays can have multiple dimensions. In theory there is no limit to how many dimensions an array may have, though there are practical limits based on the memory available for storage. In this book we focus primarily on 1-D and 2-D arrays, since they are the easiest to illustrate.

This chapter presents many of the more common functions and methods for creating and manipulating arrays. The treatment is not exhaustive, and the Numpy documentation should be consulted for further information.

7.2   Creating an Array

There are many ways of creating arrays in Numpy. The most basic is to use the `array()` function, which takes as its argument a list or tuple. Creation of a simple 1-D array is illustrated in the following code.[1]

```
> a = np.array([3, -1, 7])
> a
array([ 3, -1, 7])
```

---

[1]For the remainder of this book we will assume we have imported numpy aliased as np.

Note that this created an integer array because the input were all integers. If at least one of the inputs were a floating-point value, then the created array would be of floating-point data type. There is also an optional keyword, `dtype`, which specifies the data type of the created array regardless of the input:

```
> a = np.array([3, -1, 7], dtype=np.float_)
> a
array([ 3., -1., 7.])
```

In this example the created array is a 64-bit floating point array. Numpy data types are discussed in the next section.

A 2-D array is created by using a nested list or tuple as input to the `numpy.array()` function:

```
> a = np.array([[2, -1, 7], [6, -3, 3], [9, -4, 2]])
> a
array([[ 2, -1, 7],
       [ 6, -3, 3],
       [ 9, -4, 2]])
```

Numpy interprets the first element of the nested list as being the data for the first row of the array, the second element as the data for the second row, etc.

7.3   Numpy Data Types

There are many possible data types for Numpy objects such as arrays. Here are the most common (note the trailing underscore):

- `np.float_`: Double-precision (64-bit) floating point. May also be written as `np.float64`.
- `np.int_`: 64-bit integer. May also be written as `np.int64`.
- `np.complex_`: Complex number with real and imaginary parts, each 64-bit. May also be writte as `np.complex128`.
- `np.bool_`: Boolean (`True`/`False`).

The data type names can also be used as conversion functions:

```
> a, b, c = np.float_(4), np.int_(4.6), np.bool_(0)
> a, b, c
(4.0, 4, False)
```

The Numpy data types are different than the native Python data types such as `float`, `int`, and `complex`. Numpy also has aliases for the native Python data types. These are just the native Python names without the trailing underscores.

- `np.float` aliases to the native Python `float`.
- `np.int` aliases to the native Python `int`.

If native Python data types are used as specifiers for the `dtype` keyword when creating arrays, they are simply converted to the corresponding Numpy data type. Thus, the three arrays created in the example below all have the same data type of `numpy.float64`.

```
> a = np.array([1,2,5], dtype=float)
> b = np.array([1,2,5], dtype=np.float)
> c = np.array([1,2,5], dtype=np.float_)
```

The data type of an existing array or object may be found by using the `dtype` attribute. Changing the data type of an existing array is accomplished via its `astype()` method. An example is shown here:

```
> a = np.array([1,2,5], dtype=np.int_)
> a
array([1, 2, 5])
> b = a.astype(np.float_)
> b
array([1., 2., 5.])
> b.dtype
dtype('float64')
```

The numpy functions `float_()` and `int_()` may also be used to change the data type of an array passes as an argument to the functions, but according to the Numpy documentation using the `astype()` method is preferred.

7.4   Printing numpy Arrays

We can always neatly display the contents of a `numpy` array with the built-in `print()` function. By default, floating point values are displayed with 8 digits of precision and with scientific notation enabled. For example,

```
> X = np.array([ [np.pi, np.pi/2], \
                 [np.pi/3, np.pi/4]])*1.0e-6
> print(X)
[[3.14159265e-06 1.57079633e-06]
 [1.04719755e-06 7.85398163e-07]]
```

The `np.set_printoptions()` function provides the ability to modify the above and other default behaviors. For example, we can change the displayed precision,

```
> np.set_printoptions(precision=2)
> print(X)
[[3.14e-06 1.57e-06]
 [1.05e-06 7.85e-07]]
```

and we can suppress the use of scientific notation:

```
> np.set_printoptions(suppress=True)
> print(X)
[[0. 0.]
 [0. 0.]]
```

In the following, we restore the default precision but leave scientific notation turned off:

```
> np.set_printoptions(precision=8)
> print(X)
[[0.00000314 0.00000157]
 [0.00000105 0.00000079]]
```

Although the above two options are often the most useful, there are several other print options that can also be modified to taste—see the online documentation.

7.5   Other Array-creation Functions

Numpy contains several helper functions for creating arrays of specified shape, or patterned after existing arrays, and being filled with zeros or ones. Unitialized arrays may also be created.

7.5.1   Arrays filled with a single value

The numpy.zeros() function is used to create an array filled with zeros, while the numpy.ones() function creates an array filled with ones.

```
> a = np.zeros((2,3), dtype=np.float_)
> a
array([[ 0., 0., 0.],
       [ 0., 0., 0.]])
> b = np.ones((3,4), dtype=np.float_)
> b
array([[ 1., 1., 1., 1.],
       [ 1., 1., 1., 1.],
       [ 1., 1., 1., 1.]])
```

7.5.2   Arrays patterned from an existing array

To create a new array having the same shape and data type as an existing array *arr* we use the numpy.zeros_like(*arr*) or numpy.ones_like(*arr*) functions. The only required argument is the existing array to be used as the pattern.

7.5.3 Uninitialized arrays

Numpy also has functions for creating uninitialized arrays: `numpy.empty()` and `numpy.empty_like()`. Although these functions have 'empty' in their names you should understand that the arrays created using these functions may not be truly empty, as shown by this example:

```
> d = np.empty((2,3), dtype=np.float_)
> d
array([[ 2.07507571e-322, 4.94065646e-324,
          3.95252517e-323],
        [ 3.95252517e-323, 1.00000000e+000,
          1.00000000e+000]])
```

The array contains whatever happened to be stored in the memory locations allocated to the array. This brings up an important programming point: **Never assume that an uninitialized variable or array will either be empty, or contain zeroes!**

Why would you ever choose to use `empty()` instead of `zeros()`? You would do so only if you were a performance fanatic. Creating a large, uninitialized 100×100 floating-point array is about three times faster than creating an array populated with values. Even accounting for the fact that after you create the uninitialized array you still have to assign values to it, the uninitialized route may be faster. As an example, running a benchmark test creating a 100×100 array populated with a floating-point value of 1.0 took an average of 4.41 seconds over one million trials using

```
a = np.ones((100,100), dtype=np.float_)
```

and an average of 3.96 seconds using[2]

```
a = np.empty((100,100), dtype=np.float_)
a[:] = 1
```

7.6 Sequential Arrays

Three important functions for creating arrays filled with sequences of numbers are `numpy.arange()`, `numpy.linspace()`, and `numpy.logspace()`.

7.6.1 The arange() function

The `numpy.arange()` function has some similarity in usage to the Python `range()` function, but the output is a Numpy array instead of a `range` object,

---

[2]The specifics of this benchmark test are described in Sec. 21.9.6

and floating-point values may also be generated. As with the Python `range()` function, a striding parameter may be used, and the sequence may also be descending. A few examples:

```
> a = np.arange(0, 11, 2)
> a
array([ 0, 2, 4, 6, 8, 10])
> b = np.arange(10, -1, -3)
> b
array([10, 7, 4, 1])
> c = np.arange(0.0, 1.0, 0.2)
> c
array([ 0. , 0.2, 0.4, 0.6, 0.8])[3]
```

Note that the data type is determined by the input, although it can also be forced by providing the **dtype** keyword. Also, note again that the last value is not included in the output array.

7.6.2   The linspace() function

The `numpy.linspace()` function allows the user to specify a beginning and ending value and the number of points to create.

```
> a = np.linspace(-4, -2, 6)
> a
array([-4. , -3.6, -3.2, -2.8, -2.4, -2. ])
> b = np.linspace(-2, -4, 6)
> b
array([-2. , -2.4, -2.8, -3.2, -3.6, -4. ])
```

Unlike the `arange()` function, the results from `linspace()` include the final value.

7.6.3   The logspace() function

The `numpy.logspace()` functions works like the `numpy.linspace()` functions, but the values are logarithmically spaced. The beginning and ending values are base 10 exponents.

```
> a = np.logspace(-1, 2, 8)
> a
array([ 0.1 , 0.26826958, 0.71968567, 1.93069773,
        5.17947468, 13.89495494, 37.2759372 , 100. ])
> b = np.logspace(2, -1, 8)
```

---

[3]The extra spaces appearing in this output were placed there by the Python interpreter, and are not formatting or editing errors. This occurs in several places throughout the text. The output has been copied directly from the Python output window.

```
> b
array([ 100.   , 37.2759372 , 13.89495494, 5.17947468,
         1.93069773, 0.71968567, 0.26826958, 0.1 ])
```

Different bases can be used by setting the base keyword. For example, a natural logarithmic spacing is obtained by setting base equal to the constant, np.e:

```
> a = np.logspace(-1, 2, 8, base=np.e)
> a
array([ 0.36787944, 0.56471812, 0.8668779, 1.3307122,
         2.04272707, 3.13571476, 4.81351974, 7.3890561 ])
```

7.7 Array Indexing and Slicing

Accessing selected elements of an array is also referred to as *slicing*, and is accomplished by enclosing the indices of the elements to be selected within square brackets. For multidimensional arrays, the different axes are separated by commas. For 2-D arrays, the first index refers to the row, while the second index refers to the column. The first element of an array or axis has index zero.

One important note! Accessing arrays and assigning the value to a new variable **does not create a separate copy!** It creates a *view* or *pointer* to the original array. This is known as a *shallow copy* (see Sec. 2.12). If the original array is altered, this alteration is also reflected in the view. If an independent *deep copy* is desired, use the np.copy() function.

7.7.1 One-dimensional arrays

One-dimensional Numpy arrays are indexed and sliced just like other Python collections, such as lists and tuples, with the first index being zero (see also Sec. 2.7.1). Some examples:

```
> a
array([ 0, 1, 2, 3, 4, 5, 6, 7, 8, 9, 10])
> a[4]
4
> a[2:6]
array([2, 3, 4, 5])
> a[:5]
array([0, 1, 2, 3, 4])
> a[3:]
array([ 3, 4, 5, 6, 7, 8, 9, 10])
> a[-1]
10
```

Striding (selecting every other, every third, every fourth element, etc.) and reversing are also done just as they are for other lists and tuples. See Section 2.7.4 for a more detailed discussion. Here are some examples for illustration:

```
> a
array([ 0, 1, 2, 3, 4, 5, 6, 7, 8, 9, 10])
> a[0:12:3] # Select every-third element
array([0, 3, 6, 9])
> a[::-1] # Reverse elements
array([10, 9, 8, 7, 6, 5, 4, 3, 2, 1, 0])
> a[::-2] # Reverse, selecting every-other element
array([10, 8, 6, 4, 2, 0])
```

7.7.2   Multidimensional arrays

Indexing and slicing 2-D and higher dimensional arrays is slightly different than accessing nested lists or tuples. In the case of arrays, the indices are all contained within the same set of outer brackets instead of using a separate set of brackets for each nesting level. Using a 2-D array as an example:

```
> a
array([[1, 2, 3],
       [4, 5, 6],
       [7, 8, 9]])
> a[0,0]
1
> a[2,0]
7
> a[0,2]
3
> a[0:,2]
array([3, 6, 9])
> a[2,:]
array([7, 8, 9])
```

Note that the first index refers to the row, while the second index refers to the column. This is different than some other scientific languages such as Fortran, in which the first index of a 2-D array is for the column and the second index is for the row.

7.7.3   Indexing with lists

Lists of indices can also be used to select specific array elements. The following example shows how to extract elements 1, 3, and 7 from a 1-D array:

```
> a
array([ 0, 2, 4, 6, 8, 10, 12, 14, 16, 18, 20])
> b = a[[1, 3, 7]]
> b
array([2, 6, 14])
```

When using lists as indices, the returned result is a deep copy rather than a view. In the example above, the array b is truly independent of array a.

7.8 Broadcasting and Implicit Loops

7.8.1 Broadcasting of arrays

Once an array has been defined it can be used in a mathematical expression or as the argument to many functions, just as any other variable would be, and the operation will be performed element by element, returning another array. This is known as *broadcasting*. For example:

- A single constant value may be used to multiply or divide an entire array, or be added or subtracted from the array.

```
> a
array([ 4, -3, 2])
> a*2
array([ 8, -6, 4])
> a/4.3
array([ 0.93023256, -0.69767442, 0.46511628])
> a + 10
array([14, 7, 12])
```

- Arrays of the same shape and size may be added, subtracted, multiplied, or divided by each other.

```
> a, b
(array([ 4, -3, 2]), array([ 2, 7, -3]))
> a+b
array([ 6, 4, -1])
> a*b
array([ 8, -21, -6])
> a/b
array([ 2., -0.42857143, -0.66666667])
```

- An array may be raised to a power or used as an argument to a mathematical function.

```
> a**2
array([16, 9, 4])
> np.exp(a)
array([ 5.45981500e+01, 4.97870684e-02,
   7.38905610e+00])
```

- A powerful but potentially confusing property of broadcasting is that arrays of different shapes may be broadcast together if the following rule is satisfied: starting with the trailing dimension and working forward, each array's dimension must either be the same or equal to one. If one array has more dimensions than the other, then one assumes that the latter's dimensions are prepended with as many implied ones as necessary to make the total number of dimensions match. The final result will then have the larger of each dimension. Here is a simple example:

```
> a
array([[1, 2, 3],
       [4, 5, 6]]
> b
array([0, 1, 2]))
> a+b
array([[1, 3, 5],
       [4, 6, 8]])
```

We see here that b is added to each row of a. More elaborate examples may be found at *https://numpy.org/doc/stable/user/basics.broadcasting.html*.

7.8.2 Implicit loops

Another way to think of array broadcasting is that it is an *implicit* or *implied* loop. For example, suppose we had an array of 100 x values ranging from 0 to 4π, and we wanted to create an array of y values defined by the expression $y = \sin(x)$. We could do this using an explicit for loop as follows:

```
x = np.linspace(0, 4*np.pi, 100)
y = np.zeros_like(x)
for i, val in enumerate(x):
    y[i] = np.sin(val)
```

However, we could replace this code with two lines

```
x = np.linspace(0, 4*np.pi, 100)
y = np.sin(x)
```

The line y=np.sin(x) creates the new array y with the same shape as x and calculates each element of y based on the corresponding element of x without the need to write a **for** loop. A loop is still being performed, but it is done *implicitly* rather than *explicitly*.

Using array broadcasting as an implicit loop is much faster than writing explicit loops. As another example, suppose we have a large array of values and we want to have a new array that contains the difference in adjacent values from the original array:

```
n = 1000000   # number of data points
# Create array of random data between -500 and 500
d = 1000*np.random.random(n) - 500
diff = np.zeros(n-1)   # Array of differences

# Explicit Loop
for i in range(0, len(diff)):
    diff[i] = d[i+1] - d[i]
```

Here is an implicit loop version of the same logic:

```
# Implicit Loop
diff[0:n-1] = d[1:n] - d[0:n-1]
```

In Section 21.9.6 we show that the implicit version of this code runs in the neighborhood of 100 times faster than the explicit-loop version.

7.9 Array Statistics

Arrays have methods for returning the maximum and minimum values, as well as simple statistics. For an array named *arr* these methods are:

- *arr*.max() returns the maximum value of the array.
- *arr*.min() returns the minimum value of the array.
- *arr*.sum() returns the sum of all the values in the array.
- *arr*.mean() returns the mean value of the array.
- *arr*.std() returns the standard deviation of the array.
- *arr*.var() returns the variance of the the array.

The **numpy** module also contains functions for computing statistics from arrays. Many of these are similar to their array method counterparts, but have more options.

- max(*arr*) computes the maximum value in *arr*.
- min(*arr*) computes the minimum value in *arr*.
- median(*arr* [, *axis*]) computes the median of the values in *arr*.
- average(*arr* [, *axis*, *weights*]) computes the weighted average of the values in *arr*. The array *weights* contains the weights for the average.
- mean(*arr* [, *axis*]) computes the mean of the values in *arr*.
- std(*arr* [, *axis*]) computes the standard deviation of the values in *arr*.
- var(*arr* [, *axis*]) computes the variance of the values in *arr*.

For multidimensional data arrays the optional *axis* argument specifies along which axis to perform the calculation. This argument is simply an integer, with 0 denoting the first axis, 1 the second axis, etc. For example,

```
> a
array([[1, 2, 3],
       [4, 5, 6]])
> a.min(axis=0)
array([1, 2, 3])
> a.min(axis=1)
array([1, 4])
```

The previous functions are not suitable for data arrays containing undefined (NaN) values. To compute the mean, standard deviation, and variance for such data we can use the functions below, which ignore the NaN values.

- nanmean(*data [, axis]*) computes the mean of the values in *data* while ignoring NaN values.

- nanstd(*data [, axis]*) computes the standard deviation of the values in *data* while ignoring NaN values.

- nanvar(*data [, axis]*) computes the variance of the values in *data* while ignoring NaN values.

7.10   Finding Shape and Size

There are two very useful functions for finding the shape and size of an existing array:

- shape(*a*) returns the shape of array *a* as a tuple.

- size(*a*) returns the number of elements in *a*.

The array's shape and size attributes may also be used.

The regular Python function len() also works on Numpy arrays, but care must be exercised in interpreting the result, as it only returns the size of the first dimension. For a 1-D array the len() function returns the number of elements, but for a 2-D array it only returns the number of rows.

7.11   Reshaping, Transposing, and Shifting

Useful methods and functions for changing the shape of an array, or changing the positions of its elements, include the following:

- The *a*.flatten() array method returns a 1-D version of the multidimensional array *a*.

- The reshape(*a, ns*) function returns a copy of array *a* with a new shape *ns*. The new shape is given as a tuple. The new array must have the same number of elements as the original array. If one element of the new shape tuple is specified as −1, then that dimension is automatically computed to satisfy the size requirement.

- The roll(*a, shift*) function moves the elements of *a* by the amount *shift*. For a multi-dimensional array the additional keyword axis specifies which axis to roll. For example:

```
> a
array([0, 1, 2, 3, 4, 5, 6, 7, 8, 9])
> np.roll(a, -4)
array([4, 5, 6, 7, 8, 9, 0, 1, 2, 3])
> b
array([[ 0,  1,  2,  3,  4,  5],
       [-6, -5, -4, -3, -2, -1]])
```

```
> np.roll(b,-1, axis=0)
array([[-6, -5, -4, -3, -2, -1],
       [ 0,  1,  2,  3,  4,  5]])
> np.roll(b, -3, axis=1)
array([[ 3,  4,  5,  0,  1,  2],
       [-3, -2, -1, -6, -5, -4]])
```

- The `transpose(a)` function or `a.transpose()` array method returns a transposed copy of array *a*.

- The `rot90(a, n)` function returns a copy of *a* rotated clockwise by $n \times 90°$. A negative value of *n* will rotate *a* counterclockwise.

7.12   Sorting

An array *a* may be sorted using the `sort(a)` Numpy function or the `a.sort()` array method. The difference between the two is that the function returns a copy of the array, while the method sorts the array in-place.

7.12.1   Sorting 2-D arrays

For multidimensional arrays the `axis` keyword specifies over which axis the sorting will be accomplished. Since 2-D arrays are commonly encountered we spend some time discussing how to sort them. Recall that for a 2-D array the first axis (`axis=0`) refers to the rows, while the second axis (`axis=1`) refers to the columns. So if `axis=0` then the rows within each column are sorted, and the result is an array in which the values within each column are increasing. If `axis=1` then the columns within each row are sorted, and the result is that the values within each row are increasing.

If the `axis` keyword is omitted then it defaults to `axis=-1` which means the last axis will be sorted. For a 2-D array `axis=-1` is equivalent to `axis=1`. If the `axis` keyword is explicitly set to `None` then the array is flattened before sorting. Some examples are shown here:

```
> a
array([[ 3, -4,  2, -7],
       [-9, -1, -3,  1],
       [ 5,  2, -4,  2]])
> np.sort(a)   # column axis is sorted by default
array([[-7, -4,  2,  3],
       [-9, -3, -1,  1],
       [-4,  2,  2,  5]])
> np.sort(a, axis=0)   # row axis is sorted
array([[-9, -4, -4, -7],
       [ 3, -1, -3,  1],
       [ 5,  2,  2,  2]])
> np.sort(a, axis=1)   # column axis is sorted
array([[-7, -4,  2,  3],
       [-9, -3, -1,  1],
       [-4,  2,  2,  5]])
```

```
> np.sort(a, axis=-1)   # -1 is equivalent to 1
array([[-7, -4, 2, 3],
       [-9, -3, -1, 1],
       [-4, 2, 2, 5]])
> np.sort(a, axis=None)   # flatten and then sort
array([-9, -7, -4, -4, -3, -1, 1, 2, 2, 2, 3, 5])
```

7.12.2   Reverse sorting

If reverse sorting is desired we can simply combine the **sort()** function with
appropriate array indexing as shown here:

```
> np.sort(a, axis=0)[::-1,:]   # row axis reversed
array([[ 5, 2, 2, 2],
       [ 3, -1, -3, 1],
       [-9, -4, -4, -7]])
> np.sort(a, axis=1)[:,::-1]   # column axis reversed
array([[ 3, 2, -4, -7],
       [ 1, -1, -3, -9],
       [ 5, 2, 2, -4]])
```

7.13   Singular-dimension Arrays

Frequently a function or routine will return a multi-dimensional array that
has one or more dimensions which are singular (having only one element
along that axis). An example of such an array is the (3×1) array

```
> a = np.array([[1], [3], [-5]])
> a
array([[ 1],
       [ 3],
       [-5]])
> np.shape(a)
(3, 1)
```

This looks like a one-dimensional array, but is really a two-dimensional array
with one of the dimensions (the second in this case) being singular. Such
arrays often cause problems because the user may think they are dealing with
an array of fewer dimensions. For example, if we mistakenly assumed that
a was a truly one-dimensional array, and tried to add it to another actual
one-dimensional array, our results would be quite unexpected, as shown here.

```
> a
array([[ 1],
       [ 3],
       [-5]])
> b
array([ 4, -7, 2])
```

```
> a + b
array([[ 5, -6, 3],
       [ 7, -4, 5],
       [ -1, -12, -3]])
```

Such problems are often difficult to debug because they might not generate an error message, but instead just give unexpected results. Once the problem is identified, the `squeeze(a)` function or `a.squeeze()` method comes to the rescue. These return a copy of the array *a* with any singular dimensions removed:

```
> c = np.squeeze(a)
> c
array([ 1, 3, -5])
> c + b
array([ 5, -4, -3])
```

Although singular-dimension arrays may seem absurd, they can be quite useful. For example, a 2-D array with a singular second dimension such as the example above can be thought of as a *column vector* (it is even displayed as a column), while a 2-D array with a singular first dimension (and any 1-D array) looks like a *row vector*.

```
> a = np.array([[1], [3], [-5]])
> print(a)
[[ 1]
 [ 3]
 [-5]]
> b = np.array([[2, 4, 6]])
> print(b)
[[2 4 6]]
```

Singular-dimension arrays are useful for horizontally stacking arrays, and are discussed further in Sec. 7.16.1.

7.14 Adding or Removing Elements

7.14.1 Appending elements

Elements may be appended to the end of an existing array *a* using the `append(a, elems)` function. This returns a copy, and does not change the original array.

```
> a
array([1, 2, 3, 4, 5])
> b = np.append(a,[6,7])
> b
array([1, 2, 3, 4, 5, 6, 7])
```

7.14.2   Inserting elements

Elements may be inserted into an existing array a using the
insert(a, ind, elems) function. In this function, ind is the index before
which to insert the array elements indicated by elems.

```
> a
array([1, 2, 3, 4, 5])
> b = np.insert(a, 2, [-3, -4])
> b
array([ 1, 2, -3, -4, 3, 4, 5])
```

This operation leaves the original array unchanged.

7.14.3   Deleting elements

The delete(a, ind) function deletes the elements of array a at the specified
indices given by ind. The original array is unchanged.

```
> a
array([1, 2, 3, 4, 5, 6])
> b = np.delete(a, 3)
> b
array([1, 2, 3, 5, 6])
```

7.15   Assigning and Reassigning Elements

Elements of an array can be assigned or reassigned values using the assignment operator. Multiple elements can be assigned or reassigned at once using
ranges of indices. Here are some examples:

```
> a
array([-5, -4, -3, -2, -1, 0, 1, 2, 3, 4])
> a[3] = 99
> a
array([-5, -4, -3, 99, -1, 0, 1, 2, 3, 4])
> a[5:7] = [100, 200]
> a
array([ -5, -4, -3, 99, -1, 100, 200, 2, 3, 4])
```

7.16   Stacking and Splitting Arrays

Existing arrays may be combined into a single array, or an array may be split
into multiple subarrays.

7.16.1   Stacking

Multiple arrays may be stacked either horizontally (column-wise) or vertically
(row-wise) into a single array, using the hstack() or vstack() functions. A
vstack() example is shown here:

```
> a
array([[0, 1, 2]])
> b
array([[3, 4, 5],
       [6, 7, 8]])
> c
array([[ 9, 10, 11]])
> d = np.vstack((a,b,c))
> d
array([[ 0,  1,  2],
       [ 3,  4,  5],
       [ 6,  7,  8],
       [ 9, 10, 11]])
```

Notice that for vertical stacking the number of columns in each array must be identical (three in the example above). Also, note that the arrays to be stacked are provided as a tuple.

Horizontal stacking proceeds along the same lines, only in this case it is the number of rows which must be identical. Horizontal stacking can cause unexpected headaches if 1-D arrays are used. Any 1-D arrays must be transformed in to 2-D arrays with a singular second dimension, so that they act as *column vectors* (see Sec. 7.13) before being stacked. For example, say we have the 4×2 array

```
> a = np.array([[2,3], [8,4], [-3, 5], [0, 9]])
> a
array([[ 2,  3],
       [ 8,  4],
       [-3,  5],
       [ 0,  9]])
```

and we want to stack it with the 1-D array

```
> b = np.array([-4, -2, 0, 8])
> b
array([-4, -2, 0, 8])
```

as a new column. Since array b only has a single row we cannot horizontally stack with with array a, which has four rows. So, we must reshape array b to a 4×1 array before stacking it with array a. This is shown as follows

```
> b = np.reshape(b, (4,1))
> b
array([[-4],
       [-2],
       [ 0],
       [ 8]])
```

```
> c = np.hstack((a,b))
> c
array([[ 2,  3, -4],
       [ 8,  4, -2],
       [-3,  5,  0],
       [ 0,  9,  8]])
```

7.16.2 Splitting

An array may also be split into multiple subarrays using the `split()`, `hsplit()` or `vsplit()` functions. A `vsplit()` example is shown.

```
> a
array([[ 0,  1,  2],
       [ 3,  4,  5],
       [ 6,  7,  8],
       [9, 10, 11]])
> b = np.vsplit(a, 4)
> b
[array([[0, 1, 2]]), array([[3, 4, 5]]),
 array([[6, 7, 8]]), array([[ 9, 10, 11]])]
> c = np.vsplit(a, 2)
> c
[array([[0, 1, 2], [3, 4, 5]]),
 array([[ 6, 7, 8], [ 9, 10, 11]])]
> d = np.hsplit(a, 3)
> d
[array([[0],
        [3],
        [6],
        [9]]), array([[ 1],
        [ 4],
        [ 7],
        [10]]), array([[ 2],
        [ 5],
        [ 8],
        [11]])]
```

The integer argument to `split()`, `vsplit()` or `hsplit()` specifies how many subarrays to create, and must be such that the array can be split into same-sized subarrays. The functions return a list containing the subarrays.

Note that the subarrays created from `vsplit()` and `hsplit()` will always have more than one dimension. For example, the subarrays created from the first example above have shape 1×3, while those from the last example have shape 4×1. These are singular-dimension arrays, and if truly 1-D arrays are needed then the `squeeze()` function will need to be applied to each of the subarrrays (see Sec. 7.13).

7.17   Merging Two 1-D Arrays into 2-D Arrays

Sometimes we will have two 1-D arrays representing coordinate values, such as *x* and *y* positions or longitudes and latitudes, that we want to merge into two 2-D arrays. This is done using the `meshgrid(x, y)` function. This returns two 2-D arrays. This is illustrated here:

```
> x
array([-5, -4, -3, -2, -1, 0, 1, 2, 3, 4])
> y
array([0, 1, 2, 3, 4, 5, 6, 7])
> x2d, y2d = np.meshgrid(x, y)
> x2d
array([[-5, -4, -3, -2, -1, 0, 1, 2, 3, 4],
       [-5, -4, -3, -2, -1, 0, 1, 2, 3, 4],
       [-5, -4, -3, -2, -1, 0, 1, 2, 3, 4],
       [-5, -4, -3, -2, -1, 0, 1, 2, 3, 4],
       [-5, -4, -3, -2, -1, 0, 1, 2, 3, 4],
       [-5, -4, -3, -2, -1, 0, 1, 2, 3, 4],
       [-5, -4, -3, -2, -1, 0, 1, 2, 3, 4],
       [-5, -4, -3, -2, -1, 0, 1, 2, 3, 4]])
> y2d
array([[0, 0, 0, 0, 0, 0, 0, 0, 0, 0],
       [1, 1, 1, 1, 1, 1, 1, 1, 1, 1],
       [2, 2, 2, 2, 2, 2, 2, 2, 2, 2],
       [3, 3, 3, 3, 3, 3, 3, 3, 3, 3],
       [4, 4, 4, 4, 4, 4, 4, 4, 4, 4],
       [5, 5, 5, 5, 5, 5, 5, 5, 5, 5],
       [6, 6, 6, 6, 6, 6, 6, 6, 6, 6],
       [7, 7, 7, 7, 7, 7, 7, 7, 7, 7]])
```

7.18   Logical Operations with Arrays

7.18.1   The where() function

The `where()` function provides a way of searching through an array and identifying the position of elements that meet a simple condition. For example, say we wanted to identify all the elements of an array a that are less than 1:

```
> a
array([-3, 5, 2, -8, -4, 4, 6])
> result = np.where(a < 1)
> result
(array([0, 3, 4]),)
```

The result of the `where()` function is a tuple containing an integer array of index values for those elements of a for which the condition is `True`. These results may then be used as indexes to return the values of the array that meet the specified condition:[4]

```
> a[result]
array([-3, -8, -4])
```

7.18.2   More complex conditions

If the condition being searched for is more complex, such as identifying the elements that fall within a certain range of values, we must be a little more creative. For example, lets say we have the array

```
> a
array([-6, -5, -4, -3, -2, -1, 0, 1, 1, 2])
```

and we want to identify the elements that are greater than −5 and less than or equal to 2. If we try

```
> np.where((a > -5) and (a <= 2))
```

we get an error message that states, *"The truth value of an array with more than one element is ambiguous."* However, we can get around this by recognizing that an expression such as `a > -5` creates a Boolean array of `True/False` values. The created array is the same shape as the original array, with `True` values in all elements corresponding to where the elements in the original array, `a`, meet the condition, and `False` values elsewhere:

```
> a > -5
array([False, False, True, True, True, True,
             True, True, True, True])
```

Boolean arrays can be multiplied and added, and since `False` is equivalent to 0 while `True` is equivalent to any non-zero number, the following rules hold for Boolean multiplication and addition:

$$True \times True = True$$
$$True \times False = False$$
$$False \times False = False$$
$$True + True = True$$
$$True + False = True$$
$$False + False = False$$

---

[4]The ability to use arrays of integers or Boolean values to index Numpy arrays is sometimes referred to as *fancy indexing*.

Thus, multiplication of Boolean values is equivalent to and, while addition is equivalent to or. Armed with this, we can still use the where function with a complex condition, simply by replacing and with *, and or with +. For example:

```
> np.where((a > -5)*(a <= 1))
(array([2, 3, 4, 5, 6, 7, 8]),)
```

7.19   Random Numbers

The Numpy module named random contains functions for generating random numbers and arrays filled with random numbers.[5] Here we assume that the numpy.random module has been imported with the alias ra using the command:

```
from numpy import random as ra
```

7.19.1   Random integers

The randint(a, b) function can be used to generate uniformly distributed random integers, where a and b are the minimum and maximum values. If the size keyword is included, then an array of random integers is returned.

```
> ra.randint(-3, 8)
7
> ra.randint(-3, 8, size=10)
array([ 1, 5, 2, 6, -1, -2, 5, -2, 2, 4])
> ra.randint(-3, 8, size=(2,5))
array([[ 5, 4, -3, 0, -1],
       [ 2, 6, 1, -3, -1]])
```

7.19.2   Uniformly distributed random floating-point values

For random uniformly-distributed floating-point values we utilize the random_sample() function. The only argument is an optional size for the number of values returned. If left blank then only a single value is returned. The values are uniformly distributed between 0.0 and 1.0. If a different range of values is desired, such as from m to n, then the results may be multiplied by the quantity $(n - m)$ and then added to m. For example, to produce an array of six numbers between 2.0 and 5.0:

---

[5]Python itself also has a module named random that contains functions for generating uniformly and randomly distributed single values. The numpy.random module has the advantage of being able to create arrays of random numbers in addition to creating single values. It also provides access to a much larger set of distribution functions.

```
> (5-2)*ra.random_sample(6) + 2
array([3.08083742, 2.94845799, 2.74398572, 4.33891915,
        4.34054581, 3.63859273])
```

7.19.3   Normally distributed random floating-point values

The normal(μ, σ, s) function creates an array of s values that are normally distributed around a mean of μ with a standard deviation of σ. If the size s is omitted, then it produces a single value. For example, to create an array of six values normally distributed around a mean of 3 and a standard deviation of 1.5:

```
> ra.normal(3.0, 1.5, 6)
array([2.17863762, 3.39374718, 2.51894507, 4.25738415,
        4.46369283, 3.8629593])
```

7.20   Masked Arrays

Masked arrays are arrays in which certain elements are identified as being masked and not used in display or for calculations. A masked array actually consists of two arrays. One is an array containing the data values; the other is a Boolean array (called the mask) of the same shape as the data array, with True representing masked elements and False representing unmasked elements. Masked arrays are often used for displaying 2-D images in which some of the pixels or data are either undefined or unphysical. For example, ocean temperature data may be stored in a masked array with the land areas masked. The masked elements are not used when computing array statistics such as sum(), mean(), and so on.

Masked arrays are created using the numpy.ma module. The example below shows the creation of a simple masked 1-D integer array, with two of the middle elements masked.

```
> a = np.ma.array(np.arange(0,7),
    mask=[0, 0, 0, 1, 1, 0, 0])
> a
masked_array(data=[0, 1, 2, --, --, 5, 6],
    mask=[False, False, False, True, True, False,
    False], fill_value=999999)
```

The optional fill_value is the value assigned to the masked elements. The default value depends on the data type of the array. It can also be set on creation of the masked array. Consult the Numpy documentation for details.

7.21 Reading/Writing Arrays from/to Files

Numpy has several functions for writing arrays to files and for reading arrays from files. The usage of some of these functions is quite detailed and can be tailored with many keywords for specific applications. Here we only mention their most basic use.

7.21.1 Writing arrays to a file

The tofile() method

The least-complicated way to write all the elements of an array to a file is the `tofile()` method of Numpy arrays. This does not preserve the shape of the array but simply writes the elements consecutively. For example, if a is the 2-D array

```
a = np.array([[0,2,4],[1,3,5]])
```

then

```
> a.tofile('a-file.txt', sep=', ', format='%.2f')
```

produces a file named *a-file.txt* that has all the elements of a printed to single line with values separated by a comma and a space:

```
0.00, 2.00, 4.00, 1.00, 3.00, 5.00
```

A few notes:

- The array is printed out in row order, with the entire first row written before the next row.

- The only required argument is the name of the file.

- If the newline character, \n, is used as the separator, the values are each placed on a separate line of the file.

- If the keyword **sep** is omitted or is an empty string then a binary file is created.

- The format argument can be used to format the data written to the file.

The savetxt() function

More control in how an array *a* is written to a file can be achieved using the `numpy.savetxt()` function. Using the same 2-D array from the previous example, the code

```
> np.savetxt('a-file.txt', a, delimiter=', ',
      fmt='%3.1f', header='Start of data',
      footer='End of data')
```

produces a file containing

```
# Start of data
0.0, 2.0, 4.0
1.0, 3.0, 5.0
# End of data
```

Additional features:

- The shape of the array is preserved when written to the file.
- The only required arguments are the filename and the array.
- 1-D arrays will be written out with one value per line of the file.
- Arrays of higher dimension than 2-D can also be written to a file using `savetxt()`, but it is not a straight-forward process and is not covered here.
- The fmt keyword can be used to format the data written to the file.

7.21.2   Reading data from a text file

The fromfile() function

The simplest way to read a series of numbers from a file into a Numpy array is the `fromfile()` function. The numbers to be read should all be on a single line separated by whitespace, a comma, or some other delimiter, or each number should be on a separate line.

For example, a file named *data-file.txt* containing the data

```
0.00, 2.00, 4.00, 1.00, 3.00, 5.00
```

could be read into an array a by the simple command:

```
a = np.fromfile('data-file.txt', sep=',',
        dtype=np.float_)
```

Additional comments:

- If each data value is on a separate line, then use sep='\n'
- dtype controls the data type of the created Numpy array.

The loadtxt() function

More control in reading data from a text file into a Numpy array is provided by the `loadtxt()` function. This has the general syntax:

```
a = np.loadtxt(filename, dtype=dtype, delimiter=del,
    skiprows=sr, usecols=cols)
```

The function will read data from a file named *filename* and create the array named *a*. The only required argument is the filename. The remaining optional keywords control how the data is read.

- dtype is the data type of the created array (np.float_, np.int_, etc.)

- delimiter is a string representing the data separator, such as comma, semicolon, white space, etc. The default is any whitespace.

- skiprows is the number of lines of data to skip, and is used to move past header rows.

- usecols is a tuple giving the column indices to read. For example, if the first and third columns are desired, we would use usecols=(0,2). If only a single column is desired, a comma must still be used. For example, if only the second column is desired, the syntax would be usecols=(1,).

As an example, imagine we have a data file named *data_file.txt* that contains the following data, including a header row:

```
height (inches), weight (lbs)
69.8, 177.3
68.9, 174.7
73.2, 150.5
68.1, 132.3
73.4, 210.6
```

We can read the data into an array as follows:

```
> data = np.loadtxt('data_file.txt', dtype=np.float_,
                    delimiter=',', skiprows=1)
```

The genfromtxt() function

The most flexible and also the most complex means of reading data from a file into a Numpy array is the genfromtxt() method. For details on using this method, consult the Numpy documentation.

7.22   Saving/Loading Arrays as .npy and .npz Files

In addition to the functions and methods for reading and writing Numpy arrays described previously, Numpy also has a very simple way to create and read binary files of Numpy array data. These files will not be portable to other programming languages or platforms, but are very handy for storing and sharing array data between Python programs.

7.22.1   Numpy .npy files

The numpy.save(*filename, a*) function saves the array *a* into a binary file named *filename*. The created file will have the file extension *.npy*. Data can be read from the file into a Numpy array using the numpy.load(*filename*) function. The shape and size of the saved array are preserved when saved and loaded.

7.22.2 Numpy .npz files

Using the numpy.savez() function, multiple arrays can be saved to a Numpy array archive file. The arrays do not have to be of the same shape. Here is an example with two arrays of different shapes:

```
> a
> array([[0, 2, 4],
         [1, 3, 5]])
> b
array([-3, -2, -1, 0, 1, 2, 3])
> np.savez('a-b-file', a, b)
```

This creates a file named *a-b-file.npz* which contains both arrays. We load the data from the file using the numpy.load() function. However, with a *.npz* file the result is not an array, but a data object that contains both arrays. We access the individual arrays by first finding their names, and then using them as dictionary keys. For example:

```
> z = np.load('a-b-file.npz')
> z.files
['arr_1', 'arr_0']
> z['arr_1']
array([-3, -2, -1, 0, 1, 2, 3])
> z['arr_0']
array([[0, 2, 4],
       [1, 3, 5]])
```

The load() function automatically assigns names for each array in the *.npz* file, in this case 'arr_0' and 'arr_1'. We can force the names to be specified when we save the arrays to the file:

```
> np.savez('a-b-file', a=a, b=b)
> z = np.load('a-b-file.npz')
> z.files
['a', 'b']
> z['a']
array([[0, 2, 4],
  [1, 3, 5]])
> z['b']
array([-3, -2, -1, 0, 1, 2, 3])
```

7.23 Memory Mapping Arrays

There may be times when it is necessary to work with very large arrays that individually or collectively exceed the available physical memory of the computer. Numpy provides a capability called *memory mapping* that allows super-sized arrays to be stored on the computer's hard drive. Numpy routines can continue to operate on these memory-mapped arrays as though they were "ordinary" Numpy arrays stored in core memory. The operations will, however, be much slower than if conducted entirely from core memory.

Memory-mapped arrays are created using the Numpy `memmap()` function. The arguments include:

- *filename*, the required first argument specifying the name of the file for storing the array on disk.

- `dtype`, keyword for specifying the data type for storing data to the file. It can be any Python or Numpy data type (see Sec. 7.3).

- `mode`, keyword for specifying the mode for opening the file. Options are `'r'` for opening an existing file for read only, `'r+'` for for opening an existing file for reading or writing, or `'w+'` for creating a new file or opening an existing file for reading and writing.

- `shape`, keyword specifying the dimensions of the memory-mapped array.

There are some important options to consider before using memory mapping, and the documention should be consulted.[6] The following simple example conveys the essential idea of using memory-mapped arrays:

```
import numpy as np
filename = 'newfile.dat'
newarray = np.memmap(filename, dtype=np.float_,
                     mode='w+', shape=(2,4))
```

The above code creates a memory-mapped array with shape (2,4), using the given filename for the corresponding disk file. The `'w+'` option instructs the class to create the file, overwriting any existing file with the same name, and to use it for both reading and writing.

The memory-mapped array, `newarray`, may now be used anywhere a Numpy array can be used, with the important difference that disk space rather than core memory is allocated to accommodate the array:

```
> data = np.arange(8, dtype=np.float_)
> data.resize((2,4))
> newarray[:] = data[:]
> newarray
memmap([[0., 1., 2., 3.],
        [4., 5., 6., 7.]])
```

Note that we are careful to give the range of indices, `[:]`, for both `data[:]` and `newarray[:]`. If this were omitted and we typed `newarray=data`, then

---

[6]See *http://docs.scipy.org/doc/numpy/reference/generated/numpy.memmap.html*

`newarray` would simply be a reference, or pointer, to the original, traditional data array.

Keep in mind that operations on large arrays, whether memory-mapped or not, can create either intermediate or final results that are themselves large arrays. Failure to consider this may result in inadvertently overwhelming the physical memory of the computer.

EIGHT

FUNCTIONS AND MODULES

8.1 Functions

8.1.1 Defining functions

The basic template for defining functions is:

```
def function_name([arguments]):
    {Python statements performing
     desired tasks and calculations.}
    return [values to be returned]
```

Function definitions always begin with the `def` statement, which denotes the beginning of the block of code used to define the function. The function definition ends when the code block ends.

Immediately after the `def` statement, and on the same line, the name of the function is given, followed by parentheses. Inside the parentheses are listed any arguments that are to be input to the function. Even if the function requires no input arguments the parentheses are still required. The last statement in the code block is always a `return` statement, which when encountered returns control back to the routine or program from which the function was called. Any statements on the same line as the `return` statement will be evaluated and the results returned to the calling program or routine.

The code below shows a very simple example as to how a Python function is defined and used. This code defines a function named `sphere_area()` that takes a single argument representing a radius and returns the surface area of a sphere of that radius:

```
def sphere_area(r):
    pi = 3.1415927
    return 4*pi*r**2
```

Once this function has been defined and loaded into memory, it can be called from a program or from the interactive shell and used as shown here:

```
> sphere_area(5)
314.15927
```

8.1.2 Keywords

Keywords are optional arguments that can be used to control the flow of operations within the function or to override default parameter values. As an example, suppose that we want our function to be able to evaluate the surface area of the sphere given either a radius or a diameter. We modify the function to include a Boolean keyword named `radius` that, if `True`, instructs the function to treat the value `r` as a radius and if `False` treats `r` as a diameter. The modified function could look like this:

```
def sphere_area(r, radius=True):
    pi = 3.1415927
    if not radius:
        r /= 2.0   # Divide input value by 2
    return 4*pi*r**2
```

To calculate the area of a sphere of radius 5 units, we then may use the function as follows:

```
> sphere_area(5, radius=True)
314.15927
```

To calculate the area of a sphere of diameter 5 units:

```
> sphere_area(5,radius=False)
78.5398175
```

Note that since we defined the function with the keyword `radius` defaulted to `True`, we can also omit radius as an argument if we are treating `r` as a radius:

```
> sphere_area(5)
314.15927
```

While the example above uses a keyword of Boolean type, keywords may be of any data type.

8.1.3 The return statement

Functions may contain multiple `return` statements. However, it is very important to note that only one `return` statement is ever executed during a single function call. Once any `return` statement is encountered, control passes back to the calling routine, and no further statements within the function are executed during that call.

8.1.4 Arguments

Functions may accept multiple input arguments of any data type. The order of arguments in the function call statement must match the order of arguments in the function's definition.

Functions may also accept no arguments. In this case, the argument list between the parentheses is left empty in the function definition. When a function with an empty arguments list is called, the parentheses must still be included, or the function call will instead be treated as a bound function (see Sec. 8.1.7). Calling a zero-argument function while omitting the parentheses is a common error that is often difficult to debug.

It is also possible to design functions that accept an unlimited, or open-ended number of arguments, including keyword arguments. This is explained in Sec. 8.1.11.

8.1.5 Scoping rules

Variable scoping refers to how Python variables are shared between code blocks, calling routines, and functions. In Python, any variable that is defined prior to calling a function is a *global variable* and is available to the function, even if it was not passed explicitly. For example, we first define a function that adds the input to another variable a that is not defined within the function

```
def my_function(b):
    return(a + b)
```

and then define the variable a before calling the function.

```
> a = 10    # Global variable
> my_function(2)
12
> a
10
```

In this case, even though the variable a was not explicitly passed as an argument to my_function(), because the variable was defined before the function was called, my_function() knew about variable a and was able to use it within the function.

However, if we define a variable within a function, that variable is known only to the function. For example, if the function definition were

```
def my_function(b):
    b = 4    # Local variable
    return(a + b)
```

and then we ran

```
> a = 10    # Global variable
> my_function(2)
14
> b
NameError: name 'b' is not defined
```

an error is produced stating that b is not defined. In this case, b is a local variable to the function.

A local variable of the same name as a global variable may be defined inside of a function without conflict. For example, using the function definition

```
def my_function(b):
    a = 3    # Local variable
    return(a + b)
```

and then running

```
> a = 10    # Global variable
> my_function(2)
5
> a
10
```

shows that the local variable a defined inside the function is used for the calculation of the return value, but does not overwrite the global variable. The local variable a and the global variable a are completely separate entities.

The value of a global variable cannot be altered inside of a function unless the global statement is used. The use of the global statement makes the variable mutable within the function. We show how this is accomplished by modifying the code from the prior example, defining the function as

```
def my_function(b):
    global a    # Declares a as mutable.
    a = 3
    return(a + b)
```

and then running

```
> a = 10    # Global variable
> my_function(2)
5
> a
3
```

shows that the global variable a was altered within the function.

8.1.6 Passing arguments by value versus by reference

One aspect of arguments that can cause confusion and errors if not understood properly is how Python passes arguments to a function. For simple data objects such as integers, strings, or floating-point data Python simply passes the value to the function. However, for compound objects such as lists or arrays Python passes the reference or pointer to the actual location of the data in memory. Any modifications to the passed arguments in this case will result in modifications to the original objects. In essence, compound objects passed as arguments to functions are treated as though they are global variables.[1]

To illustrate the difference of passing by values vs. passing by reference, consider this function which simply adds 56 to the argument and then returns the result:

```
def my_function(b):
    b += 56
    return (b)
```

Passing by value

If the argument passed to `my_function()` is an integer variable, then the original value of the variable is not altered by the function, as shown here:

```
> a = 6
> print(my_function(a))
62
> a
6
```

The value of variable a is passed to the function, but a itself is not modified.

Passing by reference

If the argument passed to `my_function()` is a Numpy array then the actual array (or, more properly, a pointer or reference to the memory location storing the values of the array) is passed to the function, and the function globally modifies these values as shown:

```
> import numpy as np
> a = np.arange(0, 5)
> my_function(a)
array([112, 113, 114, 115, 116])
> a
array([112, 113, 114, 115, 116])
```

---

[1]Compound objects passed as arguments are mutable inside of the function, which can cause headaches if not accounted for.

This is very different behavior than when a simple object was passed! Failure to account for this behavior can lead to unexpected behavior and many debugging headaches. For this reason, **when passing a compound object such as an array or list to a function, a deep copy of the object** (see Sections 2.12 and 7.7) **should be passed, not the object itself.** For example:

```
> a = np.arange(0, 5)
> my_function(np.copy(a))
array([56, 57, 58, 59, 60])
> a
array([0, 1, 2, 3, 4])
```

preserves the original array a, because we sent a copy of it to the function.

8.1.7   Bound functions

Once defined, a function may be *bound* by invoking its name without parentheses. This essentially aliases the function to a different name, and primes it so that it is ready to go once arguments are provided at some later time. For example, using the function defined by

```
def my_function(b):
    return(a + b)
```

and then running

```
> a = 10
> func = my_function   # Creates bound function
> val = 100
> func(val)   # Calls bound function
110
```

shows that the bound function func can be used in place of the original function.

The value of any global variables used in the function are those in place at the time the arguments are supplied to the bound function, not at the time that it is bound. For example, if we now run the code

```
> a = 10
> func = my_function   # Creates bound function
> val = 100
> a = 30
> func(val)   # Calls bound function
130
```

note that a different result is obtained, because the value of a was 30 when arguments were supplied to the bound function.

8.1.8   The lambda operator

A simple one-line function can be quickly defined using the `lambda` operator, which has the following syntax:

```
f = lambda arguments: expression
```

When called, the created function named `f()` takes the arguments and returns the evaluated expression. As a simple example, a one-line function to return the area of a triangle of base b and height h could be defined and used as shown here:

```
> area = lambda b, h: b*h/2.0
> area(3, 5)
7.5
```

8.1.9   Querying and inspecting functions

The source code for lambdas, and some functions, can be retrieved using the `inspect` module's `getsource()` function. The name of the function or lambda is passed as the argument, and a string containing the source code is returned. The `inspect` module must first be imported.

The `getsource()` function works for user-defined lambdas and functions, but it may not work with functions imported from a library such as Numpy. For example, importing the Numpy library and then calling `inspect.getsource(np.sin)` returns an error.

The `inspect` module contains many features for inspecting objects. The online Python documentation can be consulted for more information on its capabilities and use.

User defined and built-in functions and methods have a `__name__` attribute (note double underscores) which stores the name of the function or module. For example, if we create the bound function

```
> a = round
```

we can find the name of the function via

```
> a.__name__
'round'
```

8.1.10   Unpacking arguments and keywords

In Sec. 2.13 we showed how a list or tuple may be unpacked using the `*` operator. We then gave an example using the `range()` function as to how this could be handy for passing the arguments to a function in list form. In a similar manner we can send keyword arguments to a function in dictionary form using the double-asterisk operator, `**`. For example, if we wanted to use a function that required three keywords named `metric`, `radius`, and `eccentricity`, and if these were stored in a dictionary defined as

```
kd = {'metric' : False,
      'radius' : True,
      'eccentricity' : 0.02}
```

then we could could send **kd into the function rather than type each keyword argument separately.

8.1.11   Variable number of arguments and keywords

Functions may be written to accept an open-ended number of arguments and keywords. To define a function that accept an open-ended number of arguments we simply place an asterisk before the last argument in the arguments list. Any extra arguments passed to the function will be collected into this last variable as a tuple. This concept is illustrated by the function defined here, with two required arguments, a and b.

```
def myfunc(a, b, *args):
    print('a=', a)
    print('b=', b)
    print('args=', args)
    return None
```

which operates as follows

```
> myfunc(3, 4, 5, 6, 7, 8, 'hi', 'cat')
a= 3
b= 4
args= (5, 6, 7, 8, 'hi', 'cat')
```

The last argument in the list could be named whatever you want it to be, but traditionally it appears as *args in most documentation.

To have an open-ended number of keywords we use a double asterisk before the last keyword argument. This collects any unused keywords into a dictionary, as shown here with our modified function

```
def myfunc(a, b, *args,
          metric=True, radius=4.0, **kwargs):
    print('a=', a)
    print('b=', b)
    print('args=', args)
    print('metric=', metric)
    print('radius=', radius)
    print('kwargs=', kwargs)
    return None
```

which operates as shown here, where we pass two extra keywords to the function.

```
> myfunc(3, 4, 5, 6, 7, 8, 'hi', 'cat',
        metric=False, radius=3,
        miles=False, head=True)
a= 3
b= 4
args= (5, 6, 7, 8, 'hi', 'cat')
metric= False
radius= 3
kwargs= 'miles': False, 'head': True
```

The extra keywords and their values that we passed show up in the dictionary named kwargs.

The double-starred keyword argument could be named whatever we want it to be, but most documentation uses **kwargs.

8.2 Modules

8.2.1 Creating modules

A module is simply a collection of Python statements stored in a single file. Typically modules will contain several functions and/or constants, as well as possibly some class definitions (see Chapter 9), all organized around a theme.

The name of a module is taken from the name of the file in which it is stored. For example, the simple module shown below, which contains a single constant and two functions for the area and volume of a sphere, could be named Sphere and would be stored in a Python file named Sphere.py:

```
pi = 3.1415927

def area(r):
    return 4.0*pi*r**2

def volume(r):
    return (4.0/3.0)*pi*r**3
```

8.2.2 Importing and using modules

In order to use a module it must first be imported, using the syntax

```
import module_name
```

where *module_name* is the name of the module to be imported. The individual functions or constants within the module are then accessed by specifying the module name followed by a period and the name of the function or constant.

Using the above example of the **Sphere** module, we could import it and use it as shown here:

```
> import Sphere
> Sphere.pi
3.1415927
> Sphere.area(5)
314.15927
> Sphere.volume(5)
523.5987833333334
```

Importing a module automatically imports all the functions, constants, and class definitions contained within the module. If only a single function is needed, just that function can be imported, using the following syntax:

```
from module_name import function_name
```

As an example, suppose only the **volume()** function from **Sphere** is needed by a program. We could simply import that single function and use it as shown here:

```
> from Sphere import volume
> volume(5)
523.5987833333334
```

Notice that, when using the **from/import** construct, the module name no longer needs to precede the function name when used.

8.2.3   Aliasing

A module may be aliased to a new name on importing, so that a long module name will not have to be typed every time one of its functions or constants is used. See Sec. 4.8 for details about aliasing.

8.2.4   Specifying the path to module location

When using the import command to load a module, the file containing the module must reside either in the current working directory or in one of the directories listed in **sys.path**. To view a list of these directories, simply issue the commands

```
> import sys
> sys.path
```

and the list of directories is printed to the screen.

If a module to be loaded is not saved in either the current working directory or in one of the directories listed in `sys.path`, the module's directory can easily be appended to `sys.path` via the command

```
> sys.path.append(dirname)
```

where *dirname* is the path to the directory containing the module.

8.3 Documentation Strings

Document strings are optional triple-quoted strings that appear as the very first non-commented lines in a module, function, or method. Document strings usually contain information about the purpose of the function or module and its usage. The document string becomes an attribute of the object with the name __doc__ (notice the leading and trailing double underscores) and can be printed like any other attribute. For example, we can examine the document string for the built-in `float()` function as follows:

```
> print(float.__doc__)
Convert a string or number to a
floating point number, if possible.
```

Also, when running Python in interactive mode, many interpreters will open a window when a function name is typed, and in this window the document string text will appear.

8.4 Decorators

A special type of function, called a *decorator*, is defined by the syntax @*dname*, where *dname* is the name of the decorator. Decorators are wrappers for another function or class. In this book, decorators come into play in only a few instances, these being when creating class methods, static methods, or properties (Chapter 9); for shorthand when creating widgets in Jupyter Notebook (Appendix A) ; or for optimizing code using Numba (Chapter 21).

The concept of decorators can be quite confusing. The good news is that for the purposes of this book we do not need to know a lot about them in order to use them. In fact, most readers may want to skip this section. But, for those interested in learning more about decorators we briefly describe them.

8.4.1 Interlude

Before diving into decorators, let us take a little interlude which hopefully will make decorators more understandable. Suppose that we want to create a permanent record, or log, of every time a function is called. In addition, we want to record its arguments when it was called. We could do this by creating the following function

```
def log_calls(func):
    def log(*args):
        from time import asctime
        log_name = func.__name__ + '.log'
        with open(log_name, 'a') as f:
            print(asctime(), *args, file=f)
        return func(*args)
    return log
```

Our function `log_calls()` takes another function `func()` as its sole argument. It returns a different function named `log()` which we define inside the `log_calls()` function. The `log()` function takes whatever arguments are passed to it and opens a file whose name will be that of the function used as the argument to `log_calls()`. It then gets the time from the server (see Chapter 15 for details) and appends this time and the argments to the file, and then closes the file. It then returns the original function `func()` to `log_calls()`, which then returns that same function to the calling routine.

If we send a function name (no arguments or parentheses) such as the built-in Python function `pow()` to our `log_calls()` function, and save it to another variable,

```
b = log_calls(pow)
```

we can now use `b()` just like we can the `pow()` function,

```
> b(4, 2)
16
> b(4, 3)
64
> b(2, 5)
32
```

However, notice that a text file named `pow.log` has been created, the contents of which are

```
Fri Nov 1 11:12:00 2019 4 2
Fri Nov 1 11:14:33 2019 4 3
Fri Nov 1 11:15:14 2019 2 5
```

which has recorded the time and the arguments every time we called the function `b()`.

So far, so good; but we can be sneaky if we want to be! We can hijack the `pow()` function by executing

```
pow = log_calls(pow)
```

Now, whenever we call the `pow()` function, we are really calling our `log_calls(pow)` function. The use of `pow()` is completely transparent to the user or calling routine. It behaves just like we would expect `pow()` to behave, but behind the scenes we are logging every usage of the function.

8.4.2 Back to decorators

We illustrated our `log_calls()` function with the built-in function `pow()`, but we could also use it with a user-defined function such as

```
def area(a, b):
    return a*b
```

which returns the area of a rectangle given the two sides. Using

```
area = log_calls(area)
```

we could hijack our `area` function and create a log entry everytime `area()` is called.

Decorators are just a shorthand means of accomplishing the same thing. We do this by placing the decorator `@log_calls` before our function definition for `area()`,

```
@log_calls
def area(a, b):
    return a*b
```

This code accomplishes the exact same thing as

```
def area(a, b):
    return a*b
area = log_calls(area)
```

Decorators must be placed immediately prior to the function definition. The general syntax is

```
@decname
def wrapped_func(args):
    [statements defining wrapped function]
```

The decorator name must be based on an existing function. We had to first define the function `log_calls()` before we created the decorator `@log_calls`.

NINE

DEFINING CLASSES AND METHODS

9.1 Introduction

This chapter is included to provide a quick explanation of how to define classes and create objects. It is very basic. Most readers could skip this chapter without detriment to their effective use of Python for data analysis and visualization. However, for those who want to learn how to define classes and methods this chapter can be a springboard to more detailed references.

9.2 Defining Classes

In this section we see how a class is defined and used to create, or *instantiate*, an object. Our example will be from meteorology, and the class will be for a dry *air parcel*, or volume of air. The *attributes* or data associated with the dry parcel will be the pressure, temperature, and mass. The methods for our dry air parcel will calculate and return values for the number of moles of air in the parcel, the volume of the parcel, and the density of the parcel. The code below defines the dry_parcel class.

```
class dry_parcel:
    '''Class defining a dry air parcel.
        All units m-k-s
            press, P : Pascals
            temp, T : Kelvin
            mass : kilograms'''

    # Some class attributes
    R = 8.3145      # Universal gas constant
    Md = 0.02996    # Molar mass of dry air
```

```
def __init__(self, press, temp, mass):
    self.P = press
    self.T = temp
    self.mass = mass

def moles(self):
    '''Returns number of moles in parcel.'''
    return self.mass/self.Md

def volume(self):
    '''Returns volume of parcel (m**3)'''
    return self.moles()*self.R*self.T/self.P

def density(self):
    '''Returns density of parcel (kg/m**3)'''
    return self.mass/self.volume()
```

The class definition begins with the `class` statement, followed by an optional documentation string (see Sec. 8.3). The next two lines define two attributes common to the entire class (*class attributes*). This is followed by the initialization method `__init__()`, and then any other methods belonging to `dry_parcel` objects. Recall that methods are nothing more than functions that belong to the object. Therefore, the means of defining methods is almost identical to the means for defining functions.

9.2.1   The __init__() method

A class definition may contain any number of methods. However, all class definitions must include an `__init__()` method (note the double leading and trailing underscores). This method is the *initialization method* for the class. When objects are instantiated, the initialization method is executed and sets up the attributes for the object. The attributes are passed as the arguments to the `__init__()` method. In the example, the initialization method defines the three attributes for pressure, temperature, and mass, denoted as P, T, and `mass` respectively.

The `self` preceding the object's attributes, and also appearing throughout the class definition, refers to the object that is instantiated. It may help to imagine that whenever the word `self` appears, it literally means "this object."

9.2.2   Instance methods

The three other methods defined in the example above are *instance methods*, and the `self` argument passes the instantiated object to the method. There are two other types of methods that may be encountered, *class methods* and *static methods*, which are described in Sec. 9.5.

9.3   Instantiating Objects

Once a class has been defined, it is used to *instantiate*, or create instances of the class. To use the class definition the code first needs to be executed so that the class definition is in memory. Once this is done, and even before any objects are instantiated, we have access to any of the class attributes that were defined, as shown here:

```
> dry_parcel.R
8.3145
```

To create some `dry_parcel` objects using our class definition, we simply call the class definition and provide the values for the attributes.

```
> a = dry_parcel(85000, 260, 3)
> a.P
85000
> a.T
260
> a.mass
3.0
> a.moles()
100.13351134846462
> a.volume()
2.5466543626796515
> a.density()
1.1780161626815062
```

The class attributes may also be accessed using an instantiated object's name rather than the class name:

```
> a.R
8.3145
> a.Md
0.02996
```

Once an object has been created its attributes may be altered by assigning new values. For example, we could change the temperature of our air parcel that was previously created, which also changes the volume and density.

```
> a.T = 280.0
> a.volume()
2.742550852116548
> a.density()
1.0938721510613987
```

The class attributes may also be changed interactively, but be careful and make sure you know what you are doing! Changing the class attribute may or may not retroactively affect previously instantiated objects. When multiple objects are created their class attributes are *shallow copies*, and all point to the same area in memory where the original class attribute is stored. If the class name is first used to alter the class attribute, it will change the value for all existing objects. However, once a specific object's name is used to alter the attribute, it changes for that object only (becoming a *deep copy*), leaving the class attribute unchanged for the other existing objects.

As an example, suppose we create two dry_parcel objects, a and b, and then print the value of the class attribute R,

```
> a = dry_parcel(50000, 250, 5)
> b = dry_parcel(70000, 260, 3)
> dry_parcel.R, a.R, b.R
(8.3145, 8.3145, 8.3145)
```

showing that the attribute R is the same for the class and both created objects. If we alter the attribute using the class name,

```
dry_parcel.R = 2
```

this changes the value of the attribute for both objects as well,

```
> dry_parcel.R, a.R, b.R
(2, 2, 2)
```

However, if we change the value of R using the name of one of the existing objects,

```
> a.R = 3
> dry_parcel.R, a.R, b.R
(2, 3, 2)
```

then the value only changes for that specific object. If we then further alter the value using the class name, the value for the object named a remains unchanged,

```
> dry_parcel.R = 99
> dry_parcel.R, a.R, b.R
(99, 3, 99)
```

9.4 Inheritance

Inheritance allows us to use a previously defined class called the *parent* class, and extend it to a new class called the *child* class. The child class can maintain the attributes and methods of the parent, but may also have additional or modified attributes or methods. As an example, suppose we want to extend our previously defined dry_parcel class so that we can incorporate humidity. This is done using inheritance by defining a new moist_parcel class as follows:

```
class moist_parcel(dry_parcel):
    '''A class for moist air parcel objects.  It
    inherits from the dry_parcel class.
    All units m-k-s except for q
        press, P : Pascals
```

```
            temp, T : Kelvin
            mass : kilograms
            q : grams/kilogram'''

    # Class attribute
    Mw = 0.01801     # Molar mass of water

    def __init__(self, press, temp, mass, q):
        dry_parcel.__init__(self, press, temp, mass)
        self.q = q  # Specific humidity (g/kg)

    def moles(self):
        '''Returns number of moles in parcel.'''
        q = self.q/1000. # kg/kg
        return self.mass*((1-q)/self.Md + q/self.Mw)

    def Tv(self):
        '''Returns virtual temperature in Kelvin.'''
        q = self.q/1000.0 # kg/kg
        return self.T*(1 + 0.61*q)
```

A few important points to note:

- In the class definition we include the parent class `dry_parcel` as an argument within parentheses. This is how we declare our new class to be a child of a parent class.

- In the `__init__()` method the parent class's `__init__()` method is called with the attributes that are associated with the parent class. Then, any new attributes of the child class are defined.

- Any methods of the parent class are automatically given to the child class. However, the child class can define modified methods of the same name. In our example a new method called `Tv()` is defined to return the virtual temperature of the moist air parcel, and the `moles()` method is redefined to include the addition of the water vapor to the parcel.

9.5 Types of Methods

There are three types of methods that may be defined within a class: *instance*, *class*, and *static*. They differ in what they operate on: a specific instance (object) of the class; the class itself; or neither. Before describing these methods we need to understand that the word `self` always refers to a specific, single instance of a class (an individual object of the class), while the word `cls` always refers to the class itself.

9.5.1 Instance methods

Unless specified otherwise methods defined within a class definition are considered to be instance methods, which belong to, and operate on, a single, specific instantiated object of the class. The first argument to an instance method must be the object to which it belongs. This is accomplished by having the word `self` as the first argument in the definition of the method. Note that when the user calls the method the word `self` is not explicitly typed in to the arguments list. The user (or calling program) need only provide the remaining arguments.

9.5.2 Static methods

Static methods are really just functions that are defined within the class for convenience. They do not belong to, nor operate on any specific object from the class. Whether to create a static method, or simply write a standalone function outside of the class definition, is really a matter of choice.

Static methods are defined in the same manner as instance methods, with two exceptions:

- On the line immediately prior to the `def` statement the *decorator* `@staticmethod` is written. This indicates that the following method is a static method.

- The word `self` is not included in the argument list when defining the method.

Static methods are called by the form `class.method()`, where `class` is the class name and `method` is the method name. There do not need to be any objects instantiated in order to call a static method. Confusingly, static methods may also be called from any instantiated object of the class, using the form `object.method()`, where `object` is an instantiated object.

As an example of instance vs static methods, consider the following code which defines a class of objects representing squares, with the input parameter being the area.

```
class Square:
    '''Defines square objects.'''

    # Initialization method
    def __init__(self, a):
        self.area = a  #  Attribute

    # Instance methods
    def length(self):
        return 4*np.sqrt(self.area)

    # Static method
    @staticmethod
    def combine(x, y):  # Note absence of 'self'
        '''Creates new square with combined area
           of input squares x and y'''
        return Square(x.area+y.area)
```

The class contains one instance method for returning the outside length (perimeter) of the square. There is also a static method that accepts two previously created squares and creates a new square that has the combined area of the two. This method could easily have been written as a stand-alone function outside of the class definition. Including it as a static method within the class definition is purely a matter of convenience.

The use of the class is shown with the code

```
> import numpy as np
> a = Square(5)
> b = Square(10)
> a.length()
8.94427190999916
> b.length()
12.649110640673518
> c = Square.combine(a, b)
> c.area
15
> c.length()
15.491933384829668
```

Note that the combine() static method could also have been called by using an object name rather than the class name, a.combine(a, b). This belies the fact that combine() does not really belong to the square object a.

9.5.3   Class methods

Class methods belong to the class (and subclasses) as a whole, rather than to individual members of the class. Class methods are preceded by the @classmethod decorator.

As an example of using a class method, suppose we want to extend the combine() method from the previous example of the Square class to other shapes such as circles, triangles, etc. We can accomplish this using the idea of inheritance combined with making combine() a class method. Here is the code, in which we first define a parent class for Shape objects, and then define two child classes for Circle and Square objects.

```
class Shape:
    '''Defines shape objects.'''

    # Initialization method
    def __init__(self, a):
        self.area = a   #  Attribute

    # Class method
    @classmethod
    def combine(cls, x, y):
        '''Creates new shape of class cls
            with combined area of
            input shapes x and y'''
        return cls(x.area+y.area)
```

```
class Circle(Shape):
    '''Defines circle objects.'''

    def __init__(self, a):
        Shape.__init__(self, a)

    # Instance method
    def length(self):
        return np.sqrt(4*np.pi*self.area)

class Square(Shape):
    '''Defines square objects.'''

    def __init__(self, a):
        Shape.__init__(self, a)

    # Instance method
    def length(self):
        return 4*np.sqrt(self.area)
```

The base class called **Shape** contains the class method **combine()**. Note that the first argument to **combine()** is **cls**, which is understood to mean "this class." The subclasses **Circle** and **Square** inherit from **Shape**, and therefore have access to the **combine()** method. Depending from which subclass the **combine()** is called, the method will create a new shape of that same subclass. Here are some results:

```
> import numpy as np
> a = Circle(5)   # Create Circle object
> b = Square(10)   # Create Square object
> c = Circle.combine(a, b) # Create combined Circle
> c.length()
13.729368492956533
> d = Square.combine(a, b) # Create combined Square
> d.length()
15.491933384829668
```

We could also call **combine()** from the base class **Shape**. This would create a **Shape** object with the combined areas. However, notice that **Shape** objects have no **length()** method.

```
> e = Shape.combine(a, b)
> e.area
15.0
> e.length()
AttributeError: 'Shape' object has no attribute 'length'
```

The advantage of making **combine()** a class method is that it only needs to be written one time, in the base class definition. We could create as many child classes as we want (triangles, rectangles, trapezoids, etc.), but we would never need to rewrite the `combine()` method. If we had not written `combine()` as a class method then we would have to write a modified `combine()` method for every new subclass.

9.6   Properties

Going back to our example of the `Square` class, note that the `length()` method returns the outside perimeter length of the `square` object. To access this value we had to include the empty parentheses at the end of the method name, `a.length()`. If we wanted to be able to access the length more like an attribute, without having to include the empty parentheses, we can use the `@property` decorator before defining the `length()` function. Here is the code:

```
class Square:
    '''Defines square objects.'''

    # Initialization method
    def __init__(self, a):
        self.area = float(a)   # Attribute

    @property
    def length(self):
        return 4*np.sqrt(self.area)

    # Static method
    @staticmethod
    def combine(x, y):   # Note absence of 'self'
        '''Creates new square with combined area
           of input squares x and y'''
        return Square(x.area+y.area)
```

Now, length can be accessed as though it were an attribute, with the exception that it cannot be set like a normal attribute could be.

```
> import numpy as np
> a = Square(5)
> a.length
8.94427190999916
> a.length = 7
AttributeError: can't set attribute
```

Part II

Plotting and Visualization

## TEN

1-D PLOTTING

10.1   Introduction

This chapter describes how to create basic one-dimensional (1-D) plots using the Matplotlib plotting library, which contains classes and functions for creating MATLAB-style plots and graphs. The primary submodule that we will use is `pyplot`, which is commonly imported and aliased as `plt` using the statement

```
import matplotlib.pyplot as plt
```

We then use functions from the `pyplot` submodule to create `Figure` objects and `Axes` objects.[1]

Even with identical code there may be some differences in fonts or plot boundaries generated by different Python installations and operating systems. Most of the figures shown in this book were created using the Anaconda Python installation with macOS.

10.2   A Simple 1-D Plot

The simplest way to generate a plot is to use the `pyplot.plot()` function, which generates both the `Figure` object and the `Axes` object with one command and plots the data onto the axes. This is illustrated with the following code, which generates a plot of the function $y = 2\sqrt{x}$:

---

[1]The full names of these classes are `matplotlib.figure.Figure` and `matplotlib.axes._axes.Axes`. For convenience we simplify them to `Figure` and `Axes`.

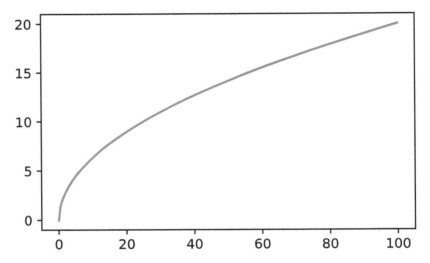

Fig. 10.1: Plot of $y = 2\sqrt{x}$ generated by the example code from Section 10.2.

```python
import numpy as np
import matplotlib.pyplot as plt
x = np.arange(0,100.5,0.5) # Generate x-axis values
y = 2.0*np.sqrt(x)   # Calculate y-values
plt.plot(x,y)     # Plot data onto axes
plt.show()   # Display plot to screen
```

When this code is executed the plot shown in Fig. 10.1 is created.

Note that the last line of the code calls the `pyplot.show()` function. This function displays the plot to the screen, and (with some exception[2]) is necessary in order to view the plot. Once `pyplot.show()`[3] is called, no more changes can be made to the figure or axes.

Using the `pyplot.plot()` function is a great way to quickly create simple plots on a single set of axes. However, it obscures what is really going on behind the scenes. It also does not allow for placing multiple axes on a single figure. In the next section we show another means of creating the same plot as in Fig. 10.1 by manually creating the figure and axes.

---

[2]Some interactive environments, as well as Jupyter notebooks, do not require the `plt.show()` command.

[3]It is important that the empty parentheses be included for the show() function. If they are omitted, no errors will be reported but the plot may not show up on the screen.

10.3 Figure and Axes Objects

A Matplotlib plot consists of a `Figure` object and at least one `Axes` object. In the previous example of a simple plot, the `Figure` and `Axes` objects were generated automatically by the `pyplot.plot()` function without us having to give them much thought. However, in order to have more control over the plotting, and to be able to have multiple axes in one figure, we need a firmer understanding of how Matplotlib sets up the figure and axes.[4]

10.3.1 Figure objects

A `Figure` object can be thought of as simply the *page* on which the plot will be displayed. A `Figure` object can be created manually using the `pyplot.figure()` function as follows:

```
fig = plt.figure()
```

This creates a `Figure` object and saves a reference to the object in a variable named `fig`.

It is common to want to control the size of the `Figure` object using the `figsize` keyword:

```
fig = plt.figure(figsize=(5,3))
```

creates a `Figure` object that is 5 inches wide and 3 inches high. One may also use the `dpi` keyword to specify the resolution in dots (or pixels) per inch. This resolution is only meaningful when saving the figure in a raster format such as PNG or JPEG.

10.3.2 Axes objects

Once a figure has been created, `Axes` objects can be created and placed upon it using the `add_axes([x,y,w,h])` method of the `Figure` object. The arguments for this method must be in the form of a list, and are as follows:

- *x* and *y* are the horizontal and vertical locations of the lower-left corner of the axes, expressed as decimal fractions (from 0.0 to 1.0) of the figure width and height, respectively. For example, a value of $x = 0.2$ would place the beginning of the axes 20% across the figure's width.

- *w* is the horizontal extent of the axes, expressed as a fraction of the figure's total width. As an example, if $x = 0.1$ and $w = 0.7$, then the axis would start at a position 10% to the right of the left-edge of the figure,

---

[4]The use of the words *axis* and *axes* can get a bit confusing. The singular *axis* refers to just one of the *x* and *y* axes (plural). When we refer to "an axes" in the singular, this is shorthand for an `Axes` object that encompasses the properties of both the horizontal and vertical axes.

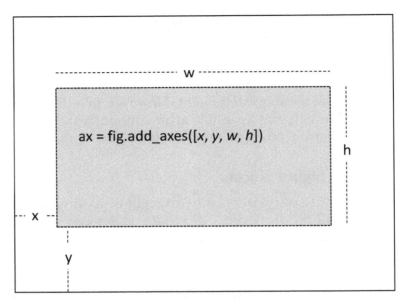

Fig. 10.2: Relationship between the arguments *x*, *y*, *w*, and *h* and the positioning of the axes on the figure. The outer, solid rectangle represents the extent of the figure, while the inner, dashed rectangle represents the extent of the axes.

and would extend to a position 80% across the width of the figure. The right-most extent of the axes will be the sum of *x* and *w*.

- *h* is the vertical extent of the axes, expressed as a fraction of the figure's total height. The uppermost extent of the axes will be the sum of *y* and *h*.

Figure 10.2 shows the relationship of the arguments *x*, *y*, *w*, and *h* and the positioning of the axes on the figure.

10.3.3   Plotting data onto axes

Once an **Axes** object is created it can be used for plotting data. This is done with the **plot(*x*, *y*)** method of the **Axes** object, where *x* and *y* are both arrays having the same dimensions. As an example, the following code generates the same plot of $y = 2\sqrt{x}$ shown in Fig. 10.1:

```
import numpy as np
import matplotlib.pyplot as plt
x = np.arange(0,100.5,0.5) # Generate x-axis values
y = 2.0*np.sqrt(x)   # Calculate y-values
fig = plt.figure()   # Create figure
ax = fig.add_axes([0.1, 0.1, 0.8, 0.8]) # Create axes
ax.plot(x,y)    # Plot data onto axes
plt.show()  # Display plot to screen
```

Plotting multiple lines of data on a single axes is accomplished by repeated use of the `pyplot.plot()` function or `Axes.plot()` method. The color and style of the plotted line can be altered from its default value, and markers can also be placed along the line. This is discussed in Section 10.7.

10.4 Discussion of pyplot.plot() and Axes.plot()

In the examples above we have illustrated two different ways of generating the same plot shown in Fig. 10.1. In Section 10.2 we illustrated how to do this using the `pyplot.plot()` function, while in Section 10.3.3 we showed how to do this using the `Axes.plot()` method. The `pyplot.plot()` function essentially performs the three separate steps shown here,

$$\text{plt.plot(x,y)} \Longleftrightarrow \begin{array}{l} \text{fig = plt.figure()} \\ \text{ax = fig.add\_axes()} \\ \text{ax.plot(x,y)} \end{array}$$

In this section we discuss the merits of each approach, and highlight the circumstances where one may be chosen over the other. We also point out some subtle differences in how the functions and methods are called for each approach.

10.4.1 Which one to use?

The `pyplot.plot()` function is most useful for creating simple plots very quickly. It requires no thought about setting up the `Figure` or `Axes` objects, since it creates both automatically when it plots the data. It is not suitable if more control over the placement of the axes on the figure is needed, or if multiple axes are to be placed on the figure. The `Axes.plot()` method gives much more control over the placement of the axes on the figure, and also allows multiple axes to be placed on the figure. It requires first manually creating the `Figure` and `Axes` objects before data can be plotted.

The choice of which procedure to use depends on the task at hand. With enough patience and knowledge it is possible to create complicated plots using the `pyplot.plot()` function, but the resulting code will likely be kludgy and inefficient compared to manually creating the `Figure` and `Axes` objects and then using the `Axes.plot()` method.

10.4.2 Methods vs. functions—revisited

This discussion gives us an opportunity to revisit the seemingly subtle difference between a method and a function.

- `pyplot.plot()` is a *function*, because pyplot itself is a *module*.
- `Axes.plot()` is a *method*, because it belongs to an `Axes` *object*.

Functions and methods are similar, but a method is distinguished from a function in that a method belongs to specific object.

- When we use `plt.plot()` we are calling the `plot()` function of the `pyplot` module (aliased as `plt`).

- When we use `ax.plot()` we are calling the `plot()` method of the `Axes` object named `ax`. Each `Axes` object will have its own `plot()` method.

10.4.3   Getting references to the current figure and axes

The `pyplot.plot()` function automatically creates the `Figure` and `Axes` objects, but it does not create references (variable names) for them. If the need arises to access the methods for the current figure or axes, two built-in functions can be used to obtain references:

- `pyplot.gcf()` (*"get current figure"*) returns a reference to the current `Figure` object.

- `pyplot.gca()` (*"get current axes"*) returns a reference to the current `Axes` object.

10.4.4   Differences in naming conventions for functions and methods

For most plotting tasks, such as placing titles, labels, and legends, there are both `pyplot` functions and `Axes` methods. Most of the `pyplot` functions and `Axes` methods have identical names and usages. However, a few of them do not. Those `Axes` methods which have different names from their corresponding `pyplot` functions are listed in Table 10.1.

The difference between the names and usage of some `pyplot` functions versus the corresponding `Axes` methods is a minor annoyance in `matplotlib`. The reason for its existence stems from the fact that in object-oriented programming there are *getter* and *setter* methods for getting and setting the attributes of objects. An axis title is essentially an *attribute* of an `Axes` object, which explains why `set_title()` is used for the `Axes` method.[5]

10.5   Clearing Figures and Axes

The `clear()` Axes method will reset the axes, removing any plotted data. It will also reset the axes limits, labels, etc. The axes will still exist as an object, and new data may be plotted on it.

The `clf()` pyplot function or `Figure` method will reset the entire figure. The figure object will still remain and new axes may be added to it.

---

[5]The setter methods also have corresponding *getter* methods that retrieve the values rather than set them. These begin with `get_` rather than `set_`.

Table 10.1: Some `pyplot` functions and corresponding `Axes` methods.

pyplot function	Axes method	Purpose	Section
title()	set_title()	Title for plot	10.9.1
xlabel()	set_xlabel()	Label for x-axis	10.9.2
ylabel()	set_ylabel()	Label for y-axis	
xlim()	set_xlim()	Limits of x-axis	10.10.1
ylim()	set_ylim()	Limits of y-axis	
xticks()	set_xticks(), set_xticklabels()	Tick marks on x-axis	10.10.2
yticks()	set_yticks(), set_yticklabels()	Tick marks on y-axis	

10.6 Elements of a Plot

Figure 10.3 shows many of the elements that can be included on a typical plot. In the rest of this chapter we discuss how to create and modify these elements to tailor plots to our specific needs. Here is a brief directory to the sections detailing how to configure plot elements:

- **Plot lines**: Section 10.7

- **Plot markers**: Section 10.7.4

- **Plot title**: Section 10.9.1

- **Axis labels**: Section 10.9.2

- **Text**: Section 10.9.4

- **Tick mark locations**: Section 10.10.2

- **Tick mark labels**: Section 10.10.2

- **Grid lines**: Section 10.11.1

- **Other lines**: Section 10.11

- **Legend**: Section 10.14

10.7 Controlling Line and Marker Properties

By default, both the `pyplot.plot()` function and `Axes.plot()` methods plot the data as a solid line. Each new call to `plot()` for the same `Axes` will result in a different color being used. In this section we discuss how to control the style, color, and thickness of the plotted lines, as well as how to include markers of various shapes, colors, and sizes.

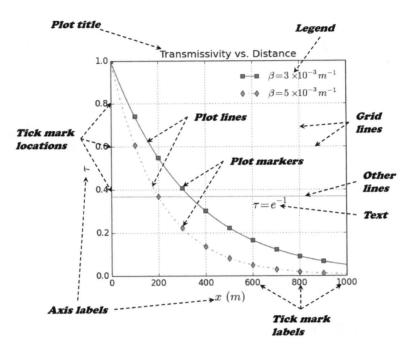

Fig. 10.3: Elements of a plot. The sections of this chapter describing each element are listed in Section 10.6.

10.7.1   Line styles

The `linestyle` keyword of `plot()` dictates the style of the line. The available line styles and their values are

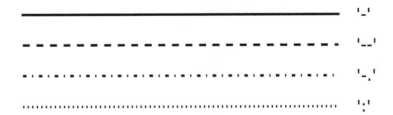

For example, to plot a dashed line, the code would be:

```
plot(x, y, linestyle='--')
```

The `linestyle` keyword can also be abbreviated as `ls`.

10.7.2   Line color

The `color` keyword (also abbreviated as simply c) specifies the color of the drawn line. There are several ways to indicate the colors. For basic colors simply use the color's name or abbreviation such as: `'blue'` or `'b'`; `'green'` or 'g'; 'red' or 'r'; 'cyan' or 'c'; 'magenta' or 'm'; 'yellow' or 'y'; 'black' or 'k'; 'white' or 'w'. For example, to plot a green dashed line:

```
plot(x, y, c='g', ls='--')
```

Colors may also be specified using HTML color names such as 'aquamarine', or by using their hexadecimal values such as '#7FFFD4'. The HTML color names and hexadecimal values are not listed here, as they are too numerous. References to these color names may be found in HTML documentation or on the web.

Colors may also be specified in RGB form via a triplet of numbers of the form (r, g, b), where r, g, and b are floating-point values in the range 0.0 to 1.0, and specify the amount of saturation of red, green, and blue, respectively. Pure red is $(1, 0, 0)$, pure green is $(0, 1, 0)$, and pure blue is $(0, 0, 1)$; black is $(0, 0, 0)$, and white is $(1, 1, 1)$.

Yet another way of specifying line color is by a string indicating a decimal value between '0.0' and '1.0'.[6] In this case the color will be a shade of grey. In this scheme, '0.0' represents black and '1.0' represents white. The closer the string is to '0.0', the darker the line will be.

10.7.3 Line thickness

The width of the plotted line is controlled using the linewidth or lw keyword argument, which takes a floating-point value representing the thickness of the line in points.

10.7.4 Markers

In addition to drawing a line, markers may be plotted at the data values. The marker style is controlled with the marker keyword, which accepts a string. The available markers and the string used to specify them are

●	'o'	■	's'	⬣	'h'
◆	'D'	★	'*'	⬟	'H'
◆	'd'	▼	'v'	●	'8'
	'None'	▲	'^'	⊥	'4'
+	'+'	◀	'<'	—	'_'
×	'x'	▶	'>'	|	'|'
•	'.'	⬠	'p'		

---

[6]A string is used as the color keyword expects a string, not a floating-point value.

The marker color, size, and spacing can be controlled using the following additional keywords:

- `markersize` or `ms`, a point value representing the size of the marker. One point is 1/72 of an inch.

- `markeredgecolor` or `mec`, the color of the outline of the marker, and is any valid color (see Sec. 10.7.2).

- `markerfacecolor` or `mfc`, the color of the interior of the marker.

- `markeredgewidth` or `mew`, the thickness of the marker outline in points.

- `markevery`, an integer value controlling the spacing of the markers. A value of 5 would plot the markers at every fifth data point.

To plot data using markers only without drawing a line, set the `linestyle` or `ls` keyword to `None`.

10.7.5   Shortcut for line and marker properties

There is a shortcut for specifying the line style, line thickness, and marker style. Instead of using the `color`, `linestyle`, and `marker` keywords separately, a string combining the color, line style, and marker type may be included as an argument to `plot()`. For example, suppose we wanted to plot a green dashed line using square markers:

```
plot(x, y, c='g', ls='--', marker='s')
```

The equivalent shorter version is simply:

```
plot(x, y, 'g--s')
```

10.7.6   Background color

The background color for the plot can be set using the `set_facecolor()` Axes method. The argument can be color names described in 10.7.2.

10.8   Logarithmic Plots

To create logarithmic axes the `plot()` function or method is replaced with one of the following, depending on which axis will be logarithmic. These accept all the same keywords as `plot()`.

- `semilogx()`, creates a logarithmic x axis.

- `semilogy()`, creates a logarithmic y axis.

- `loglog()`, creates a plot with both logarithmic x and y axes.

10.9   Placing Text on Plots

There are several `pyplot` functions and `Axes` methods for placing text onto plots. Text can be placed as a plot title, as labels for the individual axes, or at other specified locations on the plot. The size and color of textual elements can be tailored for the specific plot. Mathematical symbols and Greek alphabet characters are also available and are described in Section 10.9.7.

10.9.1   Plot titles

A title may be placed on a plot using the `pyplot.title(s)` function or the `Axes.set_title(s)` method.[7] The string *s* contains the text for the title. The size, color and other properties of the text can be controlled using the appropriate text keywords described in Section 10.9.6.

10.9.2   Axis labels

Each axis of a plot may be given a label. The `pyplot` functions for this are:

- `pyplot.xlabel(s)`, for labeling the *x* axis.
- `pyplot.ylabel(s)`, for labeling the *y* axis.

The argument *s* is a string that contains the text of the axis label.

The `Axes` method counterparts to the above functions are `ax.set_xlabel(s)` and `ax.set_ylabel(s)`, where *ax* is a reference to the `Axes` object. As with plot titles, the color, size and other properties of the axis label text can be controlled as discussed in Section 10.9.6.

10.9.3   Data coordinates versus axes coordinates

Before discussing how to place text at any specified location on a plot we must explain the difference between *data* coordinates and *axes* coordinates. Data coordinates refer to the actual data values on the *x* and *y* axes. Axes coordinates refer to the position relative to the axes width and height. In axes coordinates (0, 0) refers to the lower-left corner of the axes, and (1, 1) refers to the upper-right corner. The upper-left corner is (0, 1), and the lower-right corner is (1, 0). A position halfway across the axes, and 1/4 of the way up would be (0.5, 0.25). Figure 10.4 illustrates the relation between data and axes coordinates.

---

[7]For a discussion of the difference in name and usage between the pyplot function and corresponding `Axes` method see Section 10.4.4.

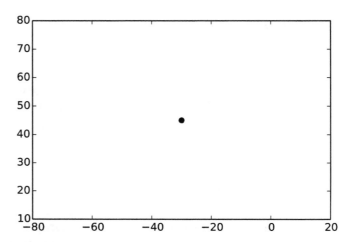

Fig. 10.4: At the location of the dot the data coordinates are $(-30, 45)$, while the axes coordinates are $(0.5, 0.5)$.

10.9.4   Placing text in the body of a plot

To place text at any specified location on the plot we use the `pyplot.text()` function or `Axes.text()` method. In both cases, the syntax is `text(x,y,s)`, where x and y are the coordinates of the position of the text and s is a string containing the text. By default, x and y are specified in *data coordinates*. If axes coordinates are to be used, the `transform=ax.transAxes` keyword must be included as an argument, where ax is a reference to the `Axes` object.[8] The color, size and other properties of the text can be specified as per Section 10.9.6.

An alternative to the `text` function or method is `annotate(s, xy)`, where xy is a tuple containing the coordinates of a point on the plot to be annotated. An optional keyword argument *xytext*, also a tuple, can be used to specify that the text itself is to positioned at a different location, and another keyword *arrowprops* can then define the properties of an arrow drawn from *xytext* to *xy*. See the online documentation for detailed options.

10.9.5   Fonts

The default font is DejaVu Sans, and the default font family is sans-serif, meaning the font has no serif.[9] Other fonts can be set using the `fontfamily` keyword within the functions or methods for setting titles, labels, etc. This may be set to a generic font family such as `'serif'`, `'sans-serif'`, `'cursive'`, `'fantasy'`, or `'monospace'`, or the name of a specific font such as `'Times New`

---

[8]If the `pyplot.text()` function is being used then the axes reference can be obtained using `ax = plt.gca()` before calling the `pyplot.text()` function.

[9]A serif is a small line attached to the top and/or bottom of a letter.

Roman', 'Arial', etc. The font change will only apply to the specific function or method in which it is used.

The font may be changed for all plot elements by importing rcParams[10] from matplotlib, and then setting the dictionary key 'font.family' to be either a generic font family, or a specific font. For example, to set the font to Times New Roman for all plot elements we would use

```
from matplotlib import rcParams
rcParams['font.family'] = 'Times New Roman'
```

To view which fonts are contained in each font family you may run this code

```
from matplotlib import rcParams
family = ['serif', 'sans-serif',
          'cursive', 'fantasy',
          'monospace']
for f in family:
    print('\n{0} family\n----'.format(f))
    rc = rcParams['font.' + f]
    for fnt in rc:
        print(fnt)
```

However, just because a particular font appears as an option does not mean it is available on your system. If you try to plot with a font that does not exist on your system a warning will be issued, and the font will revert to whatever the default font is.

Changing the font family does not effect how mathematical symbols and Greek characters are rendered when using the LaTeX-like text rendering discussed in Sec. 10.9.7. Changing those fonts is discussed in that section.

10.9.6 Text properties

The color, size, alignment, and orientation of text can be controlled using keywords in the calls to the functions and methods for creating titles, labels, and text. These keywords are described here.

- color, the color of the text specified using the color names described in Section 10.7.2.

- size, the size of the text. The text size may be specified either as a string such as 'xx-small', 'x-small', 'small', 'medium', 'large', 'x-large', or 'xx-large'; or as a numerical point value.

---

[10]rcParams is an instance of the RcParams class, and is a dictionary for setting and storing default parameters for Matplotlib.

- rotation, the orientation of the text. It may be either set as a string such as 'horizontal' or 'vertical' or a numerical value indicating the degrees of rotation.

- horizontalalignment or ha, the horizontal alignment of the text. It can be set to 'left', 'right', or 'center'.

- verticalalignment or va, the vertical alignment of the text. It can be set to 'bottom', 'top', 'center' or 'baseline'. The definitions of these terms are illustrated here,

- style, the font style. It can be set to 'normal', 'italic', or 'oblique'.

- linespacing, a numerical value indicating the spacing between lines of text. Double-spacing would use a value of 2, triple-spacing 3, etc.

- backgroundcolor is the background color over which the text is plotted.

10.9.7   Mathematical symbols and Greek characters

Mathematical symbols and Greek characters can be included in text using Matplotlib's built-in LaTeX-like syntax. The strings used for this should be *raw strings* (see Sec. 3.1.3), which are defined by including a lower-case r character prior to the leading quotes, such as r'Hello'. Raw strings are used so that the special characters in the LaTeX-like markup language are not misinterpreted as special symbols. The dollar sign character ($) precedes and follows any code that is to be interpreted as LaTeX-like markup language. Appendix B contains a quick reference for some LaTeX commands and symbols.

The default font for math symbols and Greek characters is DejaVu Sans. This is a change from older versions of Matplotlib. If you prefer the older, classic font which was Computer Modern you can change it with the following commands

```
from matplotlib import rcParams
rcParams['mathtext.fontset'] = 'cm'
rcParams['mathtext.rm'] = 'serif'
```

To change them back to the new way, either restart the kernel, or do

```
rcParams['mathtext.fontset'] = 'dejavusans'
rcParams['mathtext.rm'] = 'sans'
```

10.10   Controlling Axes Properties

In this section we discuss how to control axis limits, tick mark locations, and tick mark labels within the Python code.[11] As with controlling axis labels, the names of the `pyplot` functions and `Axes` methods differ, with the `Axes` methods being preceded by `'set_'` (see Sec. 10.9.2).

10.10.1   Axis limits

The limits of the x axis can be set using the `pyplot.xlim(`*mn*`,`*mx*`)` function or `Axes.set_xlim(`*mn*`,`*mx*`)` method. The arguments *mn* and *mx* are the minimum and maximum values for the axis. For the y axis use `pyplot.ylim(`*mn*`,`*mx*`)` function or `Axes.set_ylim(`*mn*`,`*mx*`)` method.

One of the arguments, *mn* or *mx*, may be omitted, in which case it will take on the default value. This is handy for setting the lower part of an axis to begin at zero, while letting the upper part adjust to the data values. To do this you would use something like `plt.xlim(0,)`.

Not only can these functions and methods be used to set the axes limits, but they also return the values of the axes limits. Therefore, if the current axis limits are needed the functions and methods can be called without arguments, returning a tuple with the current values of the axis limits. For example:

```
ax.set_xlim(-4, 15)  # Set new limits
al = ax.set_xlim() # Return axis limits
print(al)
```

would print the tuple $(-4.0, 15.0)$.

There are also `Axes` methods called `get_xlim()` and `get_ylim()`, the purpose of which are also to return the axis limits. Unlike `set_xlim()` and `set_ylim()`, which can either set or return the axis limits, `get_xlim()` and `get_ylim()` can only return the limits, not set them.

The orientation of an axis can be reversed by simply switching the order of the arguments *mn* and *mx* in the argument list, so that the maximum value comes before the minimum value. For example

```
plt.xlim(8,-5)
```

would reverse the x-axis with a value of 8 on the left, and a value of -5 on the right.

---

[11]In addition to controlling axes and plot properties within the code, some Python installations allow interactive control of certain axes and plot properties by clicking an icon on the plot window.

10.10.2   Tick mark location and labels

The locations and text used for tick marks can be set using either `pyplot` functions or `Axes` methods. The usage deviates significantly between the `pyplot` functions and `Axes` methods, so they are described separately.

Using pyplot functions

The `pyplot.xticks(loc,lab)` and `pyplot.yticks(loc,lab)` functions are used to both set or retrieve the locations and labels of the tick marks and have the following arguments:

- *loc* is a tuple, list, or array containing the locations of the tick marks in data coordinates.
- *lab* is a tuple, list, or array containing the text for labeling the tick marks. If *lab* is omitted, then the tick marks are labeled with the numerical value of their locations.

In addition, the text keywords `size` and `color` may be used to control the size and color of the tick labels. It is also possible to control the font used for tick mark labels, but it is not as simple as merely supplying the arguments to a keyword. See the Matplotlib documentation if such control is desired.

As an example, the code below creates the plot shown in Fig. 10.5, which is a plot of $\sin(x)$ with the x-axis labeled in fractions of π.

```
import matplotlib.pyplot as plt
import numpy as np
x = np.linspace(0, 2*np.pi)
y = np.sin(x)
plt.plot(x,y)
plt.ylim(-1.1, 1.1)
plt.xlim(0,2*np.pi)
plt.xticks([0,np.pi/2, np.pi, 3*np.pi/2, 2*np.pi],
          [r'$0$', r'$\frac{\pi}{2}$', r'$\pi$',
           r'$\frac{3\pi}{2}$', r'$2\pi$'],
          color='b', size='x-large')
plt.show()
```

Using axes methods

The `Axes` methods for setting tick mark locations are `Axes.set_xticks(loc)` and `Axes.set_yticks(loc)`, where *loc* is a tuple, list, or array containing the locations of the tick marks. Unlike the corresponding `pyplot` functions, which set both the locations and text of the tick marks, these `Axes` methods only set the locations. To set the text for the tick mark labels, use the `Axes.set_xticklabels(lab)` and `Axes.set_yticklables(lab)`,
where *lab* is a tuple, list, or array containing the text for the tick labels.

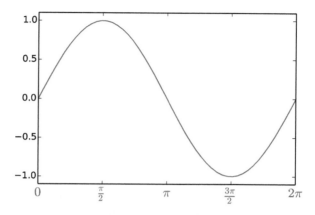

Fig. 10.5: Plot of sin x showing the x axis labels in fractions of π.

10.10.3   Retrieving tick mark locations and labels

Sometimes it is useful to be able to retrieve the tick mark locations and text from a plot. This can be accomplished using the `pyplot.xticks()` or `pyplot.yticks()` functions with empty arguments. When used in this manner they return a tuple containing a list of tick mark locations and a list of tick mark text:

```
loc, lab = plt.xticks()
```

Special consideration must be given when using the label text returned from these functions. The label list, `lab`, does not contain the label text directly, but is instead a list of Matplotlib text objects. To return the actual text from these objects we must use their `get_text()` method. This is best understood via an example. The code below

```
import matplotlib.pyplot as plt
import numpy as np
x = np.arange(0,1.1, .1)
plt.plot(x, x)
plt.xticks([0,1,2,3], ['A', 'B', 'C', 'D'])
loc, lab = plt.xticks()
print(loc)
print(lab)
```

returns

```
[0 1 2 3]
<a list of 4 Text xticklabel objects>
```

In order to actually return the text of the `Text xticklabel` objects, we would need to add the following to our program:

```
for l in lab:
        print(l.get_text())
```

which prints

```
A
B
C
D
```

The corresponding `Axes` methods for retrieving the tick mark locations is `Axes.get_xticks()` or `Axes.get_yticks()`, with empty arguments. This returns only the tick mark locations as a list. For retrieving the labels, we use `Axes.get_xticklabels()` or `Axes.get_yticklabels()`, which return the tick mark labels as a list of text objects.

10.11   Drawing Lines on Plots

10.11.1   Grid lines

Grid lines may be placed onto the axes using the `pyplot.grid()` function or `Axes.grid()` method. The `axis` keyword can be set to `'x'`, `'y'`, or `'both'` to indicate for which axis the grid lines are drawn. The `color`, `linestyle`, and `linewidth` keywords, or their aliases `c`, `ls`, and `lw`, can also be specified to control the appearance of the grid lines.

10.11.2   Horizontal and vertical lines

This section describes how to draw individual or multiple horizontal and vertical lines on plots.

Single line across an entire axes

To draw individual horizontal or vertical lines across an axes, use the `axhline(y)` or `axvline(x)` pyplot functions or `Axes` methods. The sole required argument is the x or y position of the line in data coordinates. The line will be drawn across the entire limits of the axes. The color, linestyle, and width of the line can be specified with the `color`, `linestyle`, and `linewidth` keywords, or their shortcuts `c`, `ls`, and `lw`.

To draw the line only partway across the axes the optional keywords `xmin` and `xmax` may be used for horizontal lines, and `ymin` and `ymax` for vertical lines. However, these values are in *axes coordinates* rather than *data coordinates* (see Sec. 10.9.3).

The `axhline()` and `axvline()` functions/methods can only draw a single line at a time. For drawing multiple horizontal or vertical lines, or for having more control over the starting and endpoints of single lines, use the `hlines()` and `vlines()` pyplot functions or `Axes` methods described in the next section.

Multiple horizontal or vertical lines

Horizontal lines at specified y locations may be drawn using the `pyplot.hlines(`*y,xmin,xmax*`)` function or `Axes.hlines(`*y,xmin, xmax*`)` method. If only a single line is desired, then y is a floating point or integer value indicating the y-coordinate of the line. A list or array of values can also be used for *y*, in which case horizontal lines are drawn at all the values. The other arguments, *xmin* and *xmax*, are optional and consist of either single values or lists of values indicating the x values in *data coordinates* for the beginning and ending points of the lines.

For vertical lines, the `pyplot.vlines(`*x,ymin,ymax*`)` function or `Axes.vlines(`*x,ymin,ymax*`)` method is used. In this case, x is a value or list of values for the x-coordinates of the lines, with *ymin* and *ymax* indicating the beginning and ending points in *data coordinates*.

Two additional keywords control the color and style of the lines. These are the `colors` and `linestyles` keywords. Note that they are plural! They accept either single strings, or lists of strings, indicating the colors of the lines and the style of the line. The colors are specified as per Section 10.7.2. Line styles are specified as `'solid'`, `'dashed'`, `'dashdot'`, or `'dotted'`. If a single string is given, then all the lines will be that color. If a list of strings is given, then both `colors` and `linestyles` must contain the same number of elements as does *x* or *y*.

10.11.3 Arbitrary lines and connected line segments

Drawing arbitrary lines and connected line segments is a little more involved than drawing purely horizontal or vertical lines. For this we must first import the `matplotlib.lines` module (usually aliased to `lns`):

```
import matplotlib.lines as lns
```

so that we can access the `Line2D()` function. The line object is then created by using the `Line2D` function as follows:

```
my_line = lns.Line2D(xpos, ypos, color=c,
                linestyle=ls, linewidth=lw)
```

The arguments and keywords for the function are:

- *xpos*, a list, tuple, or array containing the x coordinates of the vertexes of the line.

- *ypos*, a list, tuple, or array containing the y coordinates of the vertexes.

- `color` or `c`, the color of the line (any valid `matplotlib` color).

- `linestyle` or `ls`, the style of the line segments as given by one of the following strings `'-'`, `'--'`, `'-.'`, `':'`.

- `linewidth` or `lw`, the width of the line in points.

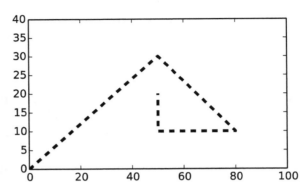

Fig. 10.6: Line segments drawn using the code from Section 10.11.3.

Once the line object has been created it is added to the axes using the `Axes.add_line()` method with the line object as the argument.

```
ax.add_line(my_line)
```

As an example, the following code would generate the plot shown in Fig. 10.6.

```
import matplotlib.pyplot as plt
import matplotlib.lines as lns
import numpy as np
fig = plt.figure()
ax = fig.add_axes([.1, .1, .8, .8])
ax.set_xlim(0, 100)
ax.set_ylim(0, 40)
l = lns.Line2D((0, 50, 80, 50, 50),
               (0, 30, 10, 10, 20),
               c='k', ls='--', lw=3)
ax.add_line(l)
plt.show()
```

10.12   Duplicate Axes

Sometimes we want axis tickmarks and labels on both sides of a figure, or we want axis labels in two different units. Both of these are accomplished using the `twinx()` or `twiny()` pyplot functions or `Axes` methods.

10.12.1   Duplicate identical axes

Suppose we want a plot with temperature as a function of time, and we want the temperature axis labels to be displayed on both the left and right hand side of the plot. We would use the `twinx()` function or method as follows:

```
import matplotlib.pyplot as plt
f = plt.figure()
a = f.add_axes([0.15, 0.1, 0.75, 0.85])
```

```
a.set_xlim(0,24)
a.set_ylim(-10, 20)
a.set_xlabel(r'Hours', size='large')
a.set_ylabel(r'$\degree$C', size='large')
b = plt.twinx(a)  # Create duplicate axes named 'b'
b.set_yticks(a.get_yticks()) # Set new axes tickmarks
plt.show()
```

which creates the axes shown in Fig. 10.7. Note in particular the use of `b.set_yticks(a.get_yticks())`, which retrieves the axis tick marks from the original `Axes` object and sets them for the new `Axes` object.

Also note that `twinx()` actually creates an additional *y*-axis on the right-hand side of the figure, while `twiny()` creates an additional *x*-axis at the top of the figure. This seems slightly counterintuitive. One way to think of this is that `twinx()` creates an *identical x* axis that has a different *y* axis.

10.12.2 Duplicate nonidentical axes

Suppose instead that we wanted the duplicate axes to be displayed in degrees Fahrenheit instead of Celsius. This would be accomplished using the following code

```
import matplotlib.pyplot as plt
f = plt.figure()
a = f.add_axes([0.15, 0.1, 0.75, 0.85])
a.set_xlim(0,24)
a.set_ylim(-10, 20)
a.set_xlabel(r'Hours', size='large')
a.set_ylabel(r'$\degree$C', size='large')
b = plt.twinx(a)  # Create duplicate axes named 'b'
limits = a.get_ylim()  # Get y-axis limits
# Convert to F and set as new axis limits
b.set_ylim(limits[0]*1.8 + 32, limits[1]*1.8 + 32)
b.set_ylabel(r'$\degree$F', size='large')
plt.show()
```

which creates the axes shown in Fig. 10.8.

10.13   Working with Multiple Axes and Figures

Here is a good spot to discuss working with multiple axes, either as duplicate axes on the same plot, or in multiple-panel plots as in Chapter 11. Most `pyplot` functions operate on the *current axes* and on the *current figure*. If there are multiple axes instances the current axes will usually be the last one that was created. In order to use the `pyplot` functions on a different axes it is necessary to set it as the current axes by using the `pyplot.sca(ax)` function, where `ax` is the variable holding the axes which is to be set as the current axes (*sca* stands for *set current axes*).

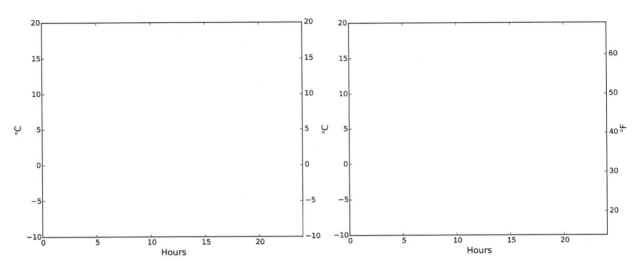

Fig. 10.7: Example of duplicate *y* axis.   **Fig. 10.8:** Duplicate *y* axis with different units.

It is also possible to work with multiple figures. Every figure object has a *number* attribute, which is an integer. The current figure can be set by using the `pyplot.figure(`*fignum*`)` function. Here, *fignum* is the number attribute of the figure to be set as the current figure. Note that the argument is the figure's *number attribute*, not the figure itself.

As an example of working with multiple figures, the code below creates and plots two figures.

```python
import numpy as np
import matplotlib.pyplot as plt
x = np.arange(0,100)
# Create 2 figures
fig1 = plt.figure()
fig2 = plt.figure()
# Make fig1 the current figure
plt.figure(fig1.number)
# Plot sqrt(x) on fig1
plt.plot(x,np.sqrt(x))
# Make fig2 the current figure
plt.figure(fig2.number)
# Plot x**2 on fig2
plt.plot(x,x**2)
plt.show()
```

Understanding the concepts of *current axes* and *current figure*, and how to obtain references to and set the current axes and figure, allows the `pyplot` function paradigm and `Axes` method paradigms to be mixed. However, doing so makes for kludgy, difficult-to-read code. For plots using multiple axes and figures we strongly recommend using the `Axes` method paradigm whenever possible, rather than the `pyplot` function paradigm.

10.14   Legends

Legends are created and placed on a plot using the `legend()` `pyplot` function or `Axes` method. In order to create the legend the `label` keyword must be used in the call to `plot()`. This keyword is set with a string that describes the data being plotted.

10.14.1   Simple legend

There are numerous keywords for controlling the placement and appearance of the legend. Before discussing these, we show an example of a simple legend. The code segment below creates the plot shown in Fig. 10.9.

```python
import matplotlib.pyplot as plt
import numpy as np
x = np.arange(0,100.0)
y1 = np.cos(2*np.pi*x/50.0)
y2 = np.sin(2*np.pi*x/50.0)
plt.plot(x, y1, 'b-', label='Cosine')
plt.plot(x, y2, 'r--', label='Sine')
plt.legend(('Cosine', 'Sine'))
plt.show()
```

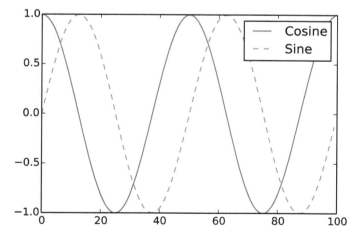

Fig. 10.9: Example of a simple legend.

10.14.2   Keywords for controlling legend appearance

The location for the legend can be controlled using the `loc` keyword which is set to an integer ranging from 0 to 10, or a string such as `'upper right'`. The allowed values for `loc` are shown in Table 10.2.

Table 10.2: Values for the legend() keyword loc. It is not clear why there is a value for 'right' but not 'left'. Also, note that 'right' seems to be identical to 'center right'.

Integer	String
0	'best'
1	'upper right'
2	'upper left'
3	'lower left'
4	'lower right'
5	'right'
6	'center left'
7	'center right'
8	'lower center'
9	'upper center'
10	'center'

Other keywords controlling legend properties are:

- fontsize, the size of the font in either point size or as a string such as 'small' or 'x-large', or a numerical value representing points.

- numpoints, an integer dictating how many data points are used in the legend lines.

- markerscale, the ratio of the legend marker size to actual plot marker size.

- frameon, a Boolean value indicating whether or not to draw a frame around the legend.

- fancybox, a Boolean value that if set to True draws the legend frame with rounded corners.

- shadow, a Boolean value indicating whether or not to draw the legend frame with a shadow effect.

- ncol, an integer indicating how many columns to use for the legend.

- mode, set to either 'expand' or None. If 'expand' is set, the legend expands horizontally to fill the width of the plot.

- title, a string for the legend title.

- borderpad, a floating-point value indicating the fractional amount of whitespace inside the legend border.

- labelspacing, the vertical spacing of the legend entries, in point values.

- columnspacing, the horizontal spacing between columns, in point values.

10.15   Saving Plots as Image Files

Plots may be saved as image files either interactively or from within the Python code. To save them interactively, click on the *save the figure* icon in the interactive plot window. This will bring up the save menu, and you can specify the file name and the file type. Typically, you would choose JPG or PNG for a raster image that could easily be imported into a presentation program or displayed on a website; for a publication-quality figure that can be included in a print document you would typically choose PDF.

Supported file types are .png, .eps, .jpg, .pgf, .pdf, .ps, .raw, .svg, and .tif. Prior to saving, the window can be resized. The image will be saved with the aspect and size of the window displayed.

To save an image from within the code, use the `Figure.savefig(`*filename*`)` method. The argument *filename* is the name of the image file. The image file type is dictated by the filename extension used. The `savefig()` method must be called prior to the `pyplot.show()` function.

Use the `Figure.set_size_inches(`*w*, *h*`)` method, where *w* and *h* are the width and height of the image in inches, to specify the size of the image file prior to saving. This must be done before using the `savefig()` method. Note that if the figure object were manually created using the `pyplot.figure()` function, then the figure size could also be specified using the `figsize` keyword, which takes the form `figsize=(`*w*, *h*`)`, where *w* and *h* are the width and height in inches.

There is no way to directly specify a figure size in pixels rather than inches. However, one can specify the pixel density in "dots per inch" (*dpi*) when creating a figure using the `dpi` keyword in the call to `figure()`. By specifying both the figure size in inches and the dots-per-inch value, the desired number of pixels for the figure's height and width can be achieved. This only applies to raster image formats such as PNG, JPG, or TIFF.

10.16   Animation

Matplotlib does contain an animation module, but it is a work in progress and is not fully functional as of this writing. There are features still missing such as the ability to readily pause, control dwell, etc. It is currently cumbersome to use, and we will not discuss it further here.

One workaround for creating animated GIF images is to use a combination of Matplotlib and the ImageMagick software.[12] To do this, first create and save a series of single GIF images with each successive GIF file having a higher

---

[12]ImageMagick is separate software that is available for Linux, Windows and Mac operating systems. It must be installed in order for this workaround to function.

number in the title than the last (e.g., *picture001.gif*, *picture002.gif*, *picture003.gif*, etc.). Then, from the operating system command line, type the command

```
convert --delay 20 --loop 0 picture*.gif
    pictureloop.gif
```

This creates the animated GIF file named *pictureloop.gif*. The delay 20 option sets the time delay between images, with larger numbers indicating a longer delay. The loop 0 option causes the loop to repeat.

Another alternative is the add-on Celluloid module, which must be installed using conda install, pip, or similar. It creates a Camera object from a matplotlib figure. With each frame update, a snapshot is taken, from which the final animation is created. Our experience with Celluloid so far is that it works well in some contexts and not quite so well in others. Nevertheless, it is simple enough to use that it's worth a try.

10.17   Other 1-D Plot Types

In addition to the basic *x*-*y* plots already discussed, Matplotlib can be used to create plots in polar coordinates, scatter plots, bar charts, pie charts, and histograms, as explained in the following sections.

10.17.1   Scatter plots

Scatter plots are created using the scatter() pyplot function or Axes method.[13] The usage is

```
scatter(x, y)
```

where *x* and *y* are arrays containing the *x* and *y* coordinates of the data points. Additional keywords are:

- marker, the marker shape, allowed values being those given in Sec. 10.7.4. Default is filled circles.
- s, the marker size in points.
- c, the color of the markers.
- linewidths or lw, the width of the marker edges (point value).
- edgecolors, the color of the marker outlines.

---

[13]When analyzing data using scatter plots, it is often desirable to also estimate the linear or polynomial relationship between the data sets. Section 21.3 discusses how to perform these operations.

Here is an example that creates the scatter plot shown in Fig. 10.10.

```
import matplotlib.pyplot as plt
import numpy as np
N = 1000
x = 3*np.random.normal(0, 1, N)
y = np.random.normal(0, 1, N) + x + 3.0
plt.scatter(x, y, s=5, c='blue', lw=0)
ax = plt.gca()
ax.set_aspect('equal')
plt.show()
```

The example specifies that the markers should be blue with a point size of 5, with no outlines for the markers. Note the use of the set_aspect() method in the example (see Sec. 12.2.2), which ensures that the plot appears square.

In the prior example we specified the same color, size, and shape for all of the points in the scatter plot. It is possible to specify different colors or sizes for each point by providing a list, tuple, or array of values to the keywords specifying the marker colors and properties. If there are more (x, y) pairs than there are sizes or colors, then the latter will cycle through the supplied list until all the points are plotted. This is not true for marker shapes, however; only one marker is possible per call. The following modified program yields the plot in Fig. 10.11:

```
import matplotlib.pyplot as plt
import numpy as np
N=6
markers = ['o', 'v', '^', '<', '>', '8', 's',
           'p', '*', 'h', 'H', 'D', 'd']
colors = ['Blue', 'Green', 'Red', 'Cyan',
          'Yellow', 'Magenta']
for i in range(len(markers)):
    x = np.random.normal(0, 1, N)
    y = np.random.normal(0, 1, N)
    z = (10*np.arange(N)/N)**2  # marker size array
    plt.scatter(x, y, c=colors, s=z,
    edgecolor='k', marker=markers[i])
ax = plt.gca()
ax.set_aspect('equal')
plt.show()
```

10.17.2   Polar coordinate plots

Plots in polar coordinates are created using the pyplot.polar(θ, r) function (there is not a similar Axes method). The required arguments are two 1-D arrays containing the angles (θ) and the radial distances (r). Many of the keywords used to control lines and markers in plot() also work with polar().

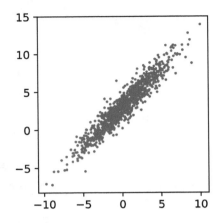

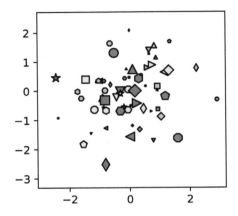

Fig. 10.10: A simple scatter plot.

Fig. 10.11: A scatter plot with variable marker sizes and colors.

As an example, the code below produces the plot shown in Fig. 10.12.

```python
import numpy as np
import matplotlib.pyplot as plt
theta = np.linspace(0,8*np.pi,100)
r = np.linspace(0,20,100)
plt.polar(theta, r, 's--')
plt.yticks(range(5, 25, 5))
plt.show()
```

The orientation and direction of the polar plot can be modified using the `set_theta_offset()` and `set_theta_direction()` Axes methods, after first getting a reference to the current axes using the `pyplot.gca()` function. To make the angles increase clockwise, use −1 as the argument to the `set_theta_direction()`. An argument of +1 causes the angles to increase counterclockwise.

The `set_theta_offset()` method specifies the location of the zero angle, with the argument in radians. Alternatively, you can use a companion method, `set_theta_zero_location()`, which takes directional arguments of the form `'NW'`, `'SE'`, `'S'`, etc. and sets the zero angle at these locations. As an example, modifying the code from the previous example to

```python
import numpy as np
import matplotlib.pyplot as plt
theta = np.linspace(0,8*np.pi,100)
r = np.linspace(0,20,100)
plt.polar(theta, r, 's--')
a = plt.gca()
a.set_theta_direction(-1) # Clockwise angle
a.set_theta_zero_location('N')
plt.yticks(range(5, 25, 5))
plt.xticks(np.radians(np.arange(0, 360, 30)))
plt.show()
```

produces the plot shown in Fig. 10.13.

Note that the same effect could be accomplished by using `a.set_theta_offset(np.pi/2)` instead of `a.set_theta_zero_location('N')`.

With polar plots the "x-axis" is really the angular axis, while the "y-axis" is really the radial axis. So the `xlim()` function controls the extent of the angular axis, while the `ylim()` function controls the extent of the radial axis. In a similar vein, the `xticks()` function controls the placement of the angle markers, and the `yticks()` function controls the placement of the radial markers. An important note is that the values to `xlim()` and `xticks()` must be in radians, though they are displayed in degrees.

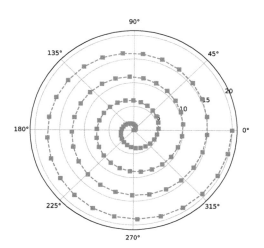

Fig. 10.12: A polar coordinate plot.

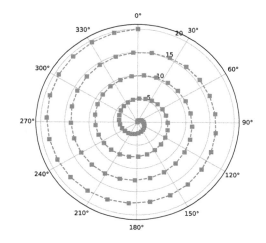

Fig. 10.13: A polar coordinate plot with a clockwise direction and the zero degree direction oriented to the North.

10.17.3 Bar charts

Bar charts are created using the `bar(x, y)` pyplot function or `Axes` method, where *x* and *y* are arrays containing the positions and lengths of the bars. The use of `bar()` is best illustrated with an example. Suppose we have data representing the temperature departures from the mean for each month of the year, and we want to plot a bar chart. The following code creates the plot in Fig. 10.14:

```
import matplotlib.pyplot as plt
import numpy as np
month = np.arange(1, 13)
departure = [1.2, -0.3, 0.1, -0.3, -1.2, 0.4,
             0.7, -0.5, -0.4, -0.1, 0.2, 0.1]
plt.bar(month, departure, width=1,
        align='center', edgecolor='black')
```

```
plt.xticks(range(1, 13), ['Jan', 'Feb', 'Mar',
                          'Apr', 'May', 'Jun',
                          'Jul', 'Aug', 'Sep',
                          'Oct', 'Nov', 'Dec'])
plt.ylabel(r'$\degree F$', size='x-large')
plt.title('Monthly Departure from Mean')
plt.xlim(0.5, 12.5)
plt.ylim(-1.5, 1.5)
plt.show()
```

Common keywords include the following:

- `color`, sets the fill color of the bars.

- `edgecolor`, sets the color for the bar outlines.

- `bottom`, sets the y-coordinates for the bottom of the bar. It is an array of the same length of the data.

- `width`, a floating-point value that sets the width of the bars.

- `linewidth` or `lw`, controls the width of the bar outlines and is a floating-point number.

- `xerr` or `yerr`, a list of floating-point numbers representing the size of the error bars in data coordinates.

- `capsize`, a floating-point value that controls the size of the error bar caps.

- `align`, controls how the error bars align with the axis labels and has a value of either `'edge'` or `'center'`.

- `orientation`, set to either `'vertical'` or `'horizontal'` it controls whether the bars are drawn vertically or horizontally.

Stacked bar charts may also be drawn, as shown by this example creating a stacked bar chart with liquid and frozen precipitation values. The results are shown in Fig. 10.15.

```
import matplotlib.pyplot as plt
import numpy as np
month = np.arange(1, 13)
liquid = [0.2, 0.3, 0.1, 1.3, 2.2, 5.4,
          4.7, 4.5, 6.4, 2.1, 1.2, 0]
frozen = [4.8, 3.3, 3.1, 0.3, 0, 0,
          0, 0, 0, 0, 2.2, 3.5]
plt.bar(month, liquid, width=.7,
        align='center', color='blue',
        edgecolor='black', label='liquid')
plt.bar(month, frozen, width=.7,
        align='center', bottom=liquid,
        color='gold', edgecolor='black',
        label='frozen')
```

```
plt.xticks(range(1, 13), ['Jan', 'Feb', 'Mar',
                          'Apr', 'May', 'Jun',
                          'Jul', 'Aug', 'Sep',
                          'Oct', 'Nov', 'Dec'])
plt.ylabel(r'Liquid Equivalent ($in$)',
    size='x-large')
plt.title('Monthly Precipitation')
plt.xlim(0.5, 12.5)
plt.ylim(0, 7)
plt.legend(('liquid', 'frozen'), loc=0)
plt.show()
```

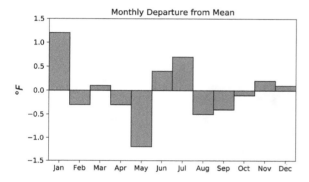

Fig. 10.14: A simple bar chart.

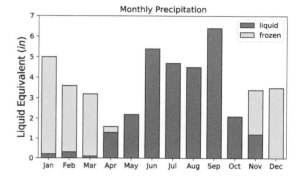

Fig. 10.15: A stacked bar chart.

10.17.4 Pie charts

The `pie()` pyplot function or `Axes` method is used to create pie charts. The simple example shown below generates a pie chart in Fig. 10.16 showing the composition of the main fixed gases in the atmosphere.

```
import matplotlib.pyplot as plt
import numpy as np
c = [0.78, 0.21, 0.009]
l = ['Nitrogen', 'Oxygen', 'Argon']
plt.pie(c, explode=[0,0.1,0.15], labels=l,
        colors=['green', 'blue', 'orange'],
        wedgeprops={'edgecolor':'black'})
plt.show()
```

Some optional keywords used with pie charts are:

- `explode`, list or tuple of offsets by which each wedge is displaced outward. The numbers represent the portion of the radius for the offset. For example, 0.1 means move the wedge outward by 10% of the total radius of the chart.

- `colors`, a list or tuple specifying the colors of the wedges.

- `shadow`, renders a shadow underneath the chart.

- labeldistance, specifies the distance away from the center at which the labels are drawn. To suppress labels set the value to None. Values less than 1.0 will place the labels within the wedges.

- startangle, the counterclockwise angle at which the first wedge is drawn with respect to the x-axis.

- counterclock, defaults to True, and is the angular direction in which the successive wedges are drawn with respect to the previous wedge.

- rotatelabels, defaults to False, and specifies whether labels are rotated to be in line with the wedge axis, or drawn horizontally.

- wedgeprops, a dictionary of arguments for drawing the wedges. For example, to draw the edge of the wedges with thick, blue, dashes lines we would set wedgeprops={'edgecolor':'blue', 'linewidth':3, 'linestyle':'dashed'}.

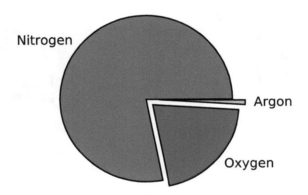

Fig. 10.16: An exploded pie chart.

10.17.5   Histograms

A histogram is created using the pyplot.hist(*x, nbin*) function or Axes.hist(*x, nbin*) method, where *x* is an array containing the data and *nbin* is the number of bins.

Besides creating the histogram plot, hist() also returns three items:

- n, an array containing the value associated with each bin.

- bins, an array containing the location of the left edge of each bin, and containing one extra value at the end that is the location of the right edge of the last bin.

- patches, a list of matplotlib.patches.Rectangle objects which represent the bars of the histogram.

The axis and label options are very similar to those for plot(). Some optional keywords are:

- density, a Boolean value which if `False` displays actual counts, and if `True` displays normalized probabilities. The default is `False`.

- cumulative, a Boolean value which if `True` plots a cumulative value for each bin of the histogram.

- color, sets the color of the histogram bars.

- edgecolor, sets the color of the bar outlines.

- linewidth or `lw`, sets the width of the bar outlines.

- linestyle or `ls`, sets the linestyle of the bar outlines, and may be `solid`, `dashed`, `dotted`, or `dashdot`.

- alpha, a floating-point value that sets the transparency of the patch. Total transparency is 0, while no transparency is 1.

- align, which dictates how the bars of the histogram are aligned horizontally. The allowed values are `left`, `mid` (default), and `right`.

- orientation, controls the orientation of the histogram, and is either `horizontal` or `vertical`.

In the example below we illustrate a comparison of two distinct normally-distributed populations. The resulting plot is shown in Fig. 10.17.

```python
import numpy as np
import matplotlib.pyplot as plt
# first population
mu, sigma = 8, 1.5
x = sigma*np.random.normal(mu, sigma, 1000)
# histogram with 50 bins
n, bins, patches = plt.hist(x, 30, density=True,
    color=(0.9,0.9,0), edgecolor ='0.2')

# second population
mu, sigma = 6, 1.2
x = sigma*np.random.normal(mu, sigma, 1000)
# second histogram , partially transparent
n, bins, patches = plt.hist(x, 20, density=True,
    color='r',edgecolor='0.2', alpha =0.5)
plt.xlabel('$X$')
plt.ylabel('Probability')
plt.title('Two histograms')
plt.grid(True, linestyle='dotted')
plt.show()
```

10.18   Plotting Outside of Boundaries

By default, plotted lines, markers, histogram bars, etc. are cropped at the edge of the plot boundaries. Most `pyplot` functions and `Axes` methods take a `clip_on` keyword that can be set as `False`. This allows plot elements to be drawn outside of the plot boundaries.

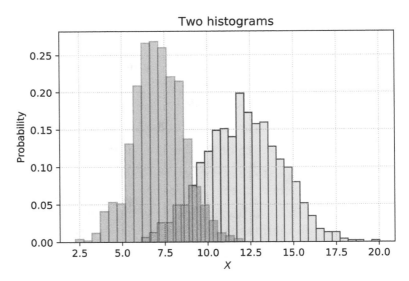

Fig. 10.17: An example histogram plot.

10.19   What is Pylab?

Many online code examples import `pylab` rather than `matplotlib`. If `pylab` is imported it actually imports `matplotlib.pyplot` and `numpy` and aliases all the functions and submodules from both of them into the `pylab` namespace. Some interactive development environments actually automatically do `from pylab import *`, so the user can simply use `plot()` without prefacing it with `pylab` or `plt`. Although this seems convenient, it can lead to unexpected clobbering of namespaces (see Sec. 4.8 to understand why this is a bad idea).

Though `pylab` is actually part of `matplotlib` the trend in the Python community is movement away from the use of `pylab` in favor of importing `matplotlib` and `numpy` separately. In fact, the website for matplotlib.org actually recommends avoiding the use of `pylab`.[14]

---

[14]*http://matplotlib.org/faq/usage_faq.html#matplotlib-pylab-and-pyplot-how-are-they-related*

MULTI-PANEL PLOTS

11.1   Introduction

Multiple axes may be placed upon a single figure by several different means. In this chapter we show three different ways to create multi-panel plots. We first show the brute-force way, using multiple calls to the `pyplot.add_axes()` function. Then we show some alternate and shortcut methods/functions for creating multiple axes.

11.2   Multiple Calls to the figure.add_axes() Method

Multiple axes may be added to a figure by simply calling the figure's `add_axes()` method multiple times. For example, if the three calls to `add_axes()` shown below are used, then the three axes shown in Fig. 11.1 are created.

```
ax1 = fig.add_axes([.1,  .1,  .35,  .3])
ax2 = fig.add_axes([.1,  .5,  .35,  .4])
ax3 = fig.add_axes([.55,  .1,  .35,  .8])
```

Note that each axes[1] must receive its own reference variable, to allow the user to specify on which axes to plot data.

11.3   The pyplot.subplot() Function

You can also add multiple axes to a figure with the $pyplot.subplot(r, c, p)$ function, were r is the number of rows, c is the number of columns, and p is

---

[1]As noted earlier, the term *axes* refers to an `Axes` object.

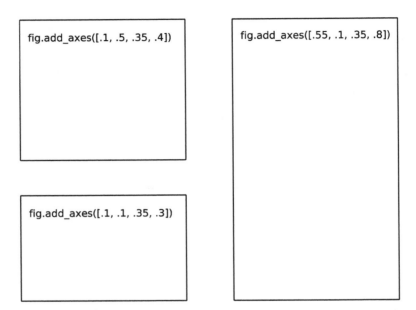

Fig. 11.1: Example of multiple axes using the add_axes() method.

the subplot number. The first call to subplot() creates both the figure and the first axes. Each subsequent call adds a new axes to the current figure.

If r, c, and p are all less than ten, then the commas separating their values may be omitted. This is often done for convenience.

As an example, the calls below create the three-row, two-column array of subplots whose layout is depicted in Fig. 11.2.

```
ax1 = plt.subplot(321)
ax2 = plt.subplot(322)
ax3 = plt.subplot(323)
ax4 = plt.subplot(324)
ax5 = plt.subplot(325)
ax6 = plt.subplot(326)
```

Although this technique is used primarily for creating equally-sized subplots, it can also be used to create irregular-sized subplots. For example,

```
ax1 = plt.subplot(211)
ax2 = plt.subplot(223)
ax3 = plt.subplot(224)
```

creates the subplots shown in Fig. 11.3.

There is also a figure-method equivalent of the pyplot.subplot() function, which can be used if a Figure object has already been created. This is the figure.add_subplot(r,c,p) method. The arguments to this method are identical to those for the pyplot.subplot() function.

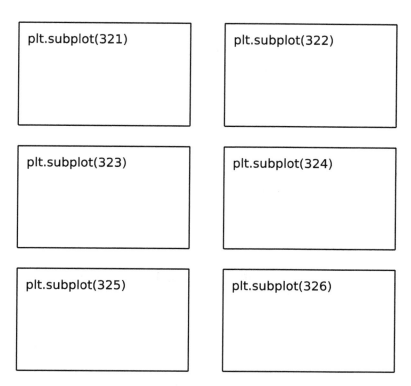

Fig. 11.2: Example of multiple axes using the `pyplot.subplot()` function.

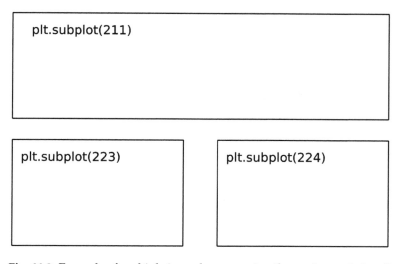

Fig. 11.3: Example of multiple irregular axes using the `pyplot.subplot()` function.

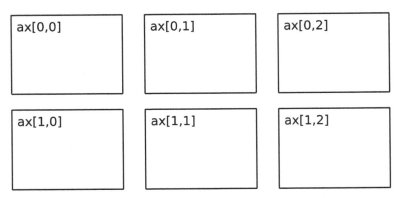

Fig. 11.4: Example of multiple axes using the `pyplot.subplots()` function.

11.4   The pyplot.subplots() Function

The `pyplot.subplots(r,c)` function (note the plural) is an easy way to create equally-sized subplots. The arguments specify the number of rows, r, and the number of columns, c. For example, to create six subplots arranged in two rows and three columns we would use

```
fig, ax = plt.subplots(2,3)
```

This creates both the figure, `fig`, and an array, `ax`, which holds references to the subplot axes. The positioning of each axes in the array is shown in Fig. 11.4.

11.5   Adjusting Subplot Position and Spacing

Adjustment of subplot positioning and spacing is often necessary in order to avoid crowding of the axis labels and tick marks on adjacent subplots. Adjustments may be made interactively by clicking the 'Configure subplot' icon in the interactive plot window, and using the sliders to adjust the keywords. The `pyplot.subplots_adjust()` function may also be used within the code itself to specify the position and spacing. The keywords to this function are:

- `left`, which specifies the left-most position of the subplots.
- `right`, which specifies the right-most position of the subplots.
- `bottom`, which specifies the bottom-most position of the subplots.
- `top`, which specifies the top-most position of the subplots.
- `wspace`, which specifies the vertical separation between the subplots.
- `hspace`, which specifies the horizontal separation between the subplots.

The values supplied to the keywords are in axes coordinates, and so must lie between 0.0 and 1.0.

Interactive adjustment is often a convenient way to determine the parameters before hard coding them into the `subplots_adjust()` function.

11.6 Sharing Axes among Subplots

If axes are shared among subplots, then axes parameters such as limits, tick mark locations and labels, etc. are also shared among the subplots. Sharing of axes is specified by setting the keywords `sharex` or `sharey` to `True`. If `sharex` is `True`, then the subplots all share a common x axis, and the x-axis labels are only plotted on the lower subplots. If `sharey` is `True`, then the subplots all share a common y axis, with labels only plotted on the left-most subplots.

As an example, the code below would generate the plot shown in Fig: 11.5. If the axes were not shared then axis labels would appear on all subplots.

```python
import matplotlib.pyplot as plt
import numpy as np
x = np.linspace(0,2*np.pi, 100) # x-axis values
fig, ax = plt.subplots(2, 2, sharex=True, sharey=True)
ax[0,0].plot(x, np.cos(x))
ax[0,1].plot(x, np.sin(x))
ax[1,0].plot(x, np.cos(2*x))
ax[1,1].plot(x, np.sin(2*x))
ax[0,0].set_xlim(0, 2*np.pi) # Sets x-axis limits
plt.show()
```

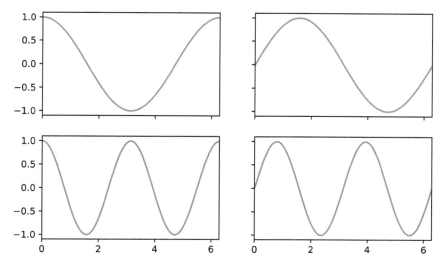

Fig. 11.5: Example of shared x and y axes. Note that x-axis labels only appear on the lower plots, and y-axis labels only appear on the left-most plots.

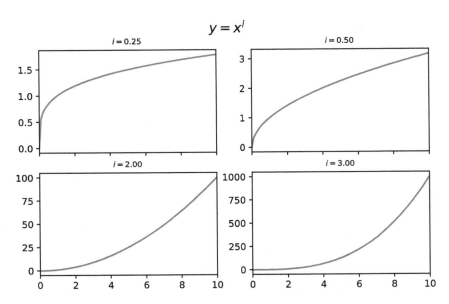

Fig. 11.6: Figure created by looping over an array of axes.

11.7   Titles

The `pyplot.title()` function and the `Axes.set_title()` method put a title on a particular axes. To place a single title on a multi-panel plot use the `pyplot.suptitle()` function or `Figure.suptitle()` method.

11.8   Looping Over an Array of Axes

Efficient code for creating multi-panel plots can often be created by looping over the array of axes that is created by the `pyplot.subplots()` function. If there are multiple rows and columns then the array must be flattened using its `flatten()` method. The code below shows an example of looping over a 2x2 multi-panel plot. The code creates the plots shown in Fig. 11.6.

```python
import numpy as np
import matplotlib.pyplot as plt
xmin, xmax = 0, 10
x = np.linspace(xmin,xmax,100)
fig, ax = plt.subplots(2, 2, sharex=True)
exponents = (0.25, 0.5, 2, 3) # Tuple of exponents
# Loop through axes
for i, a in enumerate(ax.flatten()):
    a.plot(x, x**exponents[i])
    a.set_xlim(xmin, xmax)
    ts = r'$i = {0:.2f}$'.format(exponents[i])
    a.set_title(ts, size='small')
plt.suptitle(r'$y=x^i$', size='x-large')
plt.show()
```

## TWELVE

2-D PLOTTING

12.1   Introduction

In this chapter we learn how to construct two-dimensional plots. These are primarily contour plots; however, we will also learn how to create pseudocolor plots, vectors, wind barbs, and streamlines.

12.1.1   Discussion of column vs. row ordering

A common issue when creating 2-D plots in Matplotlib is that the plots are sometimes transposed from what is expected, due to the way Matplotlib and Numpy interpret which index of a 2-D array represents the rows and which represents columns. In both Matplotlib and Numpy, the first index of an array is for the row or y-value, while the second is for the column or x-value, `my_array(row,column)`. If your data are stored in arrays which treat the first index as the x value and the second index as the y value then you will need to transpose them before plotting them. This is easily done with the `transpose()` Numpy function or array method.

12.1.2   Data sets used in the examples

The examples shown in this chapter require some 2-D data sets. Should you decide to follow along with the examples you can download the datasets from this book's resources section at the publisher's website, *www.sundogpublishing.com*. The data sets used in this chapter are titled *heights.npy* and *uandv.npz*. These files are Numpy array files, the format of which is discussed in Section 7.21.

12.2   Contour Plots

Contour plots are created using the `pyplot.contour()` function or `Axes.contour()` method. Like `pyplot.plot()` and `Axes.plot()` for 1-D plotting, the `pyplot.contour()` function creates both the `Figure` and `Axes` objects, while the `Axes.contour()` method requires an existing `Axes` object.

12.2.1   Basic contour plot

The only required argument for `contour(z)` is a 2-D array of data values, denoted here as *z*. As an example, below is a simple program that reads in a 2-D array of height values and contours them. The data file is *heights.npy*, which can be downloaded as per Section 12.1.2. When executed, this program generates the contour plot shown in Fig. 12.1.

```
import matplotlib.pyplot as plt
import numpy as np
z = np.load('heights.npy')
plt.contour(np.transpose(z))
plt.show()
```

In this example the data array is transposed before contouring, because in the original data set the first index is for the columns and the second index is for rows, which is opposite to the Matplotlib default (see Sec. 12.1.1).

If only a single data array is given as the argument, then the *x* and *y* axes are simply consecutive integers, as shown in Fig. 12.1. Since the data set *z* had a shape of (101, 75), the *x* axis runs from 0 to 100, while the *y* axis runs from 0 to 74. Two optional arrays containing the *x* and *y* values for the data points can be included, allowing the axes to be plotted in the appropriate units. For example, suppose that the data contained in array z is known to have a spacing of 5 kilometers. The code below determines the shape of the data array and creates the x and y value data arrays, which are then used in the `contour()` call. This results in the plot shown in Fig. 12.2.

```
import matplotlib.pyplot as plt
import numpy as np
z = np.load('heights.npy')
shape = np.shape(z) # Returns the shape of z
x = np.arange(0,shape[0])*5 # 1D array of x values
y = np.arange(0, shape[1])*5 # 1D array of y values
plt.contour(x, y, np.transpose(z))
plt.xlabel('km')
plt.ylabel('km')
plt.show()
```

12.2.2   Controlling the aspect ratio

Looking at Fig. 12.2 we see that 300 km along the *x* axis does not correspond to the same physical length of 300 km along the *y*-axis. We can control this behavior by using the `Axes.set_aspect()` method. It takes a single argument, the possible values of which are:

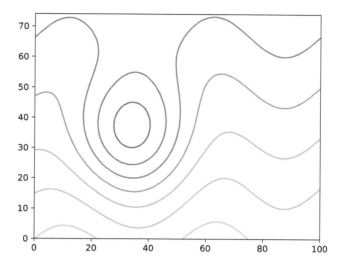

Fig. 12.1: A basic contour plot.

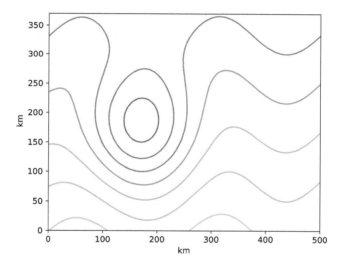

Fig. 12.2: A contour plot with axes labeled. This plot also specified the x and y arrays for the positions of the data values.

- `'auto'`, set as a string value, this is the default setting. It fills the plotting rectangle, whatever its size or aspect. If the plot is resized interactively the aspect ratio is not preserved. Figure 12.2 was created using this setting. The distances along the x axis relative to those along the y axis are arbitrary.

- `'equal'`, set as a string value, this forces the x and y axes to always be plotted proportionally to their units. If the plot is resized, both axes adjust accordingly to preserve their proportionality. Figure 12.3 was created using this setting.

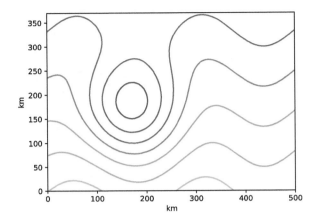

Fig. 12.3: Same plot as in 12.2, only using `set_aspect('equal')`. Note that 300 km along the x axis corresponds to the same distance as does 300 km along the y axis.

- *num*, set as either an integer or floating point value, this represents the aspect ratio of the y-axis to the x-axis. For example, `set_aspect(2)` would cause distances along the y-axis to be twice that of distances along the x-axis.

Note that `set_aspect()` is an `Axes` method. Therefore, you will need a reference to the `Axes` object in order to use it.

12.2.3 Controlling contour values and spacing

The number of contours in a contour plot can be specified by supplying a fourth, optional argument. For example, to create a plot with 10 evenly spaced contours we would use

```
plt.contour(x, y, z, 10)
```

The actual contour values will be selected automatically.

If we want to specify the values of the contours we would use the `levels` keyword, which takes a list or array of numerical values. The values do not have to be evenly spaced. For evenly spaced contours it is very convenient to simply use the `np.arange()` or `np.linspace()` functions to generate the array of contour values for use with the `levels` keyword.

12.2.4 Controlling contour properties

Colors

The colors of the contour lines are controlled using the `colors` keyword. Note that this keyword is plural! The `colors` keyword either accepts a single color, or an array or list of colors. If a single color is specified, then all the contours will have this color. If a list or array is given, each successive contour will be drawn in the next color specified. Colors are given using any of the accepted Matplotlib colors described in Section 10.7.2.

Line style and width

The style of the contour lines is controlled with the `linestyles` keyword. Again, note that this is plural. This keyword accepts either a single string, or a list or array of strings of the form `'solid'`, `'dashed'`, `'dotted'`, or `'dashdot'`.

If `colors` is set to `'black'` and no line style is specified, the contours will all be drawn in black with positive values drawn as solid lines and negative values drawn as dashed lines. If we want all contours to be drawn with solid black lines regardless of their sign, then we would set `colors='black'` and `linestyles='solid'`.

The widths of the contours are set using the `linewidths` keyword (again, note plural), which is a numerical value, or a list or array of numerical values indicating the widths of the contour lines in points.

12.2.5 Labeling contours

In order to label the contour lines, they must first be saved as a *contour set*. This is accomplished by assigning the result of the call to `contour()` to a variable, such as:

```
cs = plt.contour(z)
```

Then, the `pyplot.clabels()` function or `Axes.clabels()` method is called with the contour set as an argument, which allows label positions and formats to be specified. The labels can be either automatically or manually placed.

Automatic label placement

The default for label placement is automatic, in which the user has little control over placement. The example code below draws contours for our *heights.npy* data set, using black, dashed lines and formatting the labels with no decimal places. The result is shown in Fig. 12.4.

```
import matplotlib.pyplot as plt
import numpy as np
z = np.load('heights.npy')
cs = plt.contour(np.transpose(z),
        levels=range(5400,6000,60),
        colors='black', linestyles='dashed')
plt.clabel(cs, fmt='%.0f', inline=True)
plt.show()
```

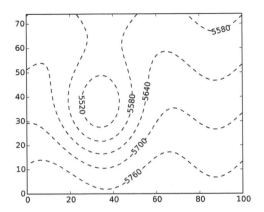

Fig. 12.4: A contour plot with in-line contour labels.

The `inline=True` keyword places the labels in line with the contours. The fmt keyword allows the contour labels to be formatted using Python 2-style format specifications, as described on p. 36.

Manual label placement

The locations for the contour labels can also be manually placed interactively. This is accomplished by setting the `manual` keyword in `clabel()` to `True`. When this keyword is set, the plot is drawn on the screen and the user can then click on the plot at each location where a contour label is to be placed. This functionality can be somewhat buggy in certain implementations, and is not guaranteed to work.

12.2.6   Other keywords for clabels()

Some other keywords for controlling contour label appearance are:

- `fontsize`, a point value for the size of the contour labels.

- `colors`, a single string, or list or array of strings, specifying the colors of the labels.

- `inline_spacing`, a numerical value indicating the number of surrounding pixels to leave blank when using in-line contour labels.

- `rightside_up`, a Boolean value specifying whether labels may be placed upside down.

12.2.7   Filled contour plots

Filled contour plots are created using `contourf()` in place of `contour()`. This does not plot the contour lines themselves, but fills in the spaces between contours with colors. If the contour lines themselves are also desired, then the call to `contourf()` would be followed by a separate call to `contour()`.

12.3 Pseudocolor and Image Plots

There are several means of displaying data contained in a 2-D array as though it were an image.[1] The primary methods and functions available are pcolormesh() and imshow().

12.3.1 pcolormesh()

Pseudocolor plots display the data from an array as pixels, with different colors for each pixel based on its value. These plots are often more attractive and more descriptive than are filled contour plots, but the trade off is that they take longer to create, and also take up more memory.

Pseudocolor plots are created using the pcolormesh() pyplot function or Axes method.[2] The usage is pcolormesh(*[x, y,] z*), where *z* is a 2-D array of data values to be displayed, and *x* and *y* are optional arrays giving the locations of the data points and which may be either 1-D or 2-D arrays. An additional keyword, edgecolor, may be set to specify the cell borders (the default is None).

As an example, the code below generates some data having a uniform, diagonally-oriented gradient with random noise superimposed. The cell sizes are also stretched from left to right and from bottom to top. The data are then plotted using pcolormesh() and the result is shown in Fig. 12.5.

```
import numpy as np
import matplotlib.pyplot as plt
n1, n2 = 101, 51
x = np.logspace(1, 2, n1)
y = np.logspace(1, 2, n2)
a, b = np.meshgrid(x, y)
data = a + b + \
    0.1*np.random.randint(0, 255, size=(n2,n1))
plt.pcolormesh(x, y, data, edgecolors='grey',
    shading='auto')
plt.show()
```

One of the unique strengths of pcolormesh() is that it can accept irregular coordinates for the corner points of data cells, as illustrated in this code example and Fig. 12.6:

---

[1]Those familiar with Geographic Information Systems (GIS) terminology know this as *raster* data.

[2]There also exists a pcolor() function/method that is used in a manner identical to pcolormesh(), but it is not as fast for plotting large arrays. We know of no reason to ever prefer it.

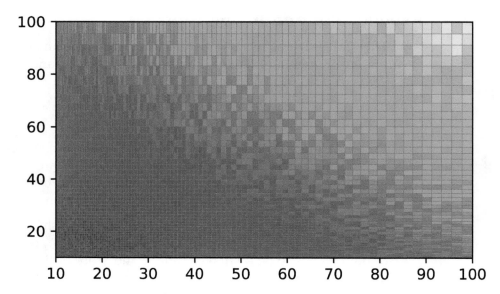

Fig. 12.5: A pseudocolor plot with cells outlined in grey. There are 101 x values (100 cell divisions in x), and 51 y values (50 cell divisions in y). The x and y values were passed to the pcolormesh() function, so that the x and y tick marks are labeled with these values.

```
x = np.array(
    [[2,  3,  6],
     [4,  5,  8],
     [6,  7, 10]])

y = np.array(
    [[5,  2,  1],
     [7,  4,  3 ],
     [9,  6,  5 ]])

data = [[0,1],
        [2,3]]

plt.pcolormesh(x, y, data)
plt.show()
```

If the coordinates are specified as latitude and longitude, then this capability is especially useful for projecting certain kinds of satellite data onto a geographic map.

12.3.2   imshow()

Another function/method for displaying raster-type data is imshow(z). This differs from pcolormesh() in several important aspects:

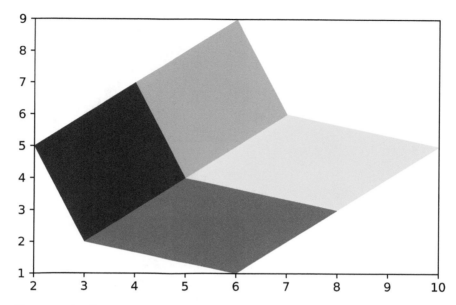

Fig. 12.6: An illustration of the ability of pcolormesh() to utilize irregular corner coordinates for each data cell.

- *Irregular cell size*: While **pcolormesh()** can display data with variable cell sizes, imshow() only displays uniform cell (pixel) sizes.

- *Cell locations:* Arrays for the locations of the *x* and *y* positions cannot be passed to imshow().

- *Orientation*: By convention image data usually is plotted with the first row at the top of the figure. This is opposite from how pcolormesh() displays the data, so data plotted using imshow() will be flipped vertically. This behavior may be controlled by using the **origin** keyword set to either **'upper'** or **'lower'**.

Plotting the data from Fig. 12.5 using imshow() results in the plot shown in Fig. 12.7. Note that the *y*-axis is reversed compared with Fig. 12.5, and that the cells are of uniform size. The axes tick marks are also different from that of Fig. 12.5 since imshow() does not accept the arrays of tick-mark values, *x* and *y*, as arguments. By default, they are simply labeled from zero to $nx - 1$ and $ny - 1$ where nx and ny are the numbers of columns and rows in the data array. This pixel-based coordinate system can be replaced by supplying the keyword argument extent=(left, right, bottom, top) with appropriate values for the axis limits.

Note that by default imshow() may use interpolation between the pixels supplied in the data array, which often leads to a smoothed image relative to the original pixel data. If this smoothing is not wanted (i.e., you want each pixel to appear with well-defined edges and a uniform color between those edges), use the optional keyword argument interpolation='nearest'.

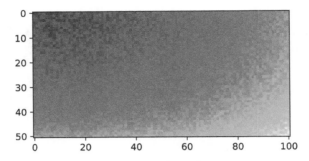

Fig. 12.7: The same data from Fig. 12.5 only plotted using imshow().

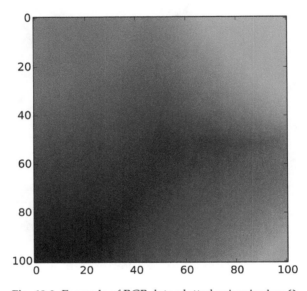

Fig. 12.8: Example of RGB data plotted using imshow().

12.3.3   Using imshow() with RGB and RGBA values

The imshow() function/method can also handle data given as RGB and RGBA color values. For those unfamiliar with the RBG and RBGA methods for specifying colors, they are briefly summarized here.

RGB

In the RGB method of specifying colors, a triplet of numbers is specified in the form (r, g, b), where r, g, and b are floating-point values in the range of 0 to 1.0, and specify the amount of saturation of red, green, and blue respectively. Pure red would be $(1, 0, 0)$, pure green would be $(0, 1, 0)$, and pure blue would be $(0, 0, 1)$. Black would be $(0, 0, 0)$, and white would be $(1, 1, 1)$.

RGBA

The RGBA method is similar to RGB but adds a fourth element specifying the opacity of the colors. If a three-dimensional array is passed to imshow(), then it is treated as RGB values. A four-dimensional array is treated as representing RGBA values. The code below generates the plot shown in Fig. 12.8.

```
import numpy as np
import matplotlib.pyplot as plt
n = 101
x = np.linspace(0, 1.0, n)
data = np.zeros((n, n, 3), dtype=np.float_)
for i in range(0, n):
    for j in range(0, n):
        red = x[i]*x[j]
        green = (1-x[i])*x[j]
        blue = (1-x[i])*(1-x[j])
        data[i,j,0] = red
        data[i,j,1] = green
        data[i,j,2] = blue
plt.imshow(data)
plt.show()
```

12.4   Color Bars

12.4.1   Adding a color bar

Filled contour plots and pseudocolor plots often include a color bar indicating the represented values. Color bars are added to the plot by assigning the result from `contourf()` to a contour set using `cs = plt.contourf(z)`, and then calling the `pyplot.colorbar()` function or `Figure.colorbar()` method with the contour set as the argument, `cb = plt.colorbar(cs)`. As an example, the code

```
import matplotlib.pyplot as plt
import numpy as np
z = np.load('heights.npy')
cs = plt.contourf(np.transpose(z))
plt.contour(np.transpose(z), colors='black')
cb = plt.colorbar(cs)   # Create color bar
cb.set_label('meters')  # Label color bar
plt.show()
```

produces the plot shown in Fig. 12.9. Note also the use of the color bar's `set_label()` method, which allows the color bar to be labeled.

By default the area allotted to the color bar takes up 15% of the axes area. This may be altered by setting the keyword `fraction` to a floating-point number that represents the decimal fraction of area for the color bar. For example, `fraction=0.1` would allot 10% of the axes area for the color bar.

The size of the colorbar itself can be changed by setting the `shrink` keyword to a decimal fraction of the default size. Setting `shrink=0.5` would cause the colorbar to shrink by 50%.

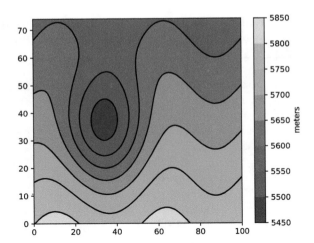

Fig. 12.9: A filled contour plot with a labeled color bar and contour lines.

The orientation of the color bar is controlled using the `orientation` keyword of `plt.colorbar()`, and can be set to either `'horizontal'` or `'vertical'`. Another `colorbar()` keyword, `extend`, allows pointed ends to be drawn at the ends of the color bars for out-of-range values. The allowed choices are `'neither'`, `'both'`, `'min'`, or `'max'`.

12.4.2   Color bars and multi-panel plots

When adding a color bar to a plot it "steals" space from the axes by readjusting the plot to make room for the color bar. When making plots with multiple axes, the space will be stolen from which ever axes is the current axes. This can be overridden by supplying the `ax` keyword to `colorbar()`. The value given to this keyword is the axes that the color bar is to steal space from.

As an example consider the code below which plots two filled contour plots.

```
import matplotlib.pyplot as plt
import numpy as np
x = np.arange(0, 101)
y = np.arange(0, 101)
z1, z2 = np.meshgrid(x, y)
fig, ax = plt.subplots(2, 1, sharex=True)
cs1 = ax[0].contourf(z1)
cs2 = ax[1].contourf(z2)
cb = plt.colorbar(cs1, ax=(ax[0], ax[1]),
    orientation='vertical')
plt.show()
```

If the `ax` keyword were not specified in the call to `colorbar()`, the color bar would steal space from the lower axes only, as that would be the current axes when `colorbar()` is called. By setting `ax=(ax[0], ax[1])` in the call to

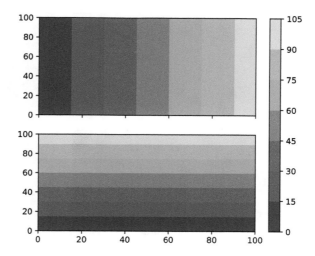

Fig. 12.10: A color bar shared between two axes.

`colorbar()`, the colorbar steals space from both axes and produces the plot shown in Fig. 12.10.

Here we show another example of sharing a color bar among four axes in a 2×2 arrangement, with the color bar stealing space equally from all four axes.

```python
import matplotlib.pyplot as plt
import numpy as np
x = np.arange(0, 100)
y = np.arange(0, 100)
z1, z2 = np.meshgrid(x, y)
z3, z4 = np.meshgrid(x[::-1], y[::-1])
fig, ax = plt.subplots(2, 2, sharex=True, sharey=True)
cs1 = ax[0,0].contourf(z1)
cs2 = ax[0,1].contourf(z2)
cs3 = ax[1,0].contourf(z3)
cs4 = ax[1,1].contourf(z4)

ax_list = [] # empty list
for a in (ax.flatten()):
    ax_list.append(a) # Create list of axes
cb = plt.colorbar(cs1, ax=ax_list, orientation='vertical')
plt.show()
```

This is accomplished by creating an empty list named `ax_list`, and then populating the list with references to all the axes in the plot. This list is then used as the value for the `ax` keyword in `colorbar()`. The **underlined code** in the example highlight the additional statements needed to accomplish the stealing of space for the color bar equally among all axes. The resultant plot is shown in Fig. 12.11.

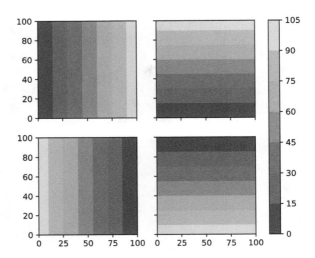

Fig. 12.11: A color bar shared between four axes arranged 2×2.

12.5   Colormaps

In Python, there are many different colormaps that can be used for filled contour, pseudocolor, and image plots in place of the default Matplotlib colormap. These are shown in Fig. 12.12 along with their names. Every colormap may be reversed by adding _r to the end of the colormap name; e.g., 'BrBG_r'.

The simplest way to change the colormap is to specify the value of the cmap keyword as the appropriate string. This is shown in the example code below (change **underlined**), which plots our original filled-contour plot with the reversed BrBG colormap.

```
import matplotlib.pyplot as plt
import numpy as np
z = np.load('heights.npy')
cs = plt.contourf(np.transpose(z), cmap='BrBG_r')
plt.contour(np.transpose(z), colors='black')
cb = plt.colorbar(cs)
cb.set_label('meters')
plt.show()
```

A list of available colormap names is returned by the function plt.colormaps().

When choosing a colormap, it's important to be aware of the different categories of colormaps. Quoting from the matplotlib documentation, we have

Sequential: change in lightness and often saturation of color incrementally, often using a single hue; should be used for representing information that has ordering.

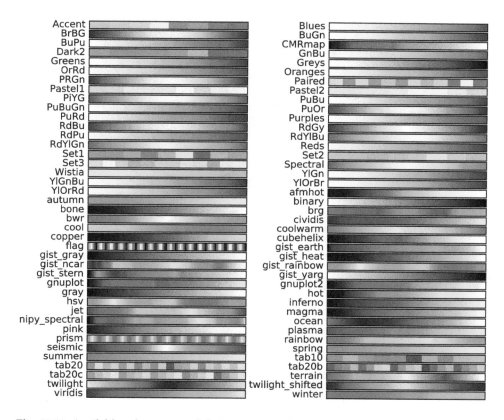

Fig. 12.12: Available colormaps and their names. Each map may be reversed by adding _r to the end of its name.

Diverging: change in lightness and possibly saturation of two different colors that meet in the middle at an unsaturated color; should be used when the information being plotted has a critical middle value, such as topography or when the data deviates around zero.

Cyclic: change in lightness of two different colors that meet in the middle and beginning/end at an unsaturated color; should be used for values that wrap around at the endpoints, such as phase angle, wind direction, or time of day.

Qualitative: often are miscellaneous colors; should be used to represent information which does not have ordering or relationships.

For more on this subject and on which colormaps fall in which categories, see *https://matplotlib.org/3.3.1/tutorials/colors/colormaps.html.*

12.6   Vectors, Wind Barbs, and Streamlines

Matplotlib has the capability to create two-dimensional plots of vector data, either as arrows, wind barbs, or streamlines.

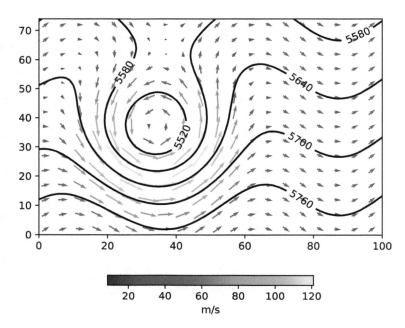

Fig. 12.13: A vector plot.

12.6.1   Vector plots

Data representing vector fields can be plotted using the
quiver(x, y, u, v [, mag]) pyplot function or Axes method, where the
arguments have the following interpretation:

- x, an array of x coordinates for the locations of the vectors.
- y, an array of y coordinates for the locations of the vectors.
- u, an array for the x-components of the vectors.
- v, an array for the y-components of the vectors.
- mag, an optional argument, this is an array for the magnitude of the
  vectors. If mag is included, then the vectors are plotted in colors representing their magnitudes. If mag is omitted, then all the vectors are
  plotted the same color.

By default, the tail of the arrow is drawn at the data point. This can be altered
by setting the pivot keyword. The possible values are 'tail', 'middle', and
'tip'.

As an example, the code below produces the plot shown in Fig. 12.13.

```
import numpy as np
import matplotlib.pyplot as plt
h = np.transpose(np.load('heights.npy'))
V = np.load('uandv.npz')
x = np.transpose(V['x'])
y = np.transpose(V['y'])
```

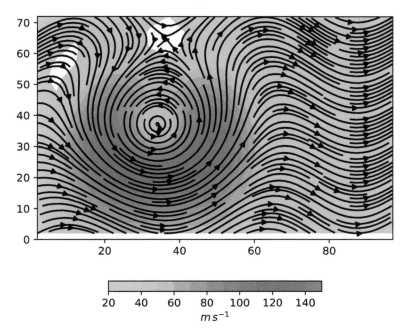

Fig. 12.14: A combined streamline and isotach plot.

```
u = np.transpose(V['u'])
v = np.transpose(V['v'])
cs = plt.contour(h, levels=range(5400,6000,60),
    colors='black')
plt.clabel(cs, fmt='%.0f', inline=True)
speed = np.sqrt(u**2+v**2)
cs2 = plt.quiver(x, y, u, v, speed, pivot='middle')
cb = plt.colorbar(cs2, orientation='horizontal',
                  fraction=0.05, shrink=0.6)
cb.set_label('m/s')
plt.show()
```

12.6.2 Wind barbs

For plotting wind barbs we would use the same code as for vectors, only replacing quiver() with barbs(). Barbs will be clipped at the edges of the diagram. If this behavior is not desired, then set the keyword clip_on=False in the call to barbs().

By convention, wind barbs are always plotted with the flags pointing toward low pressure. For plots in the Southern Hemisphere the flip_barb keyword can be set to True, which will flip the side to which the flags of the barbs point.

12.6.3   Streamlines

Streamlines are drawn using the `streamplot()` pyplot function or `Axes` method. Its usage is nearly identical to that of `quiver()` and `barbs()`. One important additional keyword is `density`, which determines the density of the streamlines on the plot. The default is 1. Higher values will increase the density of the streamlines.

The plot in Fig. 12.14 shows a combined streamline and isotach analysis for our wind data, created with the following code.

```python
import numpy as np
import matplotlib.pyplot as plt
import matplotlib.cm as cm
V = np.load('uandv.npz')
x = np.transpose(V['x'])
y = np.transpose(V['y'])
u = np.transpose(V['u'])
v = np.transpose(V['v'])
speed = np.sqrt(u**2+v**2)
cmap = cm.get_cmap('cool')
cs = plt.contourf(x, y, speed,
                  levels=range(20, 160, 10),
                  cmap=cmap)
plt.streamplot(x, y, u, v,
               density=2, color='black')
cb = plt.colorbar(cs, orientation='horizontal',
                  fraction=0.05, shrink=0.6)
cb.set_label(r'$m\/s^{-1}$')
plt.ylim(0,)
plt.show()
```

CARTOPY

13.1 Background

Cartopy is a library for plotting geographically-referenced data onto map projections. The detailed documentation for Cartopy can be found at *https://scitools.org.uk/cartopy/docs/latest/index.html*.

In Python 2 there was a very robust mapping library, Basemap, which worked quite well. Unfortunately, as happens in the open-source software environment, the developers of Basemap decided to no longer further develop it, and no one took over the chore. Cartopy seems to be a promising replacement for Basemap, but it is still in development and not all features work smoothly or correctly. As time progresses Cartopy should become more robust.

13.2 Creating a Map

Cartopy must first be imported, and for convenience we also import and alias the Cartopy coordinate reference system (crs) library. We will also need Matplotlib and eventually Numpy.

```
import cartopy
import cartopy.crs as ccrs
import matplotlib.pyplot as plt
import numpy as np
```

We can then create a projection using

```
proj = ccrs.projection_name(args)
```

where *projection_name* is the name of the desired projection, and *args* are arguments setting up the projection. Each type of projection has different keyword arguments. The available projections and their keywords are listed in Table 13.1.

Of particular importance is the Plate Carree[1] projection, which is an equirectangular projection using longitude as the x-coordinate and latitude as the y-coordinate. In contrast to the Mercator projection, the Plate Carree projection preserves the size of latitude-longitude squares at the expense of a north-south squashing distortion as you move away from the Equator. Any data set that uses longitude and latitude as the x and y coordinates is essentially in the Plate Carree projection, and we will need to specify this when we attempt to plot it onto other projections.

Most of the keywords are optional, and have default values that are used if the keyword is not specified. Many of the keywords are self-explanatory. Keywords that appear in many of the more commonly-used projections are:

- `central_longitude`, the longitude at the center of the projection. Usually defaults to 0.

- `central_latitude`, the latitude at the center of the projection. Usually defaults to 0.

- `false_easting`, the offset of the origin in the x-direction, measured in meters. Usually defaults to 0.

- `false_northing`, the offset of the origin in the y-direction, measured in meters. Usually defaults to 0.

- `standard_parallels`, the latitudes at which the map scale is true. Defaults vary by projection.

- `cutoff`, used for the Lambert conformal projection, this is the latitude beyond which the projection is not displayed. Default is -30.

13.2.1   An example

As an example, the code below creates the orthographic projection shown in Fig. 13.1.

```
import cartopy
import cartopy.crs as ccrs
import matplotlib.pyplot as plt

# Create projection and axes
proj = ccrs.Orthographic(central_longitude=-80,
                         central_latitude=40)
ax = plt.axes(projection=proj)  # creates axes
```

---

[1]Plate Carree translates to *flat square* in French.

```
ax.add_feature(cartopy.feature.LAND,
               color='tan') # Adds land
ax.add_feature(cartopy.feature.COASTLINE,
               linewidth=0.5)

# Draw meridians and parallels
ax.gridlines(xlocs=range(-180,181,60),
             ylocs=range(-90,91,15))
plt.show()
```

After creating the projection we then had to create the `GeoAxes` object on which to plot the projection[2]. We did this by the command

```
ax = plt.axes(projection=proj)
```

and setting the keyword `projection=proj` to equal the projection we created in the previous line. The several lines of code after this add land and coastlines to the map, as well as latitude and longitude lines. These and other features that may be added to the map are discussed in the next section.

Fig. 13.1: An orthographic projection created with Cartopy.

The viewable extent of the map can be set by one of two methods of the `GeoAxes` object.

- The `set_extent(ext, crs=coord)` method takes a tuple *ext* as its argument. This tuple consists of four entries, (*leftlon*, *rightlon*,

---

[2]The axes created is of the type `cartopy.mpl.geoaxes.GeoAxesSubplot`, but we shorten it to `GeoAxes` for convenience

Table 13.1: Some projections available in Cartopy

Projection name	Keywords
AlbersEqualArea	`central_longitude, central_latitude, false_easting, false_northing, standard_parallels`
AzimuthalEquidistant	`central_longitude, central_latitude, false_easting, false_northing`
EckertI thru EckertVI	`central_longitude, false_easting, false_northing`
EqualEarth	`central_longitude, false_easting, false_northing`
EquidistantConic	`central_longitude, central_latitude, false_easting, false_northing, standard_parallels`
Geostationary	`central_longitude, satellite_height, false_easting, false_northing, sweep_axis`
Gnomonic	`central_latitude, central_longitude`
InterruptedGoodeHomolosine	`central_longitude`
LambertAzimuthalEqualArea	`central_longitude, central_latitude, false_easting, false_northing`
LambertConformal	`central_longitude, central_latitude, false_easting, false_northing, standard_parallels, cutoff`
LambertCylindrical	`central_longitude`
Mercator	`central_longitude, min_latitude, max_latitude, latitude_true_scale, false_easting, false_northing, scale_factor`
Miller Cylindrical	`central_longitude`
Mollweide	`central_longitude, false_easting, false_northing`
NearsidePerspective	`central_longitude, central_longitude, satellite_height, false_easting, false_northing`
NorthPolarStereo	`central_longitude, true_scale_latitude`
Orthographic	`central_longitude, central_latitude`
PlateCaree	`central_longitude`
Robinson	`central_longitude, false_easting, false_northing`
RotatedPole	`pole_longitude, pole_latitude, central_rotated_longitude`
Sinusoidal	`central_longitude, false_easting, false_northing`
SouthPolarStereo	`central_longitude, true_scale_latitude`
Stereographic	`central_longitude, central_latitude, false_easting, false_northing, true_scale_latitude, scale_factor`
TransverseMercator	`central_longitude, central_latitude, false_easting, false_northing, scale_factor`
UTM	`zone, southern_hemisphere`

lowlat, uplat), which are the left and right longitudes, and lower and upper bounding latitudes for the map. The keyword `crs` needs to be set to the *x-y* coordinate reference system used by the data. For data in latitude and longitude coordinates you should use `crs=ccrs.PlateCarree()`.

- The `set_global()` method accepts no arguments, and sets the extent of the map to be the entire globe.

Usually neither of these needs to set explicitly. However, under certain circumstances they do need to be specified.

13.2.2 Adding features to the map

The `add_feature()` method of the `GeoAxes` object allows us to add features to the map. Several commonly used features are stored as `cartopy.feature` module constants, and are added to the map by passing them as arguments to the `add_feature()` method (see the previous example code). These constants are

`cartopy.feature.BORDERS`, for country boundaries.

`cartopy.feature.COASTLINE`, for coastlines and islands.
   The `GeoAxes.coastlines()` method may be used instead.

`cartopy.feature.LAKES`, for large lakes and reservoirs.

`cartopy.feature.LAND`, for continents and large islands.

`cartopy.feature.OCEAN`, for oceans.

`cartopy.feature.RIVERS`, for rivers.

`cartopy.feature.STATES`, for state and province boundaries.

The line styles and colors of these features can be controlled using standard keywords such as `color`, `linestyle`, and `linewidth`.

Latitude and longitude lines are added to the map using the `gridlines()` method of the `GeoAxes` object. The arguments are lists or tuples containing the values to be drawn. The color, style, and width of the gridlines may be controlled using the `color`, `linestyle`, and `linewidth` keywords. On certain projections the gridlines can also be labeled by setting the keyword `draw_labels=True`; however, as of this writing this only works for Mercator or PlateCaree projections.

13.3 Plotting Data

Data can be plotted onto a map projection using the standard `contour()`, `contourf()`, and other 2-D plotting functions and methods from Matplotlib. However, it is important that the `transform` keyword be set to the proper *x-y* coordinate system used by the data, so that Cartopy can then appropriately transform them into the coordinate system of the map.

The example below shows how to create a contour plot from data representing monthly-long-term mean 1000 mb heights onto an orthographic projection. This plot uses the data file *jan1000mb.npz*, which can be found in the "Resources" section for this book at *http://www.sundogpublishing.com*. The resulting plot is shown in Fig. 13.2.

```python
import cartopy
import cartopy.crs as ccrs
import matplotlib.pyplot as plt
import numpy as np

# Load data
data = np.load('jan1000mb.npz')
lon = data['lons'] # 1-D array of longitudes
lat = data['lats'] # 1-D array of latitudes
z = data['z']       # 2-D array of z values

# Create projection and axes
proj = ccrs.Orthographic(central_longitude=-80,
                         central_latitude=40)
ax = plt.axes(projection=proj)  # creates axes

ax.add_feature(cartopy.feature.LAND,
               color='tan')  # Adds land
ax.add_feature(cartopy.feature.COASTLINE,
               linewidth=0.5)
# ax.coastlines(color='black',
#               linewidth=.5)  # Plots coastlines

# Draw meridians and parallels
ax.gridlines(xlocs=range(-180,181,60),
             ylocs=range(-90,91,15))

ax.set_global()

# Plot data
cs = ax.contour(lon,lat,z,
                colors='black',
                levels=range(-50,200,30),
                transform=ccrs.PlateCarree())
ax.clabel(cs, fmt='%3.0f', inline=True)

plt.show()
```

A few notes about this example:

- In the call to `ax.contour()` we set the the `transform` keyword to `ccrs.PlateCarree()`, since the *x-y* coordinates of our data are longitude and latitude.

- We included the call to `ax.set_global()` so that the entire globe is viewed. With many projections this is not necessary, but if using an orthographic projection the code would not display the map without this.

- In the call to `ax.clabel(cs, fmt='%3.0f', inline=True)` we had to make the format specifier `'%3.0f'`, even though `'%.0f'` should have worked (see the example in Sec. 12.2.5).

- Related to the above difficulty, we experienced an error in getting the example code to save the resulting figure as a PDF file using the `Figure.savefig()` method. It gives a lengthy error, ending with `ValueError: Can only output finite numbers in PDF`.
  The error occurs with any format specifier having zero decimal points. Even stranger, only the orthographic projection seems effected by this error. A Robinson projection with the format specifier `'%3.0f'` saved a PDF file just fine. These errors may well be fixed by the time you are reading this.

Fig. 13.2: An orthographic projection with data contours.

13.4 Cyclic Boundaries

Many global data sets, such as that from the previous example, contain longitude values from 0 up to, but not including, 360°. In the example the longitudes ranged from 0° to 357.5°, at 2.5° intervals. When plotting projections that span the Prime Meridian this can leave a data gap, as shown in Fig. 13.3, which was plotted using the code

```
import cartopy
import cartopy.crs as ccrs
import matplotlib.pyplot as plt
import numpy as np

# Load data
data = np.load('jan1000mb.npz')
lon = data['lons'] # 1-D array of longitudes
lat = data['lats'] # 1-D array of latitudes
z = data['z']      # 2-D array of z values

# Create projection and axes
proj = ccrs.Robinson(central_longitude=-80)
ax = plt.axes(projection=proj)

ax.add_feature(cartopy.feature.LAND, color='tan')
ax.coastlines(color='black', linewidth=.5)

# Draw meridians and parallels
ax.gridlines(xlocs=range(-180,181,30),
             ylocs=range(-90,91,15))

ax.set_extent((-90,30,-10,90),
              crs=ccrs.PlateCarree())
# Plot data
plt.contourf(lon,lat, z,
             transform=ccrs.PlateCarree())

plt.show()
```

In the following sections we describe how to fix this data gap using the `add_cyclic_point()` function from Cartopy.

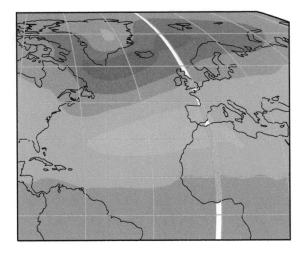

Fig. 13.3: Plot showing data gap along the Prime Meridian.

13.4.1 The add_cyclic_point() function

The `add_cyclic_point()` function from the `cartopy.util` library takes a 2-D data array and an optional 1-D coordinate array, and returns copies of these arrays. The copy of the data array contains an extra column in the right-most position. This extra column identical to the first, or left-most column. The extra element of the returned coordinate array is incremented one above the last element of the original coordinate array. The following example illustrates this.

We first import the `add_cyclic_point()` function,

```
> from cartopy.util import add_cyclic_point
```

We then create a 2-D data array and a 1-D coordinate array,

```
> a = np.array([[3, 1, 8, -4],
                [-4, 7, 2, -3]],
                dtype=np.float_)
> print(a)
[[ 3.  1.  8. -4.]
 [-4.  7.  2. -3.]]
> x = np.arange(0, 360, 90)
> print(x)
[  0  90 180 270]
```

Next, we use `add_cyclic_point()` to extend the data and coordinate arrays,

```
> ac, xc = add_cyclic_point(a, coord=x)
> print(ac)
[[ 3.  1.  8. -4.  3.]
 [-4.  7.  2. -3. -4.]]
> print(xc)
[  0  90 180 270 360]
```

13.4.2 Fixing the data gap

The data gap shown in Fig. 13.3 may be fixed using the `add_cyclic_point()` function. We first add the line

```
from cartopy.util import add_cyclic_point
```

at the beginning of the code. Then, after loading the data, we use

```
z_cyclic, lon_cyclic = add_cyclic_point(z, coord=lon)
```

to create the cyclic arrays `z_cyclic` and `lon_cyclic`. We then use these arrays in the call to `countourf()`,

```
plt.contourf(lon_cyclic,lat, z_cyclic,
    transform=ccrs.PlateCarree())
```

This creates the plot without the data gap.

3-D PLOTTING

14.1 Creating a Simple 3-D Plot

In this chapter we learn how to construct interactive three-dimensional (3-D) plots by importing the `mpl_toolkits.mplot3d.axes3d` module and using the `Axes3D()` function contained within this module. This is best illustrated using the example program shown below, which plots the 3-D spiral shown in Fig. 14.1.

```
import numpy as np
import matplotlib.pyplot as plt
import mpl_toolkits.mplot3d.axes3d as ax3d
z = np.arange(0,-100.0, -0.1)
x = np.exp(z/20.0)*np.cos(2*np.pi*z/20.0)
y = np.exp(z/20.0)*np.sin(2*np.pi*z/20.0)
fig = plt.figure()
ax = ax3d.Axes3D(fig) # Creates the 3-D axes object
ax.plot(x,y,z)
plt.show()
```

In the example we have aliased the `mpl_toolkits.mplot3d.axes3d` module as `ax3d`. Note that the `ax3d.Axes3D()` function takes the figure as the argument and creates an `Axes3D` object, which is a three-dimensional axes.[1] Once the `Axes3D` object is created, its `plot()` method can be invoked to plot the data. The `Axes3D` object's `plot()` method works similarly to the `plot()` method used for 1-D and 2-D plotting, and many of the keywords are the same.

---

[1]The full name of the class is `mpl_toolkits.mplot3d.axes3d.Axes3D`.

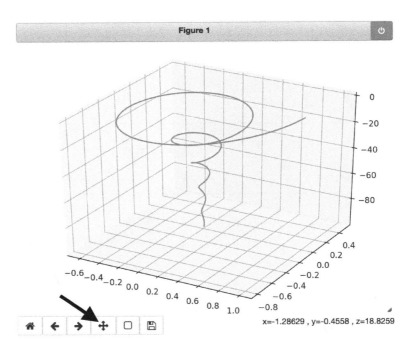

Fig. 14.1: A basic 3-D plot. The bold arrow points to the pan-and-zoom icon.

Once the plot has been created the orientation of the plot may be interactively changed by selecting the pan-and-zoom icon shown in Fig. 14.1 and then clicking and dragging the figure with the left mouse button. Clicking the right mouse button and dragging the mouse will zoom and unzoom the feature. When viewing and rotating a 3-D plot the values of azimuth and elevation are displayed in the window.

14.1.1   Orientation

The orientation of the 3-D plot may also be controlled within the code itself using the `view_init(elev=`*elevation*`, azim=`*azimuth*`)` method of the `Axes3D` object, where *elevation* and *azimuth* are expressed in degrees. If `azim` and `elev` are both set to zero then the plot will be viewed from a vantage point in the *x-y* plane and looking along the positive *x* axis. Positive values of *azimuth* cause a clockwise rotation of the plot around the *z* axis. Positive values of *elevation* result in a tilting of the *x-y* plane toward the observer.

14.1.2   Axis labels, limits, and tick marks

For 3-D plots, axes properties and labeling are controlled in the same manner as for 1-D and 2-D plots.

- Axis labels are set using the `set_xlabel()`, `set_ylabel()`, and `set_zlabel()` methods in the same manner as for 1-D and 2-D plots (see Sec. 10.9.2).

- Axis limits are set using the set_xlim(), set_ylim(), and set_zlim() methods in the same manner as for 1-D and 2-D plots (see Sec. 10.10.1).

- Axis tick mark locations are controlled using the set_xticks(), set_yticks(), and set_zticks() methods. The text for the tick-mark labels is set using the set_xticklabels(), set_yticklabels(), and set_zticklabels() methods. These are used in the same manner as for 1-D and 2-D plots (see Sec. 10.10.2).

14.1.3 Saving figure

A 3-D plotted figure may be saved either interactively or within the program using the figure's savefig() method as was done for 1-D and 2-D plots.

14.2 3-D Plots of 2-D Array Data

14.2.1 Surface plots

A 3-D surface is plotted from 2-D array data using the plot_surface(*x*,*y*,*z*) method of the **Axes3D** object. The arguments *x*, *y*, and *z* are all 2-D arrays. The example below reads in data from the 'heights.npy' file that we have used previously for 2-D plotting (see Sec. 12.1.2), and plots the surface in 3-D, shown in Fig. 14.2.

```
import numpy as np
import matplotlib.pyplot as plt
import mpl_toolkits.mplot3d.axes3d as ax3d
h = np.transpose(np.load('heights.npy'))
shp = np.shape(h)
x, y = np.meshgrid(np.arange(0,shp[1]),
                   np.arange(0, shp[0]))
fig = plt.figure()
ax = ax3d.Axes3D(fig)
ax.plot_surface(x, y, h, rstride=5,
                cstride=5, color='aqua')
ax.view_init(elev=20, azim=60)
ax.set_zlim(5200,6000)
ax.set_xlabel('x')
ax.set_ylabel('y')
ax.set_zlabel('z')
plt.show()
```

In this example we used the additional keywords rstride and cstride to control the horizontal spacing of the mesh used to create the surface. The default values for these are both 1, but at such small values the rendering of the surface may take too much time and cause delays in interactive rotation of the plot figure. The optimal values of rstride and cstride for each plot are best found through experimentation. The color keyword is also used here to show how the color of the surface may be specified. The example also shows

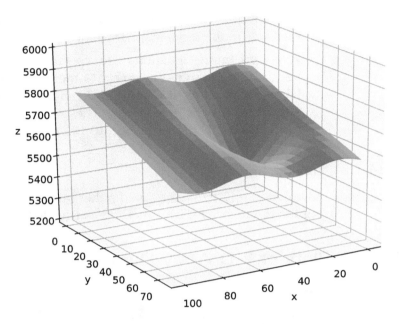

Fig. 14.2: A 3-D surface plot.

how to control axes labels and limits using the `set_zlim()` and `set_zlabel()` methods of the `Axes3D` object.

In the example the x and y data points were regularly spaced, and we used the `np.meshgrid()` function to create the 2-D arrays necessary for the `plot_surface()` method. However, there is no requirement that the data points for the `plot_surface()` method be regularly spaced, and irregularly spaced data is allowed.

A wire frame plot represents the surface with an open mesh. It is created using the `plot_wireframe()` method in the same manner as `plot_surface()`.

14.2.2   Adding contours to 3-D plots

Contour plots may be combined with surface or wire frame plots. The example below plots contours on a wire frame plot as shown in Fig. 14.3.

```
import numpy as np
import matplotlib.pyplot as plt
import mpl_toolkits.mplot3d.axes3d as ax3d
h = np.transpose(np.load('heights.npy'))
shp = np.shape(h)
x, y = np.meshgrid(np.arange(0,shp[1]),
                   np.arange(0, shp[0]))
fig = plt.figure()
ax = ax3d.Axes3D(fig)
ax.plot_wireframe(x, y, h, rstride=5,
                  cstride=5, linewidth=0.5,
                  color='0.6')
```

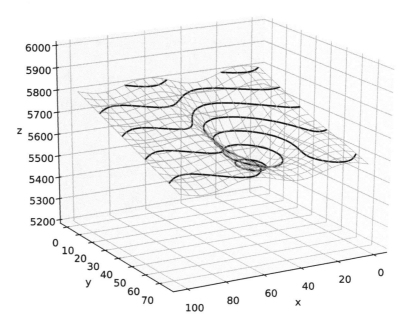

Fig. 14.3: A wire frame plot with contours.

```
ax.contour(x, y, h, colors='k', linewidths=2)
ax.view_init(elev=20, azim=60)
ax.set_zlim(5200,6000)
ax.set_xlabel('x')
ax.set_ylabel('y')
ax.set_zlabel('z')
plt.show()
```

Note that the contours are plotted at their appropriate values on the z axis. They are truly 3-D contours. We can also plot a 2-D projection of the 3-D contours. This is done by including the `offset` keyword in the call to `contour()`, which will plot the contours projected onto whatever z-level is specified. For example, if we wanted to plot the contours at the very bottom of the plotting pane we could use `offset=5200` in the call to `contour()`.

14.3   Lines and Text

14.3.1   Drawing lines

Adding lines to a 3-D plot is done in a manner similar to that for 1-D and 2-D plots (Sec. 10.11.3). The only difference is that the function to create the line comes from the `mpl_toolkits.mplot3d.art3d` module, and is called `Line3D()` instead of `Line2D()`. Their usage is similar, with the arguments being tuples of the x, y, and z vertices, and keywords specifying the line style, thickness, and color. The line is added to the plot using the `add_line()` method of the **Axes3D** object.

As an example, the code below creates the plot shown in Fig. 14.4.

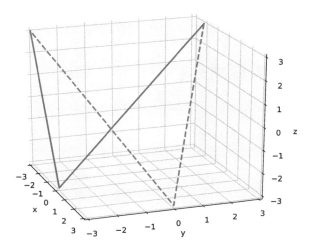

Fig. 14.4: Example of drawing 3-D lines.

```
import matplotlib.pyplot as plt
import mpl_toolkits.mplot3d.axes3d as ax3d
import mpl_toolkits.mplot3d.art3d as a3d
fig = plt.figure()
ax = ax3d.Axes3D(fig)
ax.set_xlim(-3,3)
ax.set_ylim(-3,3)
ax.set_zlim(-3,3)
ax.set_xlabel('x')
ax.set_ylabel('y')
ax.set_zlabel('z')
ax.view_init(azim=-20, elev=20)
l1 = a3d.Line3D((-3,0,-2),(-3,-3, 3),(3,-3,3),
                c='b', ls='-', lw=2)
ax.add_line(l1)
l2 = a3d.Line3D((-2,3,-3),(3, 0,-3),(3,-3,3),
                c='g', ls='--', lw=2)
ax.add_line(l2)
plt.show()
```

14.3.2   Adding text

Adding text to a 3-D plot is similar to adding text to 1-D and 2-D plots (see Sec. 10.9.4). The only difference is that the **Axes3D** method, **text()**, requires three coordinates for positioning the text. For example, to place **'Hello'** in the center of our 3-D plot from the previous example, we would use

```
ax.text(0, 0, 0, 'Hello')
```

The size and color of the text may be controlled using the keywords described in Section 10.9.4.

Part III

Additional Topics

TIME

15.1 Introduction

Working with dates and times in computer programs can sometimes be tricky, particularly when it is necessary to account for time zones, leap years, and the switch between standard time and daylight saving time (DST). Python includes some powerful features for making this easier, include the `date`, `time`, and `datetime` modules. The last of these provides a unified framework for working with both dates and times, including finding the elapsed time or number of days between two arbitrary dates, and formatting dates and times for display. Because there is potentially confusing overlap between the functionality of the different modules just mentioned, and because there is rarely any significant programming or computational penalty for taking the more general approach, we will focus here mainly on the `datetime` module.

At the outset, note that `datetime` objects can either be timezone "naive" or timezone "aware." The only difference is that in the first case, there is no timezone information attached to the object, and Python *assumes*, rightly or wrongly, that the *local* timezone is intended. This can be acceptable if there is no need to worry about the relationship between different time zones or the conversion to Universal Coordinated Time (UTC; formerly known as Greenwich Mean Time). In the second case, timezone information is an explicit attribute of the object, eliminating any ambiguity.

While we will show examples of operations using both naive and aware `datetime` objects, we strongly recommend that you make a conscious decision in the beginning as to which model is acceptable for your application and then stick with it. We will say more about timezones later.

15.2   The datetime Module

The datetime module contains several classes related to date and time:

- date provides a class and associated methods and attributes for the day, month and year.
- time provides a class and associated methods and attributes for the time in hours, minutes, seconds, and microseconds. This information is independent from any date.
- datetime provides a class and associated methods and attributes relating to combined dates and times.
- timedelta provides a class and associated methods and attributes relating to datetime *differences*.
- timezone provides a base class describing the characteristics of timezones.

A common way to import the datetime module and/or its components is as follows:

```
import datetime as dt
```

in which case we can access the datetime and timedelta classes as dt.datetime and dt.timedelta. Alternatively, we can import those classes directly as follows:

```
from datetime import datetime, timedelta, timezone
```

We will generally utilize the first convention in this chapter.

15.2.1   Basic operations

Current time

The current server time is returned by the datetime.now() method, based on the local server's clock setting.

```
> thistime = dt.datetime.now()
> print(thistime)
2020-10-04 14:21:58.293297
> thistime
datetime.datetime(2020, 10, 4, 14, 21, 58, 293297)
```

Note the difference in the output depending on whether or not one uses the print() function.

Note also that, by default, the returned value is naive; the attribute tzinfo is set to None, but the *assumed* timezone is that of the server.

```
> print(thistime.tzinfo)
None
```

The current server time corrected to UTC is similarly obtained via

```
> utc_thistime = dt.datetime.utcnow()
> print(utc_thistime)
2020-10-04 19:22:30.186541
```

Warning: this is still a naive datetime value. Subsequent operations, including the `timestamp()` method discussed below, will assume that the date/time is referenced to the local time zone.

Specifying dates/times

The basic way to create a `datetime` object initialized to a particular arbitrary time is to provide the desired time as arguments to the `datetime` class. Minimum arguments are year, month, and date, in that order; all unspecified arguments are treated as zero:

```
> sometime = dt.datetime(1995,3,21)
> print(sometime)
1995-03-21 00:00:00
> sometime = dt.datetime(1995,3,21,14,30)
> print(sometime)
1995-03-21 14:30:00
> sometime = dt.datetime(1995,3,21,14,30,22,12)
> print(sometime)
1995-03-21 14:30:22.000012
```

The final argument in the last example represents microseconds.

One may also use keyword arguments for clarity. The following is equivalent to the previous statement:

```
> sometime = dt.datetime(year=1995, month=3, day=21,
    hour=14, minute=30, second=22, microsecond=12)
> print(sometime)
1995-03-21 14:30:22.000012
```

Specifying time zones

As we have already pointed out, naive `datetime` objects can be dangerous unless you are consistently working with only local time *and* are not concerned about the ambiguities that arise during the switch between standard time and DST. Errors in time assignments to entries in a scientific data file can create serious problems that are hard to detect. For this reason, we strongly encourage you to explicitly assign timezone information whenever initializing a `datetime` object.

In our own work in meteorology, which involves datasets that are global or at least have the potential to span timezones, it is always desirable to reference times to UTC. We can easily attach the UTC timezone by invoking the `timezone.utc` object from the `datetime` module. Consider the following examples:

```
> current_time = dt.datetime.now()
> print(current_time)
2020-10-04 15:23:10.167589

> utc_current_time1 = dt.datetime.utcnow()
> print(utc_current_time1)
2020-10-04 20:23:10.167717

> utc_current_time2 = dt.datetime.now(dt.timezone.utc)
> print(utc_current_time2)
2020-10-04 20:23:10.167804+00:00
```

In first example, we obtain a naive representation of the local server time. In the second, we get a naive representation of the UTC server time. It correctly shows a time difference of five hours from our local time to UTC, but there is still no time zone information attached to the date/time value. Any subsequent operations will assume, by default, that `utc_current_time1` is actually a local time.

In the third example—the recommended approach, we not only obtain the UTC server time by passing the desired timezone as an optional argument to the `now()` method, but the displayed result shows that the time offset from UTC has been explicitly attached as +00:00, or zero hours and zero minutes. Unlike `current_time` and `utc_current_time1`, there is no potential ambiguity in the meaning of `utc_current_time2`. You can always tell whether a `datetime` object is naive or aware by printing its value and looking for the offset from UTC at the end.

To work with timezones other than UTC, you will likely want to install the library `pytz`, which provides extensive timezone support. We will not discuss it further here except to give one example:

```
> import pytz
> import datetime as dt
> tz = pytz.timezone('US/Central')
> chicago_current_datetime = dt.datetime.now(tz)
> print(chicago_current_datetime)
2020-10-04 15:46:00.545396-05:00
```

Note that the time shows the UTC offset of −5 hours.

A complete list of available timezones can be obtained via

```
for tz in pytz.all_timezones:
    print(tz)
```

The epoch and timestamps

The datetime module bases all internal computations on an arbitrary reference time called *the epoch*. Although this reference time is somewhat dependent on the operating system, it is most commonly defined as 00:00 UTC January 1, 1970. The epoch can always be determined on your system using

```
> print(dt.datetime.utcfromtimestamp(0))
1970-01-01 00:00:00
```

Time is internally expressed as the number of seconds from the epoch. Negative seconds are allowed in order to express times that occur prior to the epoch. The seconds may be either integer or floating point. The value can be accessed via the timestamp method:

```
> current_time = dt.datetime.now(dt.timezone.utc)
> current_time.timestamp()
1603661793.204501
```

If current_time were instead a naive datetime value, then the timezone would be assumed to be that of the local server. The timestamp value itself is always referenced to the epoch, which in turn is defined as a UTC date/time.

Because the timestamp is a generic integer or floating-point value, it is the only non-string representation of the date and time that is portable between programming languages. It is therefore useful for concisely and unambiguously time-tagging data elements in binary files that are intended to be shared. Again, it is important for subsequent users to ensure that the same epoch definition is being used.

15.2.2   datetime object methods and attributes

Once created, a datetime object provides a number of convenient methods and attributes in addition to those already discussed. For example, the following attributes can be accessed directly:

- year, a four-digit integer representing the year.
- month, an integer representing the month.
- day, an integer representing the day of the month.
- hour, an integer representing the hour of the day.
- minute, an integer representing the minute of the hour.
- second, an integer representing the second of the minute.
- microsecond, an integer representing the fractional second expressed in microseconds
- tzinfo, an object identifying the timezone, or None for naive datetime objects.

The individual attributes of an existing `datetime` object *d* can be changed using the *d*.`replace`(*att=new_value*, ...) method, where *att* is the attribute to be changed. This method returns a new `datetime` object (it does not modify the original object). Note that replacing the `tzinfo` attribute seems to have unpredictable effects and is not recommended.

Here are some other useful `datetime` methods not already discussed:

- `astimezone()`, preserves the time relative to UTC but translates to the specified timezone.

- `utcoffset()`, returns the offset in days and hours from UTC.

- `ctime()`, returns a standard string representation of the date and time, including day of the week; see Section 15.2.3.

- `dst()`, returns a value indicating whether DST is in effect, if known.

- `weekday()`, day of the week as an integer; Monday = 0, Sunday = 6.

- `isoweekday()`, day of the week as an integer, Monday = 1, Sunday = 7.

- `date()`, returns a `date` object only, discarding the time portion.

- `time()`, returns a `time` object only (naive), discarding the date portion.

- `timetz()`, returns a `time` object with timezone, if known.

- `toordinal()`, returns the integer number of days since the beginning of the year 1 CE.

- `strftime()`, returns a date/time string according to a format specifier passed as an argument; see Section 15.2.3.

15.2.3   Formatting datetime output

Dates and times can be formatted for human-readable output in various ways. As already noted, the `ctime()` method outputs the attributes of a `datetime` as a string in a standard format:

```
> current_time.ctime()
'Sun Oct 25 21:36:33 2020'
```

While the standard `ctime()` output might be adequate for many purposes, the `datetime.strftime(`*fmt*`)` (*string format*) method permits customized formatting of the output string based on the supplied *fmt* argument. This is a string that may include both ordinary text and format specifiers. Format specifiers are preceded with a % character, and indicate how and where the individual elements of the date and/or time are written. The available specifiers are listed in Table 15.1.

For example,

Table 15.1: Format specifiers for `strftime()` and `strptime()`.

Specifier	Meaning	Examples
%a	Abbreviated weekday name	`'Mon'`, `'Wed'`, `'Sat'`
%A	Full weekday name	`'Monday'`, `'Wednesday'`, `'Saturday'`
%b	Abbreviated month name	`'Jan'`, `'Apr'`, `'Nov'`
%B	Full month name	`'January'`, `'April'`, `'November'`
%c	Date and time	`'01/19/15 09:32:33'`
%d	Numerical day of month	`'01'`, `'19'`
%H	Hour (24-hour clock)	`'00'`, `'05'`, `'10'`, `'18'`, `'23'`
%I	Hour (12-hour clock)	`'12'`, `'05'`, `'10'`, `'06'`, `'11'`
%j	Day of year (Julian day)	`'001'`, `'095'`, `'334'`
%m	Numerical month	`'01'`, `'11'`
%M	Numerical minute	`'00'`, `'59'`
%p	A.M. or P.M. indicator	`'AM'`, `'PM'`
%S	Numerical seconds (truncated to nearest integer)	`'00'`, `'47'`
%U	Numerical week of the year, with Sunday as the first day of the week	`'00'`, `'45'`, `'53'`
%W	Numerical week of the year, with Monday as the first day of the week	`'00'`, `'45'`, `'53'`
%w	Numerical day of the week, with Sunday as 0	`'0'`, `'6'`
%x	Date only	`'01/19/15'`
%X	Time only	`'15:30:45'`
%y	Two-digit year	`'97'`, `'14'`
%Y	Four-digit year	`'1997'`, `'2014'`
%Z	Time zone	`'Eastern Standard Time'`, `'Pacific Daylight Time'`
%%	The percent % character	%

```
> current_time.strftime('%a %B %d at %X %Z'))
'Sun October 25 at 21:36:33 UTC'
> current_time.strftime('Today is Julian day %j in the
    year %Y')
'Today is Julian day 299 in the year 2020'
> current_time.strftime('Today is %A, %B %d')
'Today is Sunday, October 25
```

`datetime` objects and their format specifiers may also be used with regular Python string formatting (see Sec. 3.2) as shown here

```
> s = 'The {0:d} events occur {1:%A, %B %d} at {1:%I:%M
    %p}.'
> s.format(3, current_time)
'The 3 events occur Sunday, October 25 at 09:36 PM.'
```

15.2.4   Parsing strings representing times

strptime

The `datetime.strptime(s, `*fmt*`)` function (*string parse time*) allows a string *s* that represents a date and time to be parsed and used to create a `datetime` object. The *fmt* argument is a string giving the format of the input string, essentially the instructions for parsing. The format codes are again those given in Table 15.1.

As an example, suppose we have the string

```
> s = "Today is Wednesday November 6, 2019 at 9:18 am"
```

We can create a `datetime` object based on this string via

```
> st = dt.datetime.strptime(s, "Today is %A %B %d, %Y
    at %I:%M %p")
> st
datetime.datetime(2019, 11, 6, 9, 18)
> st.ctime()
'Wed Nov 6 09:18:00 2019'
```

dateparser module

While `strptime()` is the standard built-in method for parsing dates/times expressed as human-readable strings, it does take a little effort to construct the appropriate format string. A simpler alternative that usually works well for common formats is to install the `dateparser` module and then use the `parse` function to guess the correct format automatically:

```
> from dateparser import parse
```

The following calls then all return the same `datetime` value:

```
> parse('7-Aug-20')
> parse('August 7, 2020')
> parse('7 August 2020')
> parse('8/7/20')
datetime.datetime(2020, 8, 7, 0, 0)
```

Because no time was specified in the above examples, the default time of 00:00 is assumed. If we add a time in any reasonable format to any of the above date strings, `parse` will include that time in the returned `datetime` value, either as a naive datetime with no timezone information or with an explicit timezone:

```
> parse('8 August 2020 15:30')
datetime.datetime(2020, 8, 8, 15, 30)
> parse('8 August 2020 15:30 UTC')
datetime.datetime(2020, 8, 8, 15, 30,
            tzinfo=<StaticTzInfo 'UTC'>)
```

```
> parse('8 August 2020 10:30 CDT')
datetime.datetime(2020, 8, 8, 10, 30,
          tzinfo=<StaticTzInfo 'CDT'>)
```

If the date is omitted in the string argument, then the current date is returned.

15.2.5 timedelta objects

Objects representing time differences are called `timedelta` objects. The difference in time is expressed in terms of days, seconds, and milliseconds. A `timedelta` object can be created by calling the `dt.timedelta()` class. The arguments are supplied as the keywords `days`, `seconds`, `microseconds`, `milliseconds`, `minutes`, `hours`, and `weeks`. For example, to create a `timedelta` object representing a difference of 2 days and 12 hours we would use

```
b = dt.timedelta(days=2, hours=12)
```

Any keywords not specified are defaulted to zero.

The keyword names themselves do not need to be explicitly supplied, as long as the arguments appear in the exact order shown above. For example, we could have also defined the example above as

```
b = dt.timedelta(2, 0, 0, 0, 0, 12, 0)
```

but to avoid confusion and error we recommend supplying the keywords explicitly.

Regardless of what keywords are supplied when defining the `timedelta` object, everything is converted and stored as `days`, `seconds`, and `microseconds`, as shown here

```
> c = dt.timedelta(weeks=2, days=3, milliseconds=5040)
> c
datetime.timedelta(days=17, seconds=5,
 microseconds=40000)
```

Subtracting two `date` objects or two `datetime` objects also creates a `timedelta` object. For example,

```
> datetime2 = dt.datetime(2015, 3, 5, 13, 23, 46)
> datetime1 = dt.datetime(1997, 9, 27, 11, 17, 23)
> timediff = datetime2 - datetime1
> timediff
datetime.timedelta(6368, 7583)
> timediff.days
6368
> timediff.seconds
7583
```

15.2.6   Arithmetic with times and dates

One very useful application of `timedelta` objects is for doing arithmetic with times and dates, as shown by this example:

```
> one_week = dt.timedelta(weeks=1) # increment
> d = dt.date(1975, 2, 15)
> d2 = d + 6*one_week   # six-weeks later
> d2
datetime.date(1975, 3, 29)
> d3 = d - 12*one_week # twelve-weeks earlier
> d3
datetime.date(1974, 11, 23)
```

As an additional example, suppose we wanted to create a list of dates for all of the Sundays in March of the year 1943. We could use the code below:

```
import datetime as dt
d = dt.date(1943, 3, 1)         # starting date
end = dt.date(1943, 3, 31)      # ending date
one_day = dt.timedelta(1)       # one-day increment

while d <= end:
    if d.weekday() == 6:
        print(d.strftime('%B %d, %Y'))
    d += one_day   # advance date by one day
```

which would print the following:

```
March 07, 1943
March 14, 1943
March 21, 1943
March 28, 1943
```

This example also shows that the comparison operators (<, >, ==, <=, >=) can be used with `time`, `date`, and `datetime` objects.

15.3   Putting a Program to Sleep

While we have focused almost entirely on the `datetime` module, which encompasses most of the functionality of both the `date` module and the `time` module, there are a few specific functions accessible only via one or the other of the latter two modules.

In particular, a feature of the time module is the `time.sleep(sec)` function, which temporarily halts execution of the program for a specified duration (number of seconds) given by the argument *sec*. This may be handy for displaying a message to the user prior to executing the remainder of the program.

PANDAS

16.1 Introduction

After Numpy and Matplotlib, Pandas is probably the third-most widely used Python module in scientific programming. It was originally developed with financial applications in mind, but its power and flexibility have made it popular in a wide variety of other fields as well. It provides a rich set of tools for exploring, manipulating, subsetting, sorting, and plotting datasets.

A few specific strengths of Pandas include

- the ability to efficiently work with very large datasets;
- the ability to easily merge, subset, interpolate, and resample data sets according to arbitrary criteria and taking into account missing data and/or mismatched index values;
- improved time-based plots relative to matplotlib, including better axis labels and automatic legends;
- compatibility with Python libraries for machine learning, such as Keras and TensorFlow.

Space in this book permits only a basic overview of its functionality, focusing on the two primary data structures of `Series` and `DataFrame` objects. A Pandas `DataFrame` is a spreadsheet-like data structure, while a `Series` object is essentially a column of a spreadsheet. Both `Series` and `DataFrame` objects have methods for interacting with Matplotlib and creating plots and graphs.[1]

For those intending to use Pandas extensively for data analysis there are many books on the market devoted to this subject, one being *Python for Data Analysis* by Wes McKinney, the creator of Pandas. The online Pandas documentation may be found at *pandas.pydata.org/pandas-docs/stable/*.

---

[1]Pandas is typically imported using "`import pandas as pd.`"

16.2   Pandas Series

A Pandas `Series` object behaves much like a Numpy array in that it contains a list-like data object with an index. However, unlike Numpy arrays in which the index is simply a succession of integers beginning with zero, the index of a series can be numbers, strings, or even `datetime` objects from the `datetime` module. The only important restriction is that each index value must be unique.

This example creates a `Series` object from data representing monthly-long-term mean high temperatures for Millersville, Pennsylvania.

```
> highs_list = [39.0, 42.1, 51.3,
                62.0, 72.1, 80.6,
                85.5, 84.0, 76.7,
                65.7, 54.8, 44.2]
> highs = pd.Series(highs_list,
                index=['Jan', 'Feb', 'Mar',
                       'Apr', 'May', 'Jun',
                       'Jul', 'Aug', 'Sep',
                       'Oct', 'Nov', 'Dec'])
> highs
Jan    39.0
Feb    42.1
Mar    51.3
Apr    62.0
May    72.1
Jun    80.6
Jul    85.5
Aug    84.0
Sep    76.7
Oct    65.7
Nov    54.8
Dec    44.2
dtype: float64
```

The arguments passed to the `Series()` class are a list of data for the series, and a list representing the index values. If the keyword `index` is omitted then the series will be created with an integer index beginning with zero. The resultant series looks like a column from a spreadsheet.

16.2.1   The index

The index itself has an attribute called `name`, which defaults to `None`. We can set the name of the index as shown here.

```
> highs.index.name = 'Month'
```

If an index is named, this name appears above the index labels,

```
> highs
Month
Jan     39.0
Feb     42.1
Mar     51.3
 ...     ...
Nov     54.8
Dec     44.2
dtype:  float64
```

Naming the index is simply a convenience, and is not required. But it does have some nice uses, particularly when plotting the data (Sec. 16.2.6) or saving the data to files (Sec. 16.4).

16.2.2 Accessing data

Data within a series is accessed using the index as shown in these examples:

```
> highs['May']
72.1

> highs[['Jan', 'Apr', 'Jul', 'Oct']]
Month
Jan     39.0
Apr     62.0
Jul     85.5
Oct     65.7
dtype:  float64
```

This may appear similar to a dictionary, but a big difference is that dictionaries are unordered, while series are ordered.[2] Even though the index values are strings you can also access the values of the series by using Numpy-array-style indexing, including striding,

```
> highs[2]
51.3

> highs[3:9:2]
Month
Apr     62.0
Jun     80.6
Aug     84.0
dtype:  float64
```

---

[2]The elements of a series maintain their relative positions with respect to each other. There is always a first element and last element of a series. With a dictionary there is no one element that is considered as the first element.

However much this looks like Numpy array indexing, one key difference is that negative values for the index are not allowed! But, Pandas `Series` objects also have an `iloc` attribute (think of it as *integer location*) that works similarly to the above example, and allows negative indices as well. Note that square brackets rather than parentheses are used!

```
> highs.iloc[-2]
54.8

> highs.iloc[6:-1:2]
Month
Jul    85.5
Sep    76.7
Nov    54.8
dtype: float64
```

If you want to return just the values without the indices you can use the `values` attribute,

```
> highs[3:7].values
array([62. , 72.1, 80.6, 85.5])
```

which returns the values as a Numpy array.

A Pandas series can also be created from a dictionary,

```
> my_dict = {'mom':'Marge',
             'dad':'Homer',
             'child1':'Bart',
             'child2':'Lisa',
             'child3':'Maggie'}
> family = pd.Series(my_dict)
> family
mom        Marge
dad        Homer
child1      Bart
child2      Lisa
child3     Maggie
dtype: object
```

The index values for a series can be returned via the `index` attribute,

```
> family.index
Index(['mom', 'dad', 'child1', 'child2', 'child3'],
      dtype='object')

> family.index.values
array(['mom', 'dad', 'child1', 'child2', 'child3'],
      dtype='object')
```

16.2.3 Sorting

Two important methods for sorting series are described here.

`sort_index()`: Sorts the series based on the index labels.

`sort_values()`: Sorts the series based on the values.

Notes on these methods:

- Both methods return a copy of the series unless the keyword `inplace=True` is set, in which case the series is sorted in-place.

- Reverse sorting is achieved by setting the keyword `ascending=False`.

- Any `NaN` values are placed at the end of the sorted series, unless the keyword `na_position='first'` is set.

16.2.4 Mathematical operations with series

To illustrate the mathematical operations possible with `Series` objects we first create another series representing the monthly-mean-low temperatures for Millersville, PA,

```
> lows_list = [25.5, 27.5, 35.1,
               44.2, 54.8, 64.0,
               69.7, 68.5, 60.9,
               48.7,39.5,30.6]
> lows = pd.Series(lows_list, index=highs.index)
```

We can then combine our `highs` and `lows` series to create a new series representing the monthly-long-term mean temperatures,

```
> mean_temp = (highs+lows)/2
> mean_temp
Month
Jan    32.25
Feb    34.80
...    ...
Nov    47.15
Dec    37.40
dtype: float64
```

We can convert the high temperatures to Celsius

```
> celsius_highs = 5/9*(highs-32)
> celsius_highs
Month
Jan     3.888889
Feb     5.611111
...     ...
Nov    12.666667
Dec     6.777778
dtype: float64
```

or find the monthly-mean temperature range

```
> temp_range = highs-lows
> temp_range
Month
Jan    13.5
Feb    14.6
Mar    16.2
...     ...
Nov    15.3
Dec    13.6
dtype: float64
```

16.2.5 Statistics

The maximum and minimum can be computed directly using the `max()` and `min()` methods of the `Series` object. Simple statistics can be computed using the `mean()`, `median()`, `sum()`, `std()` and `var()` methods.

```
> highs.mean()
63.16666666666668
> highs.median()
63.85
> highs.sum()
758.0
> highs.std()
16.803264473598485
> highs.var()
282.34969696969694
```

Series also have a `corr()` method which calculates the correlation between two series. The `corr()` method from either series may be called, with the other series used as the argument,

```
> highs.corr(lows)
0.9975822383058411
```

The `cov()` method works in a similar manner only it returns the covariance between the two series,

```
> highs.cov(lows)
269.27424242424246
```

16.2.6 Plotting data

Pandas `Series` objects can be sent directly to Matplotlib plotting functions and methods. For example

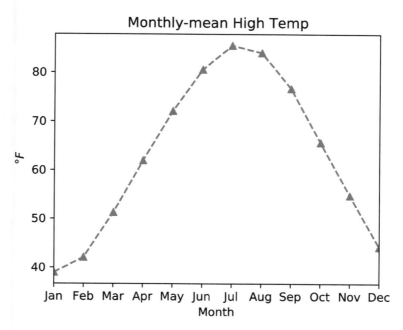

Fig. 16.1: Plot of Pandas `Series` object containing monthly-mean high temperatures.

```
import matplotlib.pyplot as plt
plt.plot(highs, c='green', ls='--', marker='^')
plt.xticks=range(0,12)
plt.ylabel(r'$\degree F$')
plt.xlabel('Month')
plt.show()
```

creates the plot of longterm-monthly-mean high temperatures shown in Fig. 16.1. Note that the *x*-axis tickmark labels are created automatically from the index values of the series.

Pandas `Series` objects also contain their own `plot()` method that acts as a wrapper for the Matplotlib plotting function of the same name, and accepts many of the same keywords. The code

```
highs.plot(c='green', ls='--', marker='^',
           xticks=range(0,12),
           title='Monthly-mean High Temp')
plt.ylabel(r'$\degree F$')
```

creates the same plot in Fig. 16.1, only using the `Series.plot()` method. One benefit of using the Pandas series method is that the index name is automatically used for labeling the *x*-axis, saving us a call to `plt.xlabel()`.

The choice of whether to use the `Series.plot()` method or standard `matplotlib` plotting methods and functions is simply a matter of preference. The two paradigms may easily be used in conjunction.

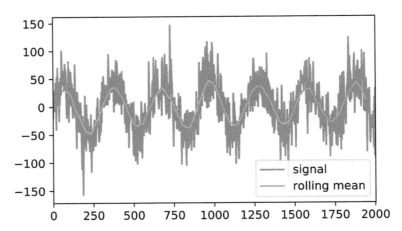

Fig. 16.2: Plot of noisy signal and a rolling mean of width 50.

16.2.7   Rolling windows

Pandas has several methods for calculating statistics over a rolling (moving) window. To illustrate these we first generate a series representing Gaussian noise superimposed upon a sine wave,

```
import numpy as np
from numpy import random as ra
x = np.arange(0, 2003, 2.5)
sig = 45*np.sin(2*np.pi/300*x)    # Sine wave
noise = ra.normal(0, 30, len(x))  # Gaussian noise
sig += noise    # Combine signal and noise
y = pd.Series(sig, index=x)    # Pandas series
```

This signal is shown in Fig. 16.2.

We now create a `Rolling` object that represents a moving window. We do this by calling the `rolling()` method of the `Series` object. The arguments are an integer representing how many data points will be in the window, and an optional Boolean keyword, `center`, which if `True` places any calculated values at the center of the window. If `center=False`, which is the default value, then the calculated values are valid at the end of the window. We desire a window of width 50 with values valid at the center of the window, and so we use

```
rolling50 = y.rolling(50, center=True)
```

Note that all this does is create our `Rolling` object and places it into the variable `rolling50`. The `Rolling` object has several different methods for calculating moving window statistics. For instance, to calculate a rolling mean, which is useful for smoothing data, we would call the `mean()` method. The example code below calculates and plots the rolling mean over the original signal, and was used to create Fig. 16.2.

```
rmean = rolling50.mean()
y.plot(label='signal')
rmean.plot(label='rolling mean')
plt.legend()
plt.show()
```

A nice feature of the rolling-window methods is that they ignore any NaN values or missing data. Some of the rolling-window methods available are:

- count(), the number of non-NaN observations in the window.

- max(), the maximum value in the window.

- mean(), the mean of the values in the window.

- median(), the median value of the window.

- min(), the minimum value in the window.

- std(), the standard deviation of the values in the window.

- sum(), the sum of the values in the window.

- var(), the variance of the values in the window.

16.2.8   Shifting of data

The shift() method of a series returns a copy of the series with the data moved forward or backward by a specified number of places, without moving the indices. A negative shift value moves the data back, while a positive value moves the data forward. As an example,

```
> d = pd.Series([5.2, -6.4, 8.1, -3.0, -1.5])
> d
0    5.2
1   -6.4
2    8.1
3   -3.0
4   -1.5
dtype: float64
> d.shift(2)
0    NaN
1    NaN
2    5.2
3   -6.4
4    8.1
dtype: float64
```

Note that undefined values are replaced with NaN. The original series remains unaltered.

16.3   Pandas DataFrames

A Pandas `DataFrame` object is essentially a spreadsheet, with the individual columns behaving like Pandas `Series` objects. We can create a data frame from two or more series. Data from spreadsheets in Excel or comma-separated value (CSV) format can also be read directly into a data frame (this is explained in Sec. 16.4).

The code below takes our two previously created `Series` objects representing the monthly high and low temperatures, and combines them into a `DataFrame` object.

```
> temps = pd.DataFrame(dict(Highs=highs, Lows=lows))
> temps
          Highs    Lows
Month
Jan        39.0    25.5
Feb        42.1    27.5
Mar        51.3    35.1
Apr        62.0    44.2
May        72.1    54.8
Jun        80.6    64.0
Jul        85.5    69.7
Aug        84.0    68.5
Sep        76.7    60.9
Oct        65.7    48.7
Nov        54.8    39.5
Dec        44.2    30.6
```

The `index` attribute is the same as it was in the original series, and represents the rows (months). A new index-like attribute, `columns` is used to reference the columns:

```
> temps.index
Index(['Jan', 'Feb', 'Mar', 'Apr', 'May', 'Jun', 'Jul',
       'Aug', 'Sep', 'Oct', 'Nov', 'Dec'],
      dtype='object')

> temps.columns
Index(['Highs', 'Lows'], dtype='object')
```

Just as we may give a name to the row index, we can also name the column index if desired,

```
> temps.columns.name = 'Temps'
```

which shows up above the row index name when the data frame is printed,

```
> temps
Temps      Highs    Lows
Month
```

```
Jan        39.0     25.5
Feb        42.1     27.5
Mar        51.3     35.1
...        ...      ...
Nov        54.8     39.5
Dec        44.2     30.6
```

Giving the columns index a name is not as useful as giving the rows index a name, and so we set it back to None for the remainder of our examples,

```
> temps.columns.name = None
```

16.3.1 Accessing data

Accessing data in the data frame is similar to using a nested list or dictionary. Some rules:

- If a single index is used it is assumed to be a column name.

```
> temps['Highs']
Month
Jan     39.0
Feb     42.1
Mar     51.3
...     ...
Nov     54.8
Dec     44.2
Name: Highs, dtype: float64
```

- If two indices are given, the first is the column and the second is the row.

```
> temps['Highs']['Mar']
51.3
```

- To retrieve a single row use the loc attribute.

```
> temps.loc['Mar']
highs     51.3
lows      35.1
Name: Mar, dtype: float64
```

Multiple columns or rows may be accessed by providing a list of indices.

```
> temps.loc[['Jan', 'May', 'Aug', 'Nov']]
        Highs    Lows
Month
Jan      39.0    25.5
May      72.1    54.8
Aug      84.0    68.5
Nov      54.8    39.5
```

```
> temps['Lows'][['Mar', 'Apr']]
Mar    35.1
Apr    44.2
Name: Lows, dtype: float64
```

The `iloc` attribute can be used to access rows and columns by their integer position. It behaves much like Numpy array indexing, and allows the use of ranges, striding, and reversing. If only a single index is given it refers to the row. If two indices are given then the first is the row and the second is the column.

```
> temps.iloc[3]
highs    62.0
lows     44.2
Name: Apr, dtype: float64

> temps.iloc[3:7]
         Highs    Lows
Month
Apr      62.0     44.2
May      72.1     54.8
Jun      80.6     64.0
Jul      85.5     69.7

> temps.iloc[3:7].values
array([[62. , 44.2],
       [72.1, 54.8],
       [80.6, 64. ],
       [85.5, 69.7]])

> temps.iloc[6:,0]
Month
Jul    85.5
Aug    84.0
Sep    76.7
Oct    65.7
Nov    54.8
Dec    44.2
Name: Highs, dtype: float64

> temps.iloc[3:7,1]
Month
Apr    44.2
May    54.8
Jun    64.0
Jul    69.7
Name: Lows, dtype: float64
```

The **values** attribute will return just the values, as a single item or an array.

16.3.2 Sorting

Sorting of data frames is performed similarly to the sorting of series described in Sec. 16.2.3, using the `sort_index()` and `sort_values()` methods, with minor modifications to specify whether the sorting takes place along rows (default) or columns, and to specify the row or column on which to sort.

- `sort_index()`, sorts the data frame based on the index labels. The `axis` keyword specifies whether to sort the row index (`axis=0` or `axis='index'`), or the column index (`axis=1` or `axis='columns'`). If `axis` is omitted then the default is sorting of the row index.

- `sort_values()`, sorts the data frame based on the row or column label specified in the `by` keyword. The `axis` keyword behaves just like described above.

As an example, if we wanted to sort the `temps` data frame on the low temperatures, in descending order, we would use

```
> temps.sort_values(by='Lows', axis=0,
                     ascending=False)
```

and if instead we wanted to sort based on the August temperatures from low to high (an admittedly trivial thing to do) we would use

```
> temps.sort_values(by='Aug', axis=1,
                     ascending=True)
```

Notes on these methods:

- Both `sort_index()` and `sort_values` return a copy of the data frame unless the keyword `inplace=True` is set, in which case the data frame is sorted in-place.

- Reverse sorting is achieved by setting the keyword `ascending=False`.

- Any `NaN` values are placed at the end of the sorted data frame, unless the keyword `na_position='first'` is set.

16.3.3 Math and statistics

Math with data frames is simple. For example, the monthly temperature ranges can be found by

```
> t_range = temps['Highs'] - temps['Lows']
>t_range
Month
Jan    13.5
Feb    14.6
...    ...
Nov    15.3
Dec    13.6
dtype: float64
```

Statistics work just like with series. The default setting is to do statistics across rows, but by setting the keyword `axis=1` the statistics will be performed across columns.

```
> temps.mean()
Highs    63.166667
Lows     47.416667
dtype: float64

> temps.mean(axis=1)
Month
Jan    32.25
Feb    34.80
Mar    43.20
...     ...
Nov    47.15
Dec    37.40
dtype: float64
```

The covariance `cov()` and correlation `corr()` methods also work for data frames, and return the covariance and correlation matrices.

```
> temps.corr()
            Highs          Lows
Highs    1.000000       0.997582
Lows     0.997582       1.000000
```

Moving window methods are also applicable to data frames. For instance, a three-month rolling average of monthly-mean temps would be calculated using

```
> rolling3 = temps.rolling(3)
> rolling3.mean()
            Highs          Lows
Month
Jan          NaN           NaN
Feb          NaN           NaN
Mar    44.133333     29.366667
Apr    51.800000     35.600000
...       ...           ...
Nov    65.733333     49.700000
Dec    54.900000     39.600000
```

16.3.4   Plotting

Calling the `plot()` method of a `DataFrame` object will make a basic plot of all the data, including a legend. The index name, if not `None`, will be used for the x-axis label. For more detailed control of the plot you can use the Matplotlib plotting features.

16.3.5 Adding and removing rows and columns

A new column may be added to an existing data frame by simply referencing the name of the new column and providing the data. For example, say we wanted to add a new column to our `temps` data frame and populate it with the mean temperature for the month. We would first calculate the mean temperatures for each month

```
> mean_temps = temps.mean(axis=1)
```

and then do

```
> temps['Means'] = mean_temps
> temps
            Highs    Lows    Means
Month
Jan         39.0    25.5    32.25
Feb         42.1    27.5    34.80
Mar         51.3    35.1    43.20
...         ...     ...     ...
Nov         54.8    39.5    47.15
Dec         44.2    30.6    37.40
```

which appends the new column and adds our calculated values.

If the column is to be inserted at a specific location, use the `insert()` method. As an example, if we wanted to insert the monthly-mean temperature ranges between the highs and lows columns in the data frame we would use

```
> tranges = temps['Highs']-temps['Lows']
> temps.insert(1, 'Ranges', tranges)
```

A new row is added by assigning its index using the `loc` attribute. For example, the code

```
> temps.loc['Bert'] = [45, 35, 40]
```

appends a new row with index `'Bert'` to the data frame. New rows cannot easily be inserted at specific locations in the middle of the data frame.

To delete a row or column from a data frame we use the `drop()` method. We use the keywords `index` or `columns` to specify whether we are deleting rows or columns. Unless the keyword `inplace=True` is used the `drop()` function does not alter the original data frame, but returns an altered copy. For example,

```
> temps.drop(index='Bert', inplace=True)
```

would delete the row named `Bert`, while

```
> temps.drop(columns='means', inplace=True)
```

would delete the `means` column.

16.4   Reading and Writing Files

Data frames and series may be written to and read from several file formats, including comma-separated and Excel formats. The following examples assume we are using a Pandas data frame named `temps` that appears as

```
> temps
          Highs   Lows    Means   Ranges
Month
Jan       39.0    25.5    32.25   13.5
Feb       42.1    27.5    34.80   14.6
Mar       51.3    35.1    43.20   16.2
Apr       62.0    44.2    53.10   17.8

...
Sep       76.7    60.9    68.80   15.8
Oct       65.7    48.7    57.20   17.0
Nov       54.8    39.5    47.15   15.3
Dec       44.2    30.6    37.40   13.6
```

16.4.1   Comma-separated value (CSV) files

Writing to CSV

A data frame or series may be written to a CSV file using the `to_csv()` method. As an example, our data frame of monthly temperatures can be written to CSV file using

```
> temps.to_csv('Monthly-temps.csv', sep=';',
               float_format='%.2f')
```

which creates a semicolon-delimited file named `Monthly-temps.csv` the contents of which are

```
Month;Highs;Lows;Means;Ranges
Jan;39.00;25.50;32.25;13.50
Feb;42.10;27.50;34.80;14.60
Mar;51.30;35.10;43.20;16.20
...
Nov;54.80;39.50;47.15;15.30
Dec;44.20;30.60;37.40;13.60
```

Note that because our index is named `'Month'` the index name appears in the header of the output file. If the index is unnamed, then the first field of the header would be blank.

Besides specifying the file name, optional keywords for the `to_csv()` method are:

- `sep`, which specifies the separator used between data values. The default is a comma. The separator may only be a single character in width.

- `float_format`, which gives the formatting for numerical values.

- `index_label`, which is the heading for the index values. If this keyword is omitted, then the index name (see Sec. 16.2.1) will be used as the heading.

- `header`, which is a list of labels to be used for the data values in the header row. If no header is desired, then set it to `False` or `None`.

Writing a series to a CSV file is similar to the example above. However, since Pandas `Series` objects do not contain column labels, a header will not appear in the data file unless specifically set using the `header` keyword. If this keyword is omitted a warning will appear. As an example, we could write our series representing high temperatures to a comma-separated file using

```
highs.to_csv('highs.csv', sep=',',
             float_format='%.1f',
             header=['High'])
```

which produces a file named `highs.csv` the contents of which are

```
Month,High
Jan,39.0
Feb,42.1
Mar,51.3
...
Nov,54.8
Dec,44.2
```

If a header were not desired we would omit the `index_label` keyword and set `header=False`.

Reading from CSV

Data from CSV files can be read into a data frame using the `pandas.read_csv()` function. For example, to read the `Monthly-temps.csv` file we created previously into a new data frame we would use

```
> temps_new = pd.read_csv('Monthly-temps.csv',
                          sep=';',
                          header=0,
                          index_col=0)
```

Besides the required filename, some optional keywords are

- `sep`, the delimiter between data values. The default is a comma.

- `header`, the row to use for the column names. The default is 0. If the file contains no header row then set `header=None`.

By default the names of the columns and of the index will be taken from the first row of the file. If the data has no header row, or if you don't want to use the header row as the column and index names, you can specify new column names here. For example,

```
> temps2_new = pd.read_csv('Monthly-temps.csv',
                            sep=';',
                            header=0,
                            names=['Bob', 'Carol',
                                   'Ted', 'Alice'],
                            index_col=0)
```

reads the data but replaces the column labels with our new choices. The data frame now looks like

```
        Bob     Carol    Ted     Alice
Jan     39.0    25.5     32.25   13.5
Feb     42.1    27.5     34.80   14.6
Mar     51.3    35.1     43.20   16.2
...     ...     ...      ...     ...
Nov     54.8    39.5     47.15   15.3
Dec     44.2    30.6     37.40   13.6
```

Since the data file only has four rows of data (not counting the months), and we only provided four labels, the labels were assigned to the columns, and the index name was set to None. If we had provided five labels, the first label would have been used for the index name, and the other four would be assigned to the columns.

16.4.2 Excel files

Writing to Excel

A data frame or series may be written to an Excel spreadsheet file using the `to_excel()` method. As an example, our data frame of monthly temperatures can be written to an Excel file using

```
> temps.to_excel('Monthly-temps.xlsx',
                  float_format='%.2f')
```

Besides specifying the file name, some optional keywords are:

- `float_format`, which gives the formatting for numerical values.
- `index_label`, which is the heading for the index values. If this keyword is omitted, then the index name (see Sec. 16.2.1) will be used as the heading.
- `header`, which is a list of names to use for the file header row. The `header` keyword applies only to the data columns, not the index column. However, if it is set to False or None then no header row is written at all.

The Excel file is either created or overwritten with every call to `to_excel`. Even though there is an optional keyword called `sheet_name` which can be set to the name of the sheet, it does not create an additional sheet in an existing Excel file, but still overwrites the file.

Writing a series to an Excel file is similar to the example above. However, since Pandas `Series` objects do not contain column labels the header will default to the index name (if present) or the integer 0, unless the `header` keyword is explicitly set. As an example, we could write our series of monthly-mean high temperatures to an Excel file using

```
highs.to_excel('highs.xlsx',
               header=['High'])
```

If a header were not desired we would omit the `index_label` keyword and set `header=False`.

Reading from Excel

Reading data from an Excel file into a data frame is accomplished via the `read_excel()` function, as shown here

```
> temps3 = pd.read_excel('Monthly-temps.xlsx',
                         index_col=0)
> temps3
         Highs   Lows    Means   Ranges
Month
Jan      39.0    25.5    32.25   13.5
Feb      42.1    27.5    34.80   14.6
Mar      51.3    35.1    43.20   16.2
...      ...     ...     ...     ...
Nov      54.8    39.5    47.15   15.3
Dec      44.2    30.6    37.40   13.6
```

We only needed to specify the data file path and which column to use as the index values. The index name and column labels are inferred automatically from the header row. Some keywords are:

- `index_col`, which specifies which column contains the index values. If this is omitted then all columns are assumed to be data columns, and a new integer index is created.

- `names`, which are optional names to use for the index and column labels. They are given as a list of strings, and there must be enough names for the index and all data columns.

- `header`, an integer which specifies which row is used for the column names. If the file has no header than set `header=None`, and the index and column names will be given integer values.

- `sheet_name`, the name of the sheet within the Excel file from which to read. If omitted, the default is always the first sheet.

16.5   Temporal Resampling

If the index of the data frame or series represents dates and/or times, then Pandas can be used to resample the data. The capability is much greater than is illustrated here, where we simply show how to take daily timeseries data and resample it to monthly-means, yearly-means, etc.

The examples in this section require the Excel file *climo.xlsx* which may be downloaded from this book's resources section at *www.sundogpublishing.com*. This data file contains daily values of max and min temperature (in Fahrenheit) and precipitation values (in inches) for a 30-year period. The data file is read using the command

```
> daily_climo = pd.read_excel('climo.xlsx', index_col=0)
```

The index values in this file are date-like, in the format year-month-day, *yyyy-mm-dd*. Pandas allows ranges to be used for such indices. For example, to obtain a week's worth of data we can simply specify the start and end date,

```
> daily_climo['2017-3-1':'2017-3-7']
                High    Low     Precip
Date
2017-03-01       69      54      0.11
2017-03-02       58      33      0
2017-03-03       37      23      t
2017-03-04       35      19      0
2017-03-05       37      13      0
2017-03-06       53      21      0
2017-03-07       63      39      0.16
```

(the 't' in the Precip column stands for *trace*, meaning precipitation was detected, but the amount was too small to measure).

To resample the data we first create a `Resampler` object using the data frame's `resample()` method

```
> monthly_climo = daily_climo.resample('A',
                                  kind='period')
```

We had to specify the time period for the resampling (in this case, annual) and the `kind` keyword to tell the resampler how we would like the index to be represented. The time periods are specified as follows:

Annual: Use `'A'` for a calendar year ending in December. If the year ends on a different month (say a fiscal year), use `'A-MMM'` where *MMM* is the three-letter month abbreviation (in all caps) representing the ending month of the year.

Quarterly: Use `'Q'`. If the year does not end in December, then use `'Q-MMM'` where *MMM* is the three-letter month abbreviation (in all caps) representing the ending month of the year. For example, climatologists would likely use `'Q-NOV'`, which would aggregate the data into the quarters Dec-Jan-Feb, Mar-Apr-May, Jun-Jul-Aug, Sep-Oct-Nov which represent climatological winter, spring, summer, and fall.

Monthly: `'M'`

Weekly: Use `'W'` for weekly sampling with weeks ending on Sunday. For weeks ending on other days use `'W-DDD'` where *DDD* is the three-letter abbreviation (all caps) for the day of the week on which the week ends.

Daily: Use `'D'` for calendar day or `'B'` for business day.

Hourly: `'H'`

Minute: Use `'T'` or `'min'`.

Second: `'S'`

To get other sampling periods not listed we simply preface the sampling period with an integer. For example, a sampling period of `'2Q'` would be two quarters (semiannual), while `'3W'` would represent three weeks.

The choices for the `kind` keyword are

- `'timestamp'`, converts the index to a datetime index.
- `'period'`, converts the index to a period index.

If `kind` is omitted then the index will be of the same type as the original data frame.

Once the `Resampler` object is created we can then apply its methods such as `mean()`, `sum()`, `median()`, `var()`, `std()`, `max()`, and `min()` to return the mean, sum, median, variance, standard deviation, maximum and mininum values.

Continuing with our example of annual resampling, we can now find the annual means by

```
> monthly_climo.mean()
        High           Low
Date
1989    60.947945      42.375342
1990    63.676712      44.575342
1991    65.210959      44.479452
...     ...     ...
2017    64.328767      44.621918
2018    62.372603      44.632877
```

Note that the `Precip` column was not included, since it contained some non-numeric data. If we would have used `kind='timestamp'` the only difference would be that the resulting index would be dates rather than years.

16.6 A Few Additional Useful Methods

A few additional methods for Pandas Series and DataFrames.

- *df*.head(n), returns the first *n* items in the DataFrame or Series, *df*.

- *df*.tail(n), returns the last *n* items in the DataFrame or Series, *df*.

- *s*.value_counts(), returns a count of each distinct value occuring in the Series, *s*.

- *df*.describe(), returns some descriptive statistics about the DataFrame or Series, *df*.

- *df*.info(), returns some basic information about the DataFrame or Series, *df*.

SCIENTIFIC DATASETS

17.1   Introduction

In the geosciences two standard formats are now widely used for storing large data sets, these being the Network Common Data Form (NetCDF) and the Hierarchical Data Format (HDF). The HDF standard has been expanded to encompass NetCDF as a special case so that modern HDF tools can work with both formats. Nevertheless, a number of Python functions specific to NetCDF exist and are widely used, so we treat HDF and NetCDF as distinct formats in the discussion here. Because both NetCDF and HDF files can contain complicated nested data structures it can be helpful to use the free application Panoply, created by NASA, to interactively explore the contents of an unfamiliar data file. Among other things, this can allow you to quickly determine what data objects and attributes are present in the file, how they are structured, and by what name to access them. Panoply is available for multiple platforms from *www.giss.nasa.gov/tools/panoply*.

17.2   Working with NetCDF

17.2.1   Overview

This section describes how to read data stored in Network Common Data Form or NetCDF. Many climate data sets and data sets from atmospheric and oceanic numerical models are stored in this format. There are three variations:

NetCDF classic: This was the original format and is still the default format for many applications.

NetCDF 64-bit: This variant supports larger variables and file sizes.

NetCDF4: This format is very similar to the HDF5 data format (discussed in Sec. 17.3).

A single NetCDF file may contain data for multiple variables, multiple times, and multiple vertical levels. There are two main types of variables in a NetCDF file:

Dimension variables: These variables hold items containing time and location information for the other variables. Examples are altitude or pressure levels, latitudes, longitudes, and date-times.

Data variables: These variables hold the actual data. Examples could be temperature, pressure, heights of pressure surfaces, wind components, etc.

17.2.2 Opening and reading NetCDF files

There are several Python modules or libraries for reading NetCDF files. Two of the most readily available are:

- `scipy.io.netcdf`: This module contains functions for reading and writing NetCDF classic files.

- `netCDF4`: This module contains functions for reading and writing both the older and newer formats of NetCDF.

The functionality of both libraries is similar. The only significant difference in usage is how the files are opened. Once the files are opened, accessing the data is the same for each module. Since the `netCDF4` module is newer and more capable we focus on it exclusively in the following discussion.

Opening a NetCDF file

To open a NetCDF file using the `netCDF4` module, use these two commands:

```
import netCDF4
f = netCDF4.Dataset(filename, 'r')
```

The first line imports the `netCDF4` module. The second line opens the NetCDF file named *filename* and assigns it to a `Dataset`[1] object named *f*. The argument `'r'` opens the file as read-only.

Exploring a NetCDF file

The `Dataset` object has an attribute named `variables` that contains the variables. This attribute is an iterable object, and so may be explored by looping over it and printing the result:

```
for v in f.variables:
    print(v)
```

---

[1]The full name of the object's class is `netCDF4._netCDF4.Dataset`

The above code prints the variable names. If you are using the `netCDF4` module it is also possible to simply use `print(f)`, which will print the variable names and other information about the file.

At this point, you may wish to try working with an actual NetCDF file. The following examples use the NetCDF file named *hgt.mon.1981-2010.ltm.nc*, available at the 'Resources' page for this book at *www.sundogpublishing.com*. You may also try working with a file of your own choosing. For the example file provided, and using the `NetCDF4` module, the code

```
import netCDF4
f = netCDF4.Dataset('hgt.mon.1981-2010.ltm.nc', 'r')
for v in f.variables:
    print(v)
```

prints the following output

```
level
lat
lon
time
climatology_bounds
hgt
valid_yr_count
```

showing that the file contains seven variables. We can further explore the variables interactively. If using the `netCDF4` module, you may type

```
> print(f)
```

which prints the following information about the file:

```
<class 'netCDF4._netCDF4.Dataset'>
root group (NETCDF3_CLASSIC data model, fileformat
  NETCDF3):
   title: monthly mean geopotential height from the
NCEP Reanalysis
   history: Created 2011/07/12 by doMonthLTM
   description:  Data from NCEP initialized
       reanalysis (4x/day).  These are interpolated to
pressure surfaces from model (sigma) surfaces.
   platform: Model
   Conventions: COARDS
   references: http://www.esrl.noaa.gov/psd/data/
       gridded/data.ncep.reanalysis.derived.html
   not_missing_threshold_percent: minimum 3% values
input to have non-missing output val
   dimensions(sizes): lon(144), lat(73), level(17),
time(12), nbnds(2)
   variables(dimensions): float32 level(level),
float32 lat(lat), float32 lon(lon), float64
```

```
time(time), float64 climatology_bounds(time,nbnds),
float32, hgt(time,level,lat,lon), int16
valid_yr_count(time,level,lat,lon)
  groups:
```

The above output reveals that the file has five *dimension* variables: `'lon'`, `'lat'`, `'level'`, `'time'`, and `'nbnds'`.

Accessing the data contained in variables

The attribute `f.variables` can be treated much like a dictionary, with the keys being the variable names. The variables themselves are stored as Numpy masked arrays. For example, typing

```
> f.variables['hgt']
```

returns the following information about the variable named hgt:

```
<class 'netCDF4._netCDF4.Variable'>
float32 hgt(time, level, lat, lon)
    long_name: Monthly Long Term mean geopotential
    height
    valid_range: [ -700. 35000.]
    units: m
    add_offset: 0.0
    scale_factor: 1.0
    missing_value: -9.96921e+36
    precision: 0
    least_significant_digit: 0
    GRIB_id: 7
    GRIB_name: HGT
    var_desc: Geopotential height
    dataset: CDC Derived NCEP Reanalysis Products
    level_desc: Multiple levels
    statistic: Long Term Mean
    parent_stat: Mean
    actual_range: [ -198.80215 32228.03    ]
unlimited dimensions:
current shape = (12, 17, 73, 144)
filling on, default _FillValue of 9.969209968386869e+36
    used
```

This variable is stored in 32-bit floating-point format, and is a 4-D array with the dimensions time, level, lat, and lon in that order. Any attributes of the variable are also displayed, and their values given. This variable has 16 attributes, one of which is `units`, which tells us the data are stored in meters.

To access the data contained in the variables we use `f.variables[key][:]` where *key* is the name of the variable. For example,

```
> f.variables['level'][:]
```

yields the following output

```
masked_array(data=[1000.,    925.,    850.,    700.,    600.,
    500.,    400.,    300.,
                     250.,    200.,    150.,    100.,     70.,
    50.,     30.,     20.,
                      10.],
            masked=False,
        fill_value=1e+20,
            dtype=float32)
```

which shows that the 'level' variable is stored as a masked array, and also shows us the values. If we simply want to view the data without all the extra information we can access the data attribute as shown here,

```
> f.variables['level'][:].data
array([1000.,    925.,    850.,    700.,    600.,    500.,    400.,
    300.,    250.,
        200.,    150.,    100.,     70.,     50.,     30.,     20.,
    10.],
    dtype=float32)
```

Doing the same for the 'time' variable is shown here,

```
> f.variables['time'][:].data
array([    0.,     31.,     59.,     90.,    120.,    151.,    181.,
    212.,    243.,    273.,    304.,    334.])
```

For time there are 12 entries, one for each month of the year. The values represent how many days have elapsed since the beginning of the year at the start of the month in question. The month of January is represented by zero, since at the beginning of January 1st, no days have elapsed.[2] At this point you are encouraged to do the same for the other dimension variables, 'lon' and 'lat', to see their values and ranges.

Now that we know the values and ranges of all the dimension variables, we can access the data in the data variables. In our example the main data variable is 'hgt', which is the height of a pressure surface. To see the order in which the data variables are stored, we look at its dimensions attribute by typing

```
> f.variables['hgt'].dimensions
```

---

[2]The values in the 'time' variable can vary from file to file. Sometimes it is expressed in days, such as in our example file. Other times it may be hours, minutes, or even seconds.

which prints the following:

```
('time', 'level', 'lat', 'lon')
```

This tells us that to access the height values we have to give the indices for time, level, lat, and lon in that order. Since the data are stored as Numpy arrays, we give the indices the same way we would for Numpy arrays.

As an example, suppose we wanted to see all the data for the 850 hPa level for the month of April. We would ask for

```
> f.variables['hgt'][3, 2, :, :].data
```

as time index 3 is for April,[3] and level index 2 is for 850 hPa.

To find out in what units the data are stored we can call the units attribute of the variable (if the creator of the data file was kind enough to include it). The example below shows us that the height variable is stored in meters, while the time values are in days since January 1st of the year one.[4]

```
> f.variables['hgt'].units
'm'
> f.variables['time'].units
'days since 0001-01-01 00:00:0.0'
```

Once we are finished with a NetCDF data set we should close it using

```
> f.close()
```

Plotting data from NetCDF files

We can plot data extracted from a NetCDF file using our normal plotting procedures from Matplotlib. For example, the following code creates the plot of global 850 hPa average heights for the month of April, shown in Fig. 17.1:

```
import netCDF4
import matplotlib.pyplot as plt
import numpy as np
f = netCDF4.Dataset('hgt.mon.1981-2010.ltm.nc', 'r')
z = f.variables['hgt'][3, 2, :, :]
lat = f.variables['lat'][:]
lon = f.variables['lon'][:]
```

---

[3]For this data set the time variable has 12 entries, one for each month of the year. January would have index 0, February would be 1, March would be 2, and so on.

[4]Since this data file represents long-term monthly mean data over many years, referencing the year 0001 is really meaningless. The time values in this case just represent the number of days since the start of a year.

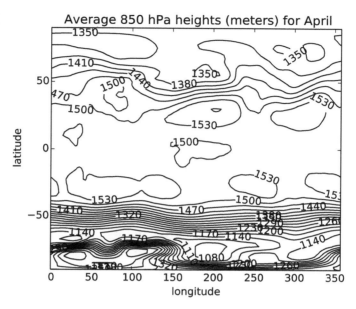

Fig. 17.1: An example plot of data extracted from a NetCDF file.

```
cs = plt.contour(lon, lat, z,
    levels = np.arange(990, 1700, 30),
    colors = 'black')
plt.clabel(cs, fmt = '%.0f', inline = True)
plt.xlabel('longitude')
plt.ylabel('latitude')
plt.title('Average 850 hPa heights (meters) for April')
plt.show()
f.close()
```

17.2.3 Writing NetCDF files

Here we describe and give a simple example of how to create and write data to a NetCDF file. For the example we will use the Numpy array archive data file, *uandv.npz*, from Sec. 12.1.2, which may be downloaded from this book's resources section at the publisher's website, *www.sundogpublishing.com*. This data file contains *u* and *v* wind components and *x* and *y* locations. We will read this data and then use it to create and write a NetCDF file.

The next few lines of code read the wind data from the Numpy array archive file so that we can use it to create our NetCDF file.

```
import numpy as np
import netCDF4
wind = np.load('uandv.npz')
u_comp = wind['u'] # m/s  2-D Array
v_comp = wind['v'] # m/s  2-D Array
easting = 50*wind['x'][:,0]  # km  1-D Array
northing = 50*wind['y'][0,:]  # km  1-D Array
```

The `easting` and `northing` variables are 1-D arrays of the x and y locations of the data, in kilometers.

Open file for writing

The first thing we must do is to open the NetCDF file for writing,

```
f = netCDF4.Dataset('wind.nc', 'w')
```

We have named the new file *wind.nc*. If the file already exists then it will be overwritten.

Creating the dimensions for the file

The variables in our file will have two dimensions, the x and y locations. We create the dimensions by calling the `createDimension()` method, as shown in these two lines of code

```
f.createDimension('x', easting.size)
f.createDimension('y', northing.size)
```

The arguments are the name of the dimension, and the size of the dimension.

Creating variables

The dimensions we created in the prior step are *not the same thing* as the *dimension variables*. We now need to create the dimension variables for the x and y locations, which is accomplished via the `createVariable()` function.

```
x = f.createVariable('x', 'i',
                     dimensions=('x'))
y = f.createVariable('y', 'i',
                     dimensions=('y'))
```

The arguments are the name of the variable, the data type of the variable, and the dimensions of the variable. The data type is expressed as a string. Common data types and their strings descriptors are

integer: Use `'i'` for 32-bit or `'i8'` for 64-bit.

floating-point: Use `'f'` for 32-bit or `'f8'` for 64-bit.

There are many other possible data types, and a complete list may be found at *http://unidata.github.io/netcdf4-python/netCDF4/ index.html#netCDF4.Dataset.createVariable*.

To assign data to the variables we use the assignment operator. The next two lines of code assign data to our dimension variables,

```
x[:] = easting
y[:] = northing
```

Creating and assigning data to our data variables proceeds along the same lines

```
u = f.createVariable('u', 'f8',
                     dimensions=('x','y'))
u[:] = u_comp  # Assign data
v = f.createVariable('v', 'f8',
                     dimensions=('x','y'))
v[:] =  v_comp  # Assign data
```

Closing the file

And finally, we always remember to properly close the file

```
f.close()
```

We can now check the results by opening our new file and reading it,

```
f = netCDF4.Dataset('wind.nc', 'r')
print(f)
```

which prints out

```
<class 'netCDF4._netCDF4.Dataset'>
root group (NETCDF4 data model, file format HDF5):
    dimensions(sizes): x(20), y(15)
    variables(dimensions): int32 x(x), int32 y(y),
    float64 u(x,y), float64 v(x,y)
    groups:
```

Creating attributes

NetCDF data sets and variables can have user-defined attributes which provide descriptions or other metadata about the data set or variable. The attributes are assigned before the file is closed.

For example, we could create an attribute giving a description of the data set, and another giving its date of creation,

```
f.description='U and V wind components'
f.date='October 29, 2019'
```

We have complete control over naming of the attributes, and are not limited any predefined names.

It is a good idea to create an attribute for each variable that explains in what units it is stored, so we could add to our program the following lines

```
x.units = 'km'
y.units = 'km'
u.units = 'm/s'
v.units = 'm/s'
```

Groups

The NetCDF4 format allows the creating of *groups*, which are collections of variables that are related. A data set can contain multiple groups, and each group can contain groups of its own. You may think of it like the directories or folders on your computer, with the dataset being the root directory, and the groups being subdirectories.

Groups and subgroups are created with the `createGroup()` method of either a data set or group. The only required argument is the name of the group to be created. For instance, to create a group named `surface` to hold meteorological variables valid at the ground we would use

```
sfc = f.createGroup('surface')
```

We could then create variables within this group by calling its `createVariable()` method.

17.3   Working with HDF

17.3.1   Overview

The Hierarchical Data Format (HDF) was developed at the National Center for Supercomputing Applications (NCSA) starting in the late 1980s and was adopted by NASA in the early 1990s as the standard format for distributing data collected by the Earth Observing System.

Two versions of HDF have come into wide use: the older HDF4 and the current HDF5.[5] The latter is significantly more flexible and efficient to work with in Python and will be our focus here. The official description reads as follows: *"HDF5 is a data model, library, and file format for storing and managing data. It supports an unlimited variety of datatypes, and is designed for flexible and efficient I/O and for high volume and complex data."*

The main thing you initially need to know about HDF5 files is that they are hierarchical collections of just two generic kinds of named objects.

Datasets are structured as homogeneous, multidimensional data objects that may be indexed or sliced exactly like NumPy arrays. An important feature of HDF5 is that very large datasets can be efficiently accessed from within a program without loading the entire dataset into the computer's memory.

Groups can be thought of as folders or directories. They generally contain datasets and/or other groups. The HDF5 file itself the top-level group.

---

[5]Readers who would like to understand the differences between the two versions can visit *hdfgroup.org/h5h4-diff.html*.

Both types of objects usually have small chunks of text or other data that are attached as *attributes*. These usually contain information about the file itself or about various components of the data within it, including perhaps dates, times, instrument properties, units, etc.

17.3.2 Opening and reading HDF5 files

For HDF5 files, we use the h5py module:

```
import h5py
f = h5py.File(filename, mode='r')
```

The second line opens the HDF5 with the name given by *filename* and assigns it to the file object whose name is represented by *f*. The argument 'r' opens the file as read-only.

To illustrate the process with real data, we will use a file identical to those distributed by NASA for a satellite instrument called the Global Precipitation Measurement (GPM) Microwave Imager (GMI). The orbit file is called 'GMI_sample.HDF5' and it may be downloaded from the book's resources page at *www.sundogpublishing.com*. Our goal will be to extract the microwave image for one channel and produce a simple display.

Once the file has been downloaded and saved to your working directory, it may be opened as follows:

```
import h5py

filename = 'GMI_sample.HDF5'
f = h5py.File(filename, mode='r')
```

Examining the structure and contents of an HDF5 file

If you are working with a particular dataset for the first time, you are likely to have no idea how it is organized or even what information is included. Fortunately, it is straightforward to examine the contents of an HDF5 file interactively in a manner that resembles listing the contents of a hierarchy of folders or directories on your hard disk.

The data set attributes are stored in an object attribute named `attrs`. The first thing you may want to do is find all the attributes of the data set. To do this we can loop through the attributes with this code

```
for a in f.attrs:
    print(a)
```

which results in

```
FileHeader
InputRecord
NavigationRecord
FileInfo
XCALinfo
```

The `attrs` attribute of a file, or of any group or dataset contained in the file, behaves like a Python dictionary. Using the name of the attribute as the dictionary key yields the value of that particular attribute.

For example, we can display the `FileHeader` attribute by typing

```
> print(f.attrs['FileHeader'])
```

which yields a very cumbersome byte string (see Sec. 3.7). We can easily convert this to a simple text string and print it as shown here,

```
s = f.attrs['FileHeader']
print(s.decode('utf-8'))
```

which produces the more readable output

```
DOI=10.5067/GPM/GMI/GPM/GPM1C;
AlgorithmID=1CGMI;
AlgorithmVersion=2014-N;
FileName=
    1C.GPM.GMI.XCAL2014-N.20140312-S135912-E153139.
    000201.V03B.HDF5;
SatelliteName=GPM;
InstrumentName=GMI;
GenerationDateTime=2014-09-03T13:41:01.000Z;
StartGranuleDateTime=2014-03-12T13:59:12.614Z;
StopGranuleDateTime=2014-03-12T15:31:40.282Z;
GranuleNumber=201;
NumberOfSwaths=2;
NumberOfGrids=0;
GranuleStart=SOUTHERNMOST_LATITUDE;
TimeInterval=ORBIT;
ProcessingSystem=PPS;
ProductVersion=V03B;
EmptyGranule=NOT_EMPTY;
MissingData=0;
```

The next step might be to list the names of the objects (groups or datasets) that are found just below the top level. All of the actual data in the file (as opposed to the *metadata* found in the global attributes) will be found in one or more of these objects.

```
for name in f:
    print(name)
```

which yields

```
S1
S2
```

The names aren't terribly informative, but a little exploration confirms that the data we want will be found in the group S1. We create a reference to that group for convenient access to its attributes and to the datasets and/or groups it contains:

```
S1=f['S1']
print('Attribute names:')
for a in S1.attrs:
    print(a)
print('\nObject names:')
for name in S1:
    print(name)
```

This code produces the following output:

```
Attribute names:
S1_SwathHeader
S1_IncidenceAngleIndex

Object names:
ScanTime
SCstatus
Latitude
Longitude
Quality
incidenceAngle
sunGlintAngle
incidenceAngleIndex
Tc
```

This time, the object names listed are datasets, not groups, though you can't necessarily tell that just by looking at the names. The ones we care about are Latitude and Longitude, which contain the geolocation data, and Tc, which contains the image data. We set references to each of these and determine their dimensions:

```
> Latitude = S1['Latitude']
> print(Latitude.shape)
(2959, 221)
> Longitude = S1['Longitude']
> print(Longitude.shape)
(2959, 221)
> Tc = S1['Tc']
> print(Tc.shape)
(2959, 221, 9)
```

We examine their attributes as shown:[6]

```
print('Attributes for Latitude:\n')
for a in Latitude.attrs:
    print(a, ':', Latitude.attrs[a].decode('utf-8'))
print('\nAttributes for Tc:\n')
for a in Tc.attrs:
    print(a, ':', Tc.attrs[a].decode('utf-8'))
```

with the resulting output

```
Attributes for Latitude:

DimensionNames : nscan1,npixel1
Units : degrees
CodeMissingValue : -9999.900391

Attributes for Tc:

DimensionNames : nscan1,npixel1,nchannel1
Units : K
CodeMissingValue : -9999.900391
LongName :
Intercalibrated Tb for channels
 1) 10.7 GHz V-Pol 2) 10.7 GHz H-Pol
 3) 18.7 GHz V-Pol 4) 18.7 GHz H-Pol
 5) 23.8 GHz V-Pol
 6) 36.5 GHz V-Pol 7) 36.5 GHz H-Pol
 8) 89.0 GHz V-Pol and 9) 89.0 GHz H-Pol
```

From the above, we infer the structure of our dataset:

- The image data is organized as an array of 2959 scans, each scan consisting of 221 pixels, and each pixel having 9 channel brightness temperatures (Tb) whose values are given in K (degrees Kelvin). The names of the nine channels are given in terms of the microwave frequency and polarization.

- The latitude data, given in degrees, is likewise organized as an array of 2959 scans by 221 pixels, with one value per pixel. The same is true for longitude data (not shown).

- Missing data is indicated by a value of approximately -9999.9.

---

[6]This data set apparently saved the attributes as byte strings, which is why we have to use the decode() method to convert them to text strings.

Accessing the data contained in variables

We can now access the actual numerical data of interest in a manner analogous to Numpy arrays, all of dimension (2959, 221).[7] Note that we are selecting just one of the nine channels, in this case 37 GHz H-Pol:

```
lats = Latitude[:,:]
lons = Longitude[:,:]
T37H = Tc[:,:,6]
```

Note that all of the following ways of accessing the image data are completely equivalent in view of the previously assigned values of S1 and Tc:

```
T37H = f['S1/Tc'][:,:,6]
T37H = S1['Tc'][:,:,6]
T37H = Tc[:,:,6]
```

As always, one should close the file once finished with it so as to free up computer resources.

```
f.close()
```

Putting it together

The following short script demonstrates the complete process of opening the HDF5 file, extracting the data of interest, and making a simple image plot:

```
import h5py
import matplotlib.pyplot as plt
import numpy as np

filename = 'GMI_sample.HDF5'
f = h5py.File(filename, mode='r')

lats = f['S1/Latitude'][:,:]
lons = f['S1/Longitude'][:,:]
t37h = f['S1/Tc'][:,:,6]

# Mark as missing out-of-range values
t37h[(t37h < 100.0)] = np.nan

# Don't try to plot pixels falling outside of map range
t37h[(lats > 60.0)+(lats < 30.0)
    +(lons<100.0)+(lons>150.0)] = np.nan
```

---

[7]If you need actual Numpy arrays for vector operations, then you should add the np.array() operator to the right hand side of these assignments.

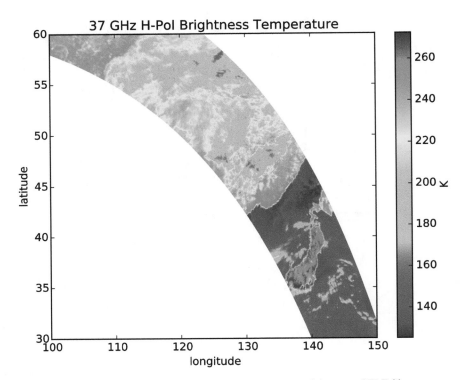

Fig. 17.2: An example plot of data extracted from an HDF file.

```
# Plot the data on a simple lat/lon map
plt.scatter(lons, lats, c=t37h, s=2,
            cmap=plt.cm.jet, edgecolor='',
            linewidth=0.)
plt.xlabel('longitude')
plt.ylabel('latitude')
plt.xlim((100, 150.0))
plt.ylim((30., 60.))
plt.colorbar(label='K')
plt.title('37 GHz H-Pol Brightness Temperature')

plt.show()
f.close()
```

The resulting plot is shown in Fig. 17.2.

REGULAR EXPRESSIONS

18.1   Introduction

Regular expressions provide a means of searching text for a specific pattern
of characters. The advantage of using regular expressions is that not only
can literal characters be searched for, but patterns such as "three lower-case
letters followed by two digits," or more complex patterns can be used as
search targets. Regular expressions are not unique to Python, and are found in
numerous other programming languages. They are incorporated into Python
through the built-in `re` module.

This chapter is not an exhaustive treatment of regular expressions. It is meant
to give a flavor of their usefulness, and it only scratches the surface of how
they can be used. Entire books have been written on regular expressions, and
the reader desiring to know more than this brief overview provides should
consult a more comprehensive reference, such as one of the following:

Friedl, J. E. F. *Mastering Regular Expressions.* O'Reilly Media, 2006.

Fitzgerald, M. *Introducing Regular Expressions.* O'Reilly Media, 2012.

Stubblebine, T. *Regular Expression Pocket Reference: Regular Expressions for Perl,
Ruby, PHDP, Python, C, Java and .NET.* O'Reilly Media, 2007.

18.2   The re.findall() Function

To use regular expressions in Python we must first create a *pattern* that describes the target of the search. The pattern is simply a raw string[1] of the

---

[1]Raw strings are discussed in Section 3.1.3.

form r'mouse' or r'4', which directs the regular expression engine to search for the word mouse or the digit 4. The pattern, *p*, along with the string, *s*, to be searched, are used as arguments to the re.findall(*p*,*s*) function, which returns a list containing all non-overlapping matches. This is best shown with an example:

```
> import re
> s = 'Honolulu, Hawaii'
> re.findall(r'H', s)
['H', 'H']
> re.findall(r'lu', s)
['lu', 'lu']
> re.findall(r'x', s)
[]
```

If the target is not found, findall() returns an empty list.

Matches returned by findall() are nonoverlapping. For example,

```
> re.findall(r'xax', 'xaxaxax')
['xax', 'xax']
```

returns only two matches, even though the target xax appears three times in the string to be searched.

18.3   Regular Expression Syntax

Table 18.1 contains a summary of the syntax used in regular expression patterns. Each syntax element is described in detail in the following subsections.

18.3.1   Matching the beginning or ending of a string

To find matches only appearing at the beginning of a string, the pattern is preceded with either \A or ^ as illustrated here,

```
> s = 'omnivore omnibus'
> re.findall(r'om', s)    # Match 'om' anywhere
['om', 'om']
> re.findall(r'^om', s)   # Match 'om' at start
['om']
> re.findall(r'^vore', s)   # Match 'vore' at start
[]
```

Likewise, to match only at the end of a string, the pattern is ended with either \Z or $ as this example shows,

```
> re.findall(r'bus$', s)    # Match 'bus' at end
['bus']
> re.findall(r'omni$', s)   # Match 'omni' at end
[]
```

Table 18.1: Regular expression syntax elements and where they are discussed in this text.

Syntax	Purpose	Section
^ or \A	Matches the beginning of a string.	18.3.1
$ or \Z	Matches the ending of a string.	18.3.1
\b	Matches the beginning or ending of a word.	18.3.2
.	Matches any character except newline, \n.	18.3.3
\d	Matches any digit.	18.3.3
\D	Matches any non-digit.	18.3.3
\s	Matches any whitespace character.	18.3.3
\S	Matches any non-whitespace character.	18.3.3
\w	Matches any alphanumeric character.	18.3.3
\W	Matches any non-alphanumeric character.	18.3.3
c*	Matches zero or more consecutive occurrences of the group or character denoted by c. Matches the maximum number of occurrences possible.	18.3.4
c+	Matches one or more consecutive occurrences of the group or character denoted by c. Matches the maximum number of occurrences possible.	18.3.4
c?	Matches zero or one occurrence of the group or character denoted by c.	18.3.4
c*?	Matches zero or more consecutive occurrences of the group or character denoted by c. Matches the minimum number of occurrences possible.	18.3.4
c+?	Matches one or more consecutive occurrences of the group or character denoted by c. Matches the minimum number of occurrences possible.	18.3.4
c??	Matches zero or one occurrence of the group or character denoted by c. Matches the minimum number of occurrences possible.	18.3.4
$c\{m\}$	Matches exactly m consecutive occurrences of the group or character denoted by c.	18.3.4
$c\{m,n\}$	Matches at least m and at most n consecutive occurrences of the group or character denoted by c. If there are more than n consecutive occurrences a match will still be made, but only up to n are returned.	18.3.4
$c\{m,n\}$?	Matches at least m and at most n consecutive occurrences of the group or character denoted by c. Matches the minimum number of occurrences possible.	18.3.4
$c\{m,\}$	Matches at least m consecutive occurrences of the group or character denoted by c.	18.3.4
$c\{,n\}$	Matches from zero to n consecutive occurrences of the group or character denoted by c. Same as $c\{0,n\}$	18.3.4
[set]	Matches any of the characters included in set.	18.3.5
[^set]	Matches any of the characters *not* included in set.	18.3.5
(expr)	Matches the expression expr as a group.	18.3.6
expr1|expr2	Matches either expr1 or expr2.	18.3.7
expr1(?=expr2)	Matches expr1 only if it is immediately followed by expr2.	18.3.8
expr1(?!expr2)	Matches expr1 only if it *is not* immediately followed by expr2.	18.3.8
(?<=expr1)expr2	Matches expr2 only if it is immediately preceded by expr1.	18.3.9
(?<!expr1)expr2	Matches expr2 only if it *is not* immediately preceded by expr1.	18.3.9

18.3.2 Matching the beginning or ending of a word

To find a match occurring only at the beginning or ending of a word[2] the \b character is used:

```
> s = 'Honolulu, Hawaii'
> re.findall(r'lu\b', s)    # Find 'lu' at word end
['lu']
> re.findall(r'\blu', s)    # Find 'lu' at word start
[]
> re.findall(r'\bHa', s)    # Find 'Ha' at word start
['Ha']
```

18.3.3 Matching classes of characters

Regular expressions can be used to match classes of characters, such as "all digits," "all nondigits," "all non-whitespace characters," etc., as illustrated in the following examples.

Any non-newline character

The period . matches any character other than a newline, \n.

```
> re.findall(r'.', 'Hello \r and \t good\nbye')
['H', 'e', 'l', 'l', 'o', ' ', '\r', ' ', 'a', 'n', 'd',
    ' ', '\t', ' ', 'g', 'o', 'o', 'd', 'b', 'y', 'e']
```

Any digit or nondigit

The pattern \d will match any digit, while \D will match any nondigit.

```
> s = 'USS Enterprise (CVN-65)'
> re.findall(r'\d', s)    # Find all digits.
['6', '5']
> re.findall(r'\D', s)    # Find all non-digits.
['U', 'S', 'S', ' ', 'E', 'n', 't', 'e', 'r', 'p', 'r',
    'i', 's', 'e', ' ', '(', 'C', 'V', 'N', '-', ')']
```

Any whitespace or nonwhitespace character

The pattern \s will match any whitespace character, while \S will match any nonwhitespace character.

```
> s = 'F-4 \t Phantom II\n'
> re.findall(r'\s', s)    # Find all whitespace
[' ', '\t', ' ', ' ', '\n']
```

---

[2]A word is usually defined as consecutive letters, digits, or underscore characters. However, this is somewhat dependent on the regular expression engine used, so there may be variations between software packages.

```
> re.findall(r'\S', s)  # Find all non-whitespace
['F', '-', '4', 'P', 'h', 'a', 'n', 't', 'o', 'm',
    'I', 'I']
```

Any alphanumeric or non-alphanumeric character

The pattern \w will match any alphanumeric character, while \W will match any non-alphanumeric character. Alphanumeric characters are defined as any letters or digits.

```
> s = 'F-4 \t Phantom II\n'
> re.findall(r'\w', s)  # Find all alphanumeric
['F', '4', 'P', 'h', 'a', 'n', 't', 'o', 'm', 'I', 'I']
> re.findall(r'\W', s)  # Find all non-alphanumeric
['-', ' ', '\t', ' ', ' ', '\n']
```

18.3.4 Matching consecutive occurrences

The characters *, +, and ? are used within regular expression patterns to indicate consecutive occurrences (*repetitions*) of the previous character or group (see Sec. 18.3.6 for more on groups). There are also ways to match specific numbers of repetitions.

Matching zero or more consecutive occurrences

To match zero or more consecutive occurrences of a character an asterisk * is used after the character. If used by itself it will match as many repetitions as possible. If followed by a question mark, *?, it will match as few repetitions as possible.

```
> s = 'xxoxooxooxoooo'
> re.findall(r'xo*', s)
['x', 'xo', 'xoo', 'xoo', 'xoooo']
> re.findall(r'xo*?', s)
['x', 'x', 'x', 'x', 'x']
```

The pattern xo* is interpreted as, "Find every x that is followed by zero or more o's, returning the x and as many o's as possible." The pattern xo*? is interpreted as, "Find every x that is followed by zero or more o's, returning the x and as few o's as possible."

Note that the * only applies to the character immediately preceding it. In the examples just given, it only applies to the character o, not the entire expression xo. Matching consecutive occurrences of substrings containing multiple characters is much more involved, and beyond the scope of this simple treatment. The reader who needs to perform more complicated searches is directed to one of the references mentioned in Section 18.1.

Matching one or more consecutive occurrences

To match one or more consecutive occurrences of a character, a + is used after the character. If used by itself it will match as many repetitions as possible. If followed by a question mark, +?, it will match as few repetitions as possible.

```
> s = 'xxoxooxooxoooo'
> re.findall(r'xo+', s)
['xo', 'xoo', 'xoo', 'xoooo']
> re.findall(r'xo+?', s)
['xo', 'xo', 'xo', 'xo']
```

The pattern xo+ is interpreted as, "Find every x that is followed by one or more o's, returning the x and as many o's as possible." The pattern xo*? is interpreted as, "Find every x that is followed by one or more o's, returning the x and as few o's as possible."

As with *, a + only applies to the character immediately preceding it. In the examples just given, it only applies to the character o, not the entire expression xo.

Matching zero or one occurrence

To match zero or one occurrences of a character, a ? is used after the character. If used by itself it will match as many repetitions as possible. If followed by another question mark, ??, it will match as few repetitions as possible.

```
> s = 'xxoxooxooxoooo'
> re.findall(r'xo?', s)
['x', 'xo', 'xo', 'xo', 'xo']
> re.findall(r'xo??', s)
['x', 'x', 'x', 'x', 'x']
```

The pattern xo? is interpreted as, "Find every x that is followed by zero or one o, returning the x and as many o's as possible." The pattern xo?? is interpreted as, "Find every x that is followed by zero or one o, returning the x and as few o's as possible."

As with the * and +, the ? only applies to the character immediately preceding it. In the examples above it only applies to the character o, not the entire expression xo.

Matching a specified number or range of consecutive occurrences

To match a specified number or range of consecutive occurrences of a character c, use the syntax c{m,n}, where m is the lowest number of repetitions and n is the highest number of repetions in the range. This syntax is interpreted as, "Find no less than m repetitions and up to n repetitions of character c." If this syntax is followed by a ? then it means, "match as few repetitions as possible."

We illustrate this with the following examples, which search a string for digits.

```
> s = 'abc34abm5634zqr342er'
> re.findall(r'\d{2}', s)
['34', '56', '34', '34']
> re.findall(r'\d{2,3}', s)
['34', '563', '342']
> re.findall(r'\d{2,3}?', s)
['34', '56', '34', '34']
```

If *m* is omitted, such as {,*n*}, this is interpreted as 0 to *n* repetitions. If *n* is omitted, {*m*,}, this means find at least *m* repetitions.

18.3.5 Matching sets of characters

A set of characters is denoted by enclosing the characters within square brackets, []. For example, the pattern r'[aeiou]' would match any lower-case vowels. The complement of a set is denoted by the ^ character preceding the set. For example, the pattern r'[^aeiou]' would match any character that was not a lower-case vowel.

```
> s = 'The quick brown fox.'
> re.findall(r'[aeiou]', s)   # Match all vowels.
['e', 'u', 'i', 'o', 'o']
> re.findall(r'[^aeiou]', s)   # Match all non-vowels.
['T', 'h', ' ', 'q', 'c', 'k', ' ', 'b', 'r', 'w',
    'n', ' ', 'f', 'x', '.']
```

Ranges of characters can be denoted using a hyphen (-). For example, if we want to search a string for any capitalized letters we could use the pattern r'[A-Z]' rather than writing out each letter as a member of the set:

```
> s = 'The quick Brown fox.'
> re.findall(r'[A-Z]', s)  # Match all upper-case
['T', 'B']
```

More than one range may be included in a single set. For example, to search for all letters, either upper or lower case, the set would be [A-Za-z].

```
> s = 'USS Enterprise (CVN-65)'
> re.findall(r'[A-Za-z]', s)   # Match all letters.
['U', 'S', 'S', 'E', 'n', 't', 'e', 'r', 'p', 'r',
    'i', 's', 'e', 'C', 'V', 'N']
```

18.3.6 Groups

A group is an expression contained within parentheses. When a group is used in a regular expression pattern, the string is searched for the entire pattern but findall() only returns that part of the matched string that is within the parentheses. Study the following two examples, both of which search a string for one or more digits that are immediately followed by the letter C. In the first example the entire match of 23C is returned, while in the second example only the digits 23 are returned, since the digits were contained with a group.

```
> s = 'The temperature was 23C and the pressure was
    1004mb.'
> re.findall(r'\d+C', s)
['23C']
> re.findall(r'(\d+)C', s)
['23']
```

The *, +, ?, and {*m,n*} syntax that are used to find multiple consecutive occurrences of a character (refer to Sec. 18.3.4) can also be applied to groups. For example,

```
> s = 'xxoxoooxooxoooo'
> re.findall(r'(xo)+', s)
['xo', 'xo', 'xo']
> re.findall(r'(xo){2,}', s)
['xo']
> re.findall(r'(xo+)+', s)
['xoooo']
```

Some of these results can be difficult to interpret, and may not be what is intuitively expected. Again, the interested reader who wishes to delve more into a mastery of regular expressions is encouraged to study references such as those listed in Section 18.1.

18.3.7 Matching a choice of two patterns

The | character in a regular expression is interpreted as "or." For example, the pattern r'rat|mouse' will match either rat or mouse.

```
> s = 'There was a rat in the house.'
> t = 'There was a mouse in the house.'
> u = 'There was a cat in the house.'
> re.findall(r'rat|mouse', s)
['rat']
> re.findall(r'rat|mouse', t)
['mouse']
> re.findall(r'rat|mouse', u)
[]
```

18.3.8 Matching text immediately following or not immediately following a specific expression

The syntax *expr1*(?=*expr2*) matches *expr1* only if it is immediately followed by *expr2*. For example:

```
> s = 'tabby cat, calico cat, hound dog, water dog, tom
  cat'
> re.findall(r'(\w+)\s(?=dog)', s)
['hound', 'water']
```

searches for one or more alphanumeric characters (\w+) followed by a white-space (\s) and then followed by dog.

The syntax *expr1*(?!*expr2*) matches *expr1* only if it *is not* immediately fol-lowed by *expr2*. For example:

```
> s = 'tabby cat, calico cat, hound dog, water dog, tom
  cat'
> re.findall(r'(\w+)\s(?!dog)', s)
['tabby', 'calico', 'tom']
```

searches for one or more alphanumeric characters (\w+) followed by a white-space (\s) and not followed by dog.

18.3.9 Matching text immediately preceding or not immediately preceding a specific expression

The syntax (?<=*expr1*)*expr2* matches *expr2* only if it is immediately pre-ceded by *expr1*. For example:

```
> s = 'liters decaJoules kilograms picoFarads
  kilometers'
> re.findall(r'(?<=kilo)\w+\b', s)
['grams', 'meters']
```

searches for one or more alphanumeric characters (\w+) at the end of a word (\b) that are also preceded by kilo.

The syntax (?<!*expr*) matches *expr2* only if it *is not* immediately preceded by *expr1*.

18.4 More Functions in the re Module

In addition to re.findall() there are other useful functions contained in the re module.

18.4.1 The re.sub() and re.subn() functions

The re.sub(*p*, *t*, *s*) and re.subn(*p*, *t*, *s*) functions both search the string *s* for the pattern *p* and substitute the text *t* in place of the pattern. The only difference between the two functions is that re.sub() returns a copy of the string with the replacements made, while re.subn() returns a tuple containing a copy of the string and a count of how many substitutions were made. In the following,

```
> s = '123abc821xyz'
> re.sub(r'\d', 'X', s)
'XXXabcXXXxyz'
> re.subn(r'\d', 'X', s)
('XXXabcXXXxyz', 6)
```

both commands replace digits with X, but re.subn() also tells us that six substitutions were made.

The re.sub() function can be a very useful means of removing extra white-space from a string, as this example shows.

```
> s = 'Here is  a string with     some    extra
    whitespace.'
> re.sub(r'\s{2,}', ' ', s)
'Here is a string with some extra whitespace.'
```

18.4.2   The re.split() function

The re.split(p, s) function splits the string s based on the pattern p, and returns a list containing the portions of the string.

```
> s = '34.5    76.2 -89.6      -12.34'
> re.split(r'\s+', s)    # Split on whitespace
['34.5', '76.2', '-89.6', '-12.34']
```

18.5   Regular Expression Pattern Objects

A regular expression Pattern object, denoted here by r, is an object created from a regular expression pattern p using the re.compile(p) function. Regular expression Pattern objects have methods associated with them that perform many of the same tasks as the re.findall(), re.split(), re.sub(), and re.subn() functions. Which paradigm to use (re functions or Pattern methods) is strictly a choice made by the programmer. Either paradigm may be used for a specific task. In this section we describe the methods associated with using Pattern objects.

18.5.1   The re.compile() function

The re.compile(p) function creates a Pattern object from the regular expression pattern, p. By including the option flag re.I, the Pattern object will be *case-insensitive*, meaning it will not distinguish between uppercase and lowercase letters. Here are some examples:

```
> r = re.compile(r'[a-z]')      # lower-case only
> r = re.compile(r'[A-Z]')      # upper-case only
> r = re.compile(r'[a-z]', re.I)   # both
> r = re.compile(r'[A-Z]', re.I)   # both
> r = re.compile(r'[A-Za-z]')   # both
```

18.5.2 The *r*.findall() method

The *r*.findall(*s*) method of a `Pattern` object works nearly identically to the re.findall(*p*, *s*) function. The following two examples illustrate how each is used.

- The re.findall() function:

```
> s = 'Honolulu, Hawaii'
> re.findall(r'lu', s)
['lu', 'lu']
```

- The *r*.findall() method:

```
s = 'Honolulu, Hawaii'
> r = re.compile(r'lu')
> r.findall(s)
['lu', 'lu']
```

18.5.3 The *r*.sub() and *r*.subn() methods

The *r*.sub() and *r*.subn() methods work nearly identically to their corresponding `re` functions of the same names, as the following two examples illustrate.

- The re.sub() and re.subn() functions:

```
> s = 'ABC123'
> re.sub(r'\d', 'x', s)
'ABCxxx'
> re.subn(r'\d', 'x', s)
('ABCxxx', 3)
```

- The *r*.sub() and *r*.subn() methods:

```
> s = 'ABC123'
> r = re.compile(r'\d')
> r.sub('x', s)
'ABCxxx'
> r.subn('x', s)
('ABCxxx', 3)
```

18.5.4 The *r*.split() method

The *r*.split() regular expression method works nearly identically to the re.split() function, as shown below.

- The re.split() function:

```
> s = 'Splitting a string on vowels'
> re.split(r'[aeiouAEIOU]', s)
['Spl', 'tt', 'ng ', ' str', 'ng ', 'n v', 'w', 'ls']
```

- The `r.split()` method:

```
> s = 'Splitting a string on vowels'
> r = re.compile(r'[aeiou]', re.I)
> r.split(s)
['Spl', 'tt', 'ng ', ' str', 'ng ', 'n v', 'w', 'ls']
```

In the previous example the `re.I` option flag was set so that the pattern was not case-sensitive.

18.6   Conclusion

As mentioned several times already, the use and mastery of regular expressions is neither intuitive nor without confusion. This chapter was meant only to give an overview of their use. It is not a comprehensive reference or cookbook for regular expressions. Those needing a comprehensive understanding of regular expressions are directed to the references listed in Section 18.1.

NINETEEN

LINEAR ALGEBRA

A great many scientific computations involve matrix operations, and efficient routines for these are provide as part of several Python modules. Two of the most important are the Numpy and SciPy modules, each of which contains a `linalg` submodule. Generally speaking, the `scipy.linalg` submodule is more comprehensive, while `numpy.linalg` offers the benefit of more flexible broadcasting, such as linear solutions of stacked arrays. Here we will use the `numpy.linalg` library for some basic operations, followed by the `scipy.linalg` library for some more complex applications.

It should be noted that NumPy provides a subclass of arrays that are specifically intended to represent matrices. However, use of this class is no longer recommended. Instead, matrix operations are now normally applied to ordinary NumPy floating point arrays, and there are several built-in operators in Python 3 to invoke these.

19.1 Matrix Products

Beginning with Python 3.5, the @ operator works with numpy arrays to perform conventional matrix multiplication:

```
> a
array([[ 1., -4.,  0.],
       [-1., -2., -1.],
       [ 2.,  0., -3.]])
> b
array([[ 2., -1.,  3.],
       [-2., -6.,  2.],
       [ 0.,  2.,  3.]])
```

```
> a@b
array([[ 10.,   23.,   -5.],
       [  2.,   11.,  -10.],
       [  4.,   -8.,   -3.]])
> c
array([[ 3],
       [-2],
       [ 6]])
> a@c
array([[ 11.],
       [ -5.],
       [-12.]])
```

Interestingly, in addition to the @ operator, there are several other equivalent ways to achieve matrix multiplication, using np.dot() or np.matmul(). All of the following give identical results for the arrays a and b defined above:

```
> a@b
> np.dot(a,b)
> a.dot(b)
> np.matmul(a,b)
```

The matmul() function has the advantage that it can operate on stacked matrices as well as single matrices.

The np.dot() method (or function) is nominally the dot-product operator for row vectors,

```
> d = np.array([1, 2, 3])
> d.dot(d)
14
> np.dot(d,d)
14
```

but it works on two-dimensional matrices as well, as shown earlier. However, if c is a column vector with shape $(N, 1)$, as defined above for example, then one must ensure compatible shapes for matrix multiplication as follows:

```
> c.T.dot(c)
array([[49]])
> c.dot(c.T)
array([[  9,   -6,   18],
       [ -6,    4,  -12],
       [ 18,  -12,   36]])
```

where the T attribute provides the transpose of c. Note the first result is not a scalar but rather a 1×1 array, while the second result is the outer product of c.

Some additional matrix functions is listed in Table 19.1.

Table 19.1: A selection of common matrix functions provided by NumPy. See the online documentation for optional arguments and for additional functions.

`np.dot(a, b)`	Dot product of two arrays.
`np.inner(a, b)`	Inner product of two arrays.
`np.outer(a, b)`	Compute the outer product of two vectors.
`np.matmul(x1, x2)`	Matrix product of two arrays.
`np.tensordot(a, b)`	Compute tensor dot product along specified axes.
`np.linalg.cholesky(a)`	Cholesky decomposition.
`np.linalg.qr(a)`	Compute the qr factorization of a matrix.
`np.linalg.svd(a)`	Singular Value Decomposition.
`np.linalg.eig(a)`	Compute the eigenvalues and right eigenvectors of a square array.
`np.linalg.eigh(a)`	Return the eigenvalues and eigenvectors of a complex Hermitian (conjugate symmetric) or a real symmetric matrix.
`np.linalg.norm(x)`	Matrix or vector norm.
`np.linalg.cond(x)`	Compute the condition number of a matrix.
`np.linalg.det(a)`	Compute the determinant of an array.
`np.linalg.matrix_rank(M)`	Return matrix rank of array using SVD method
`np.trace(a)`	Return the sum along diagonals of the array.
`np.linalg.solve(a, b)`	Solve a linear matrix equation, or system of linear scalar equations.
`np.linalg.inv(a)`	Compute the (multiplicative) inverse of a matrix.

19.2   Systems of Linear Equations

The `np.linalg` module contains functions for solving systems of linear equations using matrix methods. This section discusses how to use these functions.

19.2.1   Background

A system of linear equations such as

$$5x - 3y - 5z = 20$$
$$2x + 6y + 3z = -12$$
$$8x + 5y - 9z = 11$$

can be written in matrix form as

$$\begin{pmatrix} 5 & -3 & -5 \\ 2 & 6 & 3 \\ 8 & 5 & -9 \end{pmatrix} \begin{pmatrix} x \\ y \\ z \end{pmatrix} = \begin{pmatrix} 20 \\ -12 \\ 11 \end{pmatrix}. \tag{19.1}$$

This can also be written as

$$\mathbf{Cx} = \mathbf{b},\tag{19.2}$$

where **C** is the coefficient matrix,

$$\mathbf{C} = \begin{pmatrix} 5 & -3 & -5 \\ 2 & 6 & 3 \\ 8 & 5 & -9 \end{pmatrix},$$

x is the column-vector of unknown values,

$$\mathbf{x} = \begin{pmatrix} x \\ y \\ z \end{pmatrix},$$

and **b** is the column-vector representing the values on the right-hand side,

$$\mathbf{b} = \begin{pmatrix} 20 \\ -12 \\ 11 \end{pmatrix}.$$

One way to solve the system of equations (19.1) or (19.2) is to manipulate the system to get the coefficient matrix into the form of the identity matrix,

$$\mathbf{I} = \begin{pmatrix} 1 & 0 & 0 \\ 0 & 1 & 0 \\ 0 & 0 & 1 \end{pmatrix}.$$

Once this is accomplished, the system of equations will be of the form

$$\begin{pmatrix} 1 & 0 & 0 \\ 0 & 1 & 0 \\ 0 & 0 & 1 \end{pmatrix} \begin{pmatrix} x \\ y \\ z \end{pmatrix} = \begin{pmatrix} s_x \\ s_y \\ s_z \end{pmatrix},$$

where

$$\mathbf{x} = \mathbf{s} = \begin{pmatrix} s_x \\ s_y \\ s_z \end{pmatrix},$$

and the values of x, y, and z are now known.

19.2.2   Solving a system of equations using np.linalg.solve()

The np.linalg.solve() function solves a system of equations such as (19.1) or (19.2) using Gaussian elimination. We first need to create Numpy arrays to represent the coefficient matrix, **C**, and the right-hand side vector, **b**. These arrays are then passed as arguments to the solve(C, b) function, which returns a 1-D array representing the solution vector, **s**.

The code below creates the necessary arrays and solves the system of equation from (19.1).

```
import numpy as np
C = np.array([[5, -3, -5],
              [2, 6, 3],
              [8, 5, -9]],
              dtype=np.float_)
b = np.array([20, -12, 11], dtype=np.float_)
s = np.linalg.solve(C, b)
print(s)
```

The result is

```
[ 1.8683274 , -2.22419929, -0.79715302]
```

or $x = 1.868$, $y = -2.224$, and $z = -0.797$.

19.2.3 LU decomposition

Sometimes it is necessary to solve a large systems of equations of the form (19.2) where the coefficient matrix **C** does not change but the right-hand side vector **b** may be different from one application to the next. Solving each new system of equations using np.linalg.solve() can be very time consuming, especially if the coefficient matrix is large. Fortunately, there is a mathematical technique called *LU decomposition* which is handy for such applications. This problem is an example for which the more comprehensive scipy.linalg module is useful.

The underlying mathematics is not important for our purposes. We will concentrate simply on describing how to implement LU decompositon. This is accomplished in two steps:

1. The first step is to call the scipy.linalg.lu_factor(*C*) function, which returns the LU decomposition matrix, *lu*, given the coefficient matrix *C*.

2. The second step is to pass the LU decomposition *lu* and the right-hand side vector *b* to the scipy.linalg.lu_solve(*lu*, *b*) function, which returns the solution vector, *s*.

In the following example code we solve (19.1) using LU decomposition.

```
import numpy as np
from scipy.linalg import lu_factor, lu_solve
C = np.array([[5, -3, -5],
              [2, 6, 3],
              [8, 5, -9]],
              dtype=np.float_)
b = np.array([20, -12, 11], dtype=np.float_)
lu = lu_factor(C)    # LU decomposition of matrix
s = lu_solve(lu, b)  # Solution
print(s)
```

which gives the same result as the `scipy.linalg.solve()` function shown in the previous section.

The advantage to using LU decomposition is that for large matrices the most time consuming part of solving the system of equations is finding the LU decomposition of the coefficient matrix. But once the LU decomposition is known, solving the system of equations is rather quick. If the same coefficient matrix is used for different right-hand side vectors, **b**, the LU decomposition need only be performed once. This situation often arises in modeling applications using finite-element analysis or finite-differencing for both solids and fluids.

19.2.4   Banded matrices

In many modeling applications using finite-element analysis or finite differencing, the coefficient matrix is a special type of sparse matrix called a *banded matrix*. This means that most of the elements of the matrix are zero except for elements along or near the main diagonal of the matrix. An example of a banded coefficient matrix (with dots in place of the zero elements) is:

$$\begin{pmatrix} c_{0,0} & c_{0,1} & c_{0,2} & c_{0,3} & \cdot & \cdot & \cdot & \cdot \\ c_{1,0} & c_{1,1} & c_{1,2} & c_{1,3} & c_{1,4} & \cdot & \cdot & \cdot \\ c_{2,0} & c_{2,1} & c_{2,2} & c_{2,3} & c_{2,4} & c_{2,5} & \cdot & \cdot \\ \cdot & c_{3,1} & c_{3,2} & c_{3,3} & c_{3,4} & c_{3,5} & c_{3,6} & \cdot \\ \cdot & \cdot & c_{4,2} & c_{4,3} & c_{4,4} & c_{4,5} & c_{4,6} & c_{4,7} \\ \cdot & \cdot & \cdot & c_{5,3} & c_{5,4} & c_{5,5} & c_{5,6} & c_{5,7} \\ \cdot & \cdot & \cdot & \cdot & c_{6,4} & c_{6,5} & c_{6,6} & c_{6,7} \\ \cdot & \cdot & \cdot & \cdot & \cdot & c_{7,5} & c_{7,6} & c_{7,7} \end{pmatrix} . \tag{19.3}$$

The subscript on the elements denote the row and column, $c_{row,col}$. In this example there are $u = 3$ *upper* diagonals and $l = 2$ *lower* diagonals. The *bandwidth* of a banded matrix is defined as $l + u + 1$, so the example has a bandwidth of six.

A banded matrix such as (19.3) may be represented in a more compact form as

$$\begin{pmatrix} \cdot & \cdot & \cdot & c_{0,3} & c_{1,4} & c_{2,5} & c_{3,6} & c_{4,7} \\ \cdot & \cdot & c_{0,2} & c_{1,3} & c_{2,4} & c_{3,5} & c_{4,6} & c_{5,7} \\ \cdot & c_{0,1} & c_{1,2} & c_{2,3} & c_{3,4} & c_{4,5} & c_{5,6} & c_{6,7} \\ c_{0,0} & c_{1,1} & c_{2,2} & c_{3,3} & c_{4,4} & c_{5,5} & c_{6,6} & c_{7,7} \\ c_{1,0} & c_{2,1} & c_{3,2} & c_{4,3} & c_{5,4} & c_{6,5} & c_{7,6} & \cdot \\ c_{2,0} & c_{3,1} & c_{4,2} & c_{5,3} & c_{6,4} & c_{7,5} & \cdot & \cdot \end{pmatrix} .$$

Note that the upper diagonals are padded with leading zero elements, while the lower diagonals are padded with trailing zero elements. You may think of this as simply rotating (19.3) counterclockwise until the diagonals become rows.[1] In general, an $n \times n$ banded matrix with u upper and l lower diagonals will be represented as a $(u + l + 1) \times n$ rectangular matrix.

An example of a system of equations having a banded coefficient matrix is

$$\begin{pmatrix} 2 & -3 & 1 & 0 & 0 & 0 & 0 \\ 1 & 7 & -1 & 2 & 0 & 0 & 0 \\ 0 & -1 & 2 & -1 & 3 & 0 & 0 \\ 0 & 0 & -1 & -1 & 2 & 1 & 0 \\ 0 & 0 & 0 & 2 & 2 & 1 & -1 \\ 0 & 0 & 0 & 0 & -1 & -1 & -1 \\ 0 & 0 & 0 & 0 & 0 & 2 & 1 \end{pmatrix} \begin{pmatrix} x_0 \\ x_1 \\ x_2 \\ x_3 \\ x_4 \\ x_5 \\ x_6 \end{pmatrix} = \begin{pmatrix} 20 \\ -12 \\ 11 \\ 0 \\ -5 \\ 7 \\ -4 \end{pmatrix}. \tag{19.4}$$

The coefficient matrix for (19.4) in banded form is

$$\mathbf{C}_b = \begin{pmatrix} 0 & 0 & 1 & 2 & 3 & 1 & -1 \\ 0 & -3 & -1 & -1 & 2 & 1 & -1 \\ 2 & 7 & 2 & -1 & 2 & -1 & 1 \\ 1 & -1 & -1 & 2 & -1 & 2 & 0 \end{pmatrix}, \tag{19.5}$$

with $u = 2$ and $l = 1$.

Efficient methods have been developed for solving large systems of equations having sparse banded coefficient matrices. These methods can be quicker than using either Gaussian elimination or LU decomposition. The

```
scipy.linalg.solve_banded((l, u), Cb, b)
```

function is used to solve banded systems. The arguments are

- (l, u), a tuple containing the number of lower and upper diagonals.
- Cb, a 2-D array representing the banded coefficient matrix in the form of (19.5).
- b, a 1-D array representing the right-hand-side vector.

The code below shows how to solve (19.4).

```
import numpy as np
from scipy.linalg import solve_banded
Cb = np.array([[0, 0, 1, 2, 3, 1, -1],
               [0, -3, -1, -1, 2, 1, -1],
               [2, 7, 2, -1, 2, -1, 1],
               [1, -1, -1, 2, -1, 2, 0]],
              dtype=np.float_)
```

[1]This is the way that Python's Scipy module represents a banded matrix. Other software packages or program libraries may do it differently. Always consult the documentation for the package you are using!

```
b = np.array([20, -12, 11, 0, -5, 7, -4],
             dtype=np.float_)
s = solve_banded((1,2), Cb, b)
print(s)
```

which gives the result for $[x_0, x_1, ..., x_6]$ as

```
[ 7.03149606 -0.47637795  4.50787402 -5.59448819
    -1.36220472  1.63779528 -7.27559055]
```

FOURIER ANALYSIS

20.1 Introduction

Fourier analysis is a tool that allows most mathematical functions to be written as a sum of sinusoids of different wavenumbers[1] and amplitudes. The amplitudes of the sinusoids are known as the *Fourier* or *spectral coefficients*. If the Fourier coefficients are known then the original function can be reconstructed from them. For continuous, periodic functions, the form of Fourier analysis that is used is the *Fourier series*. For discrete data, we use the *discrete Fourier transform*, or *DFT*. A commonly used computer algorithm for computing discrete Fourier transforms is the *fast Fourier transform* or *FFT*.[2]

For scientific data analysis we mainly use data collected in digital form, which means that the discrete Fourier transform is most applicable for our purposes. The Numerical Python (Numpy) module has functions for easily computing the Fourier coefficients for both 1-D and 2-D data arrays. In this chapter, we first discuss the basics of the discrete Fourier transform and then describe the Numpy functions for computing the Fourier coefficients.

---

[1]For spatial data Fourier analysis decomposes the function into sinusoids of different wavenumbers. For temporal data the decomposition is in terms of frequency. The underlying mathematics is the same in either case.

[2]The terms FFT and DFT are often used interchangeably; however, the term FFT really only refers to the fast Fourier transform algorithm for computing a DFT.

20.2   The Discrete Fourier Transform

20.2.1   Common form of the discrete Fourier transform

The commonly used equations for defining the discrete Fourier transform and its inverse are:

$$U_m = \frac{1}{N} \sum_{j=0}^{N-1} u_j \exp\left(-\iota 2\pi jm/N\right) \tag{20.1}$$

$$u_j = \sum_{m=0}^{N-1} U_m \exp\left(\iota 2\pi jm/N\right). \tag{20.2}$$

Here the Greek letter iota, ι, denotes the imaginary number $\iota = \sqrt{-1}$. Equation (20.1) is called the *forward transform*, and returns the spectral coefficients, U_m, from the input function, u_j. Equation (20.2) is called the *inverse transform*, *reverse transform*, or *backward transform*, and returns the original function from the spectral coefficients. In these equations j is the data point number (beginning with zero), m is the spectral coefficient index, and N is the total number of data points. The number of spectral coefficients returned by the DFT is equal to the number of data points. The wavenumbers of the spectral coefficients are given by

$$k_m = \frac{2\pi m}{Nd}; \quad m = 0, 1, 2, \cdots, N-1, \tag{20.3}$$

where d is the separation (time or space) between grid points. Due to symmetry properties of the DFT, the wavenumbers for $m > N/2$ can also be thought of as being negative wavenumbers using the following identity

$$k_{N/2+b} = -k_{N/2-b} \tag{20.4}$$

for any integer $0 \le b \le N/2 - 1$. The wavenumbers are then given by

$$k_m = \begin{cases} 2\pi m/Nd, & \text{for } 0 \le m \le N/2 \\ 2\pi\left(m - N\right)/Nd, & \text{for } N/2 + 1 \le m \le N - 1. \end{cases} \tag{20.5}$$

Since there is a direct relation between the index m in (20.1) and the wavenumbers, k_m, using either (20.3) or (20.5), we can refer to the Fourier coefficients using either U_m or U_{k_m}. In the first notation, U_m, m is always positive and represents the index running from 0 to $N-1$, where N is the number of data points. In the second representation, U_{k_m}, k_m is the wavenumber associated with index m, and may be either positive or negative.

20.2.2   Alternate form of the discrete Fourier transform

Equations (20.1) and (20.2) are not the only possible definitions for the DFT. An equally valid (though less common) definition for the forward and inverse transforms is

$$U_m = \sum_{j=0}^{N-1} u_j \exp\left(-\iota 2\pi jm/N\right) \tag{20.6}$$

$$u_j = \frac{1}{N} \sum_{m=0}^{N-1} U_m \exp\left(\iota 2\pi jm/N\right), \tag{20.7}$$

with the normalization factor, $1/N$, applied to the inverse transform rather than to the forward transform. **Unfortunately, Numpy uses these alternate forms, (20.6) and (20.7), as the definition of the discrete Fourier transform and inverse transform!** This is important to remember when interpreting the results returned by using the numpy.fft module. This is why the Fourier coefficients calculated using the numpy module may differ by a factor of N compared with those calculated using other software packages.

20.2.3 A DFT example

Here we illustrate the results of taking the DFT of an array (in Sec. 20.4 we will show the Python code used to generate this example). Our array consists of 101 data points with indices ranging from $j = 0$ to 100, and a spacing of one meter. The values of u_j on this grid are generated using the equation

$$\begin{aligned} u_j = 1.5 + \cos(5k_0 j) + 4\cos(15k_0 j) \\ - 3\cos(30k_0 j) + 2.5\cos(40k_0 j) + 2\sin(8k_0 j) \\ + 3\sin(15k_0 j) - 5\sin(35k_0 j), \quad (20.8) \end{aligned}$$

where $k_0 = 2\pi/N$. The data consists of four cosine functions and three sine functions. One of the sine functions shares the same wavenumber as one of the cosine functions. All the other sines and cosines have separate wavenumbers. A plot of u_j is shown in the top panel of Fig. 20.1.

When we take the DFT of u_j it results in 101 spectral coefficients, U_m. Even though the input function, u_j, is real-valued, the spectral coefficients are complex-valued. Plots of the real and imaginary components of the spectral coefficients as functions of wavenumber are shown in the middle and bottom panels of Fig. 20.1. The real part of the spectral coefficients (middle panel) corresponds to the cosine terms in the original function, while the imaginary part (bottom panel) corresponds to the sine terms.

Note that when considering only the positive wavenumbers, there are four spectral spikes on the plot of $\text{Re}(U_m)$ corresponding to the four cosine terms in (20.8), and three spectral spikes on the plot of $\text{Im}(U_m)$ corresponding to the three sine terms. The same is true when looking at the negative wavenumbers only. Each spectral spike corresponds to half the amplitude of the wave given by the corresponding term in (20.8). For example, in (20.8) the term $\cos 5k_0 j$ corresponds to the spikes on the plot of $\text{Re}(U_m)$ at $k = \pm 0.31$ rad m^{-1}. Each

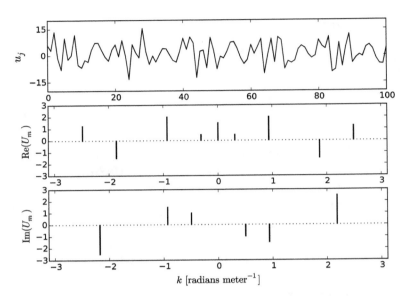

Fig. 20.1: The top panel shows a plot of u_j from (20.8). The middle panel shows the real part of the Fourier coefficients, which correspond to the cosine terms. The bottom panel shows the imaginary part of the Fourier coefficients, which correspond to the sine terms. The horizontal axis is angular wavenumber, k. Note that the negative wavenumbers are redundant, and could be ignored with no loss of information.

of these spikes has amplitude of 0.5, since the original cosine wave in (20.8) had an amplitude of one.

At wavenumber $k = 0$ on the plot of $Re(U_m)$ there is a spike of amplitude 1.5. This corresponds to the very first term in (20.8), which had a constant value of 1.5.

20.2.4   Real versus complex DFTs

For real-valued input u_j the Fourier coefficients for the negative wavenumbers ($k < 0$) are the complex-conjugates[3] of those for the positive wavenumbers ($k > 0$), and do not contain any additional information. It is therefore redundant to compute the coefficients for both positive and negative wavenumbers if the input function is real-valued. Instead, we can just compute the coefficients for the zero and positive wavenumbers. Many software applications, Numpy included, have a *real DFT* function for doing this, which cuts the computational time and memory usage in half compared to using the complex

---

[3]The conjugate of a complex number $z = a + \iota b$ is defined as $z^* = a - \iota b$, and is achieved by simply switching the sign on the imaginary part of the complex number.

DFT. It is important to remember that the coefficients themselves will still be complex-valued even if the input is real-valued. An example of using the Numpy functions for real-valued DFTs is shown in 20.5.

The reason that DFTs accept complex-valued input is that they can actually perform DFTs on two real-valued signals at the same time. If one data set is loaded into the real part of the input and a second data set is loaded into the imaginary part of the input, the resultant Fourier coefficients actually contain information about both input data sets. The information is intertwined, but can be separated using simple formulas. For example, if we had two real-valued datasets denoted by u_j and v_j, we could combine them into a complex-valued array using the formula

$$z_j = u_j + \iota v_j. \tag{20.9}$$

After taking the DFT of z_j we would have the complex-valued Fourier coefficients, Z_{k_m}. The Fourier coefficients corresponding to the two original signals are then recovered using the formulas

$$U_{k_m} = \frac{1}{2}(Z_{k_m} + Z^*_{-k_m}) \tag{20.10}$$

$$V_{k_m} = -\frac{\iota}{2}(Z_{k_m} - Z^*_{-k_m}) \tag{20.11}$$

where Z^* denotes the complex-conjugate of Z, and $k_m \geq 0$.

For practical applications we would like formulas (20.10) and (20.11) expressed in terms of index number, m, rather than wavenumber, k_m. These are

$$U_m = \begin{cases} \frac{1}{2}(Z_m + Z^*_m), & \text{for } m = 0; \\ \frac{\iota}{2}(Z_m + Z^*_{N-m}), & \text{for } 1 \leq m \leq N/2. \end{cases} \tag{20.12}$$

$$V_m = \begin{cases} -\frac{1}{2}(Z_m - Z^*_m), & \text{for } m = 0; \\ -\frac{\iota}{2}(Z_m - Z^*_{N-m}), & \text{for } 1 \leq m \leq N/2. \end{cases} \tag{20.13}$$

20.2.5 The power spectrum

The square of the magnitude of the Fourier coefficients, $P_m = |U_m|^2$, is called the *power*, and a plot of P_m vs k_m is the *power spectrum*. The power spectrum is real-valued, and gives an indication of how much energy is contained at a particular wavenumber. The power spectrum is often the end goal in performing spectral analysis.

20.2.6 Leakage

The discrete Fourier transform assumes that the data sequence is periodic. If the data array u_j has a length of N (indices running from $j = 0$ to $N - 1$), the DFT algorithm assumes that if there were one additional data point at the end of the array, $j = N$, then $u_0 = u_N$. Note that it does not assume that $u_0 = u_{N-1}$.

The assumption of periodicity is an important constraint when taking the DFT of a data set. In the example shown in Fig. 20.1, by defining $k_0 = 2\pi/N$, all the wave components had wavelengths that were perfectly periodic over the domain $0 \leq x \leq N$. If instead we define $k_0 = 2\pi/(N-1)$, then the wavelengths are not quite perfectly periodic, and the Fourier coefficients now are those shown in Fig. 20.2. Instead of having four discrete spikes for the cosine functions and three for the sine functions, the spikes are now smeared over adjacent wavenumbers. This phenomenon is called *leakage*.

To mitigate leakage, data sets are sometimes *tapered* to cause the endpoints to smoothly transition to zero prior to taking the DFT. Three commonly used tapering windows defined for a window of N data points are:

Hanning window: The Hanning window is defined as

$$h[j] = \frac{1}{2} - \frac{1}{2}\cos\frac{2\pi j}{N-1} \text{ for } 0 \leq j \leq N-1.$$

Hamming window: The Hamming window is defined as

$$h[j] = 0.54 - 0.5\cos\frac{2\pi j}{N-1} \text{ for } 0 \leq j \leq N-1.$$

Blackman window: The Blackman window is defined as

$$h[j] = 0.42 - 0.46\cos\frac{2\pi j}{N-1} + 0.08\cos\frac{4\pi j}{N-1} \text{ for } 0 \leq j \leq N-1.$$

Whichever window is used, once it is defined it is multiplied with the dataset to be tapered, and the result will be the tapered dataset. Numpy has functions creating each of these tapered windows, which are appropriately named hanning(), hamming(), and blackman(). Their sole argument is an integer representing the number of data points in the window.

Using a tapered window is not a cure-all for unperiodic data. Windowing decreases the magnitude of the computed Fourier coefficients, and also decreases the spectral resolution. To account for the decreases in magnitude of the Fourier coefficients when using a tapered window it is common to multiply the calculated Fourier coefficients by a factor of 2.0 for the Hanning window, 1.85 for the Hamming window, and 2.8 for the Blackman window.

20.2.7 Noisy data

In many applications the data will contain random noise, which will manifest itself as spikes in the power spectrum. The noise can be suppressed by breaking the data into smaller parts and performing a DFT on each. The Fourier coefficients from each piece of the signal can then be averaged, which will reduce the spikes from the random noise while preserving the spikes from the data signal. An example of this is shown in Sec. 20.5.

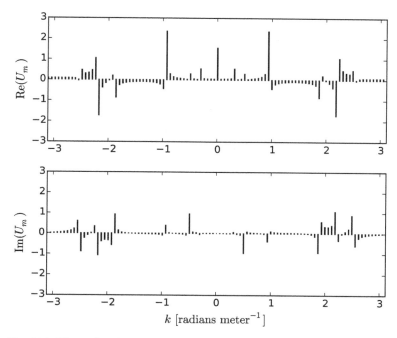

Fig. 20.2: The real and imaginary parts the Fourier coefficients corresponding to a data set whose wave components are not perfectly periodic over the interval $0 \leq x \leq N$, causing *leakage* and a smearing of the Fourier coefficients over adjacent wavenumbers. Compare to Fig. 20.1.

20.3   The numpy.fft Module

In this section we describe the numpy.fft module for calculating discrete Fourier transforms.[4] Recall that the numpy.fft module defines the DFT and inverse DFT using the alternate forms, (20.6) and (20.7), which will result in larger Fourier coefficients (by a factor of N) than will the traditional definitions in (20.1) and (20.2).

20.3.1   Forward and inverse DFT functions

The functions within the numpy.fft module for taking discrete Fourier transforms are:

- fft(u), which takes a complex array, *u*, and returns a complex array of the same dimension as *u* containing the Fourier coefficients. The Fourier

---

[4]We will be using the Numpy numpy.fft module for computing Fourier coefficients. Scientific Python (Scipy) also has a module, scipy.fftpack for computing Fourier coefficients. It is unclear from the documentation what the relation, if any, is between these two modules, or whether one is better.

coefficients are calculated using (20.6). If the DFT of only one data set is to be calculated, the data set is loaded into the real portion of the data array u. If the DFTs of two data sets are to be calculated, one is loaded into the real portion of u, while the other is loaded in the imaginary portion. Equations (20.10) and (20.11) can be used to recover the Fourier coefficients for the two data sets.

- `ifft(U)`, which takes a complex array U representing Fourier coefficients and performs the inverse DFT using (20.7) to return a complex array of the data set.

The fully qualified names of these functions are `numpy.fft.fft()` and `numpy.fft.ifft()`. To avoid having to type all of this in, it is easier to import the `numpy.fft` module aliased as FFT, using the command

```
import numpy.fft as FFT
```

20.3.2   Frequencies/wavenumbers for Fourier coefficients

The frequencies/wavenumbers associated with the Fourier coefficients returned by the `fft()` function are ordered first with the positive frequencies in ascending order, followed by the negative frequencies in descending order. This is explained more fully below, for a signal with N data points, and the array index represented as i. The frequency values depend on whether the number of data points is even or odd.

Even number of data points

- The first element, $i = 0$, contains the Fourier coefficient for the zero frequency (the mean) of the signal.

- The elements $1 \leq i \leq N/2 - 1$ contain the Fourier coefficients for the positive frequencies in ascending order, but do not include the highest frequency (the *Nyquist* frequency).

- Element $i = N/2$ contains the Fourier coefficient for both the positive and negative Nyquist frequencies.[5]

- The remaining elements, $N/2 + 1 \leq i \leq N - 1$, contain the Fourier coefficients for the negative frequencies in increasing order (more negative to less negative).

As an example, for a data input with 10 data points and a spacing of 1 unit, the frequencies would be

$$k = [0,\ 0.1,\ 0.2,\ 0.3,\ 0.4,\ 0.5,\ -0.4,\ -0.3,\ -0.2,\ -0.1].$$

In this instance the Nyquist frequency is ± 0.5.

---

[5]The Fourier coefficients are identical for both the positive and negative Nyquist frequency.

Odd number of data points

- The first element, $i = 0$, contains the Fourier coefficient for the zero frequency (the mean) of the signal.
- The elements $1 \leq i \leq (N-1)/2$ contain the Fourier coefficients for the positive frequencies in ascending order, up to and including the Nyquist frequency.
- Elements $i = (N+1)/2 \leq i \leq N-1$ contains the Fourier coefficients for the negative frequencies in increasing order (more negative to less negative), beginning with the negative Nyquist frequency.

As an example, for a data input with 9 data points and a spacing of 1 unit, the frequencies would be

$$k = [0,\ 0.1\bar{1},\ 0.2\bar{2},\ 0.3\bar{3},\ 0.4\bar{4},\ -0.4\bar{4},\ -0.3\bar{3},\ -0.2\bar{2},\ -0.1\bar{1}].$$

In this instance the Nyquist frequency is $\pm 0.4\bar{4}$.

The fftfreq() helper function

Calculating the frequencies associated with the Fourier coefficients can be confusing, given the different rules for data sets containing an even versus an odd number of data points. Fortunately there is a helper function called `fftfreq(N, d)` that returns the frequencies for a data set having N data points and a data interval of d. This works for both even and odd values of N. Note that if N is even the negative Nyquist frequency is returned, rather than positive Nyquist frequency. This is not an issue since the Fourier coefficient for the negative Nyquist frequency is identical to that for the positive Nyquist frequency.

20.3.3 The fftshift() function

The `fftshift(U)` function takes the input array U of Fourier coefficients and shifts it such that the zero frequency is in the middle of the array. The frequencies then go from most negative to most positive. This is sometimes convenient for making plots of the coefficients. This function can also be used to shift the frequency array returned by the `fftfreq()` function.

The `ifftshift(U)` function is simply the inverse of the `fftshift()` function, putting the zero frequency coefficient at the beginning of the array, followed by the positive frequency coefficients in ascending order and then the negative coefficients in ascending order.

20.3.4 Real DFTs

Since taking the DFT of a purely real input results in redundancy in that the negative frequencies provide no additional information, Numpy provides functions for taking DFTs that return the Fourier coefficients for the positive frequencies only. These functions operate just like those already discussed, but are usually prefaced with an 'r' before the function name. These functions are briefly described here.

- rfft(*u*) takes the DFT of a real-valued signal *u* and returns the Fourier coefficients for the positive frequencies only.

- irfft(*U*) takes the inverse DFT of the Fourier coefficient array *U*, assuming that *U* represents coefficients for the positive frequencies only.

- rfftfreq(*N*, *d*) returns an array of the positive frequencies for the Fourier coefficients represented by the result of rfft(). The arguments *N* and *d* are defined the same as for the fftfreq() function.

If you have a real-valued function and want to take the DFT, whether you use Numpy's complex DFT functions or its real DFT functions is strictly a matter of preference. Either will provide you with the spectrum. Section 20.5 contains an example of using Numpy's real-DFT functions.

20.3.5   Multi-dimensional DFTs

The numpy.fft module also has functions for taking the DFT of data in two or more dimensions. The reader should consult the Numpy documentation for the use of these functions.

20.4   Example Using Numpy's Complex DFT functions

In this section we show the code that was used to generate Fig. 20.1. This code makes use of Numpy's functions for performing DFT on complex-valued input. Keep in mind though that the input we are using is real-valued, and we could have just as easily using the real FFT functions.

```python
import numpy as np
import numpy.fft as FFT
import matplotlib.pyplot as plt

figure, (ax1,ax2,ax3) = plt.subplots(3,1,
                                      sharex=False)

N = 101              # Number of data points
x = np.arange(0,N)   # x values
d = 1.0              # sample spacing

k_not = 2*np.pi/N # wave with wavelength of N

Ac = (1.0,  4.0,  -3.0,  2.5)    # Cosine amplitudes
kc = (5.0,  15.0,  30.0,  40.0) # Cosine multipliers
As = (2.0,  3.0,  -5.0)          # Sine amplitudes
ks = (8.0,  15.0,  35.0)         # Sine multipliers
```

```
# Generate signal
u = 1.5*np.ones(N,dtype=np.float64)
for i, j in enumerate(kc):
    u += Ac[i]*np.cos(j*k_not*x)
    print(j*k_not)
for i , j in enumerate(ks):
    u += As[i]*np.sin(j*k_not*x)
    print(j*k_not)

U = FFT.fft(u)/N  # Spectral coefficients
f = 2*np.pi*FFT.fftfreq(N, d)  # wavenumbers

# Top Panel
ax1.plot(x,u,'k-')
ax1.set_ylim(-20,20)
ax1.set_xlim(0,x[-1])
ax1.set_yticks([-15,0,15])
ax1.set_ylabel(r'$u_j$', size='x-large',
                rotation='vertical')
ax1.set_xlabel(r'$j$')

# Middle Panel
ax2.set_xlim(np.min(f), np.max(f))
ax2.set_ylim(-3,3)
ax2.axhline(0, c='black', ls=':')
ax2.bar(f,np.real(U),width=0.01, bottom=0,
                color='k')
ax2.set_ylabel(r'$\mathrm{Re}(U_m)$', size='large',
                rotation='vertical')

# Bottom Panel
ax3.set_xlim(np.min(f), np.max(f))
ax3.set_ylim(-3,3)
ax3.axhline(0, c='black', ls=':')
ax3.bar(f,np.imag(U),width=0.01, bottom=0,
                color='k')
ax3.set_ylabel(r'$\mathrm{Im}(U_m)$', size='large',
                rotation='vertical')
ax3.set_xlabel(
   r'$k\/\mathrm{[radians\/meter}^{-1}\mathrm{]}$',
                size='large')

plt.show()
```

20.5 DFT Example with Noisy Data

Here we demonstrate an application of spectral analysis to a realistically noisy digital signal, and will also use the real FFT functions from the Numpy library (though we could use the complex ones if we so choose). The example will be for 10 seconds worth of data at a sampling rate of 1000 Hz (1000 samples

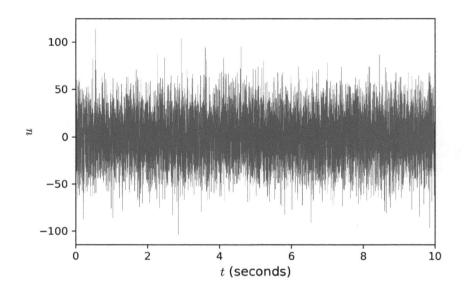

Fig. 20.3: Noisy signal.

per second). The data will consist of two sinusoidal signals at frequencies of 25 and 300 Hz, and amplitudes of 2.5 and 4 units respectively. Onto these signals we impose normally-distributed random noise having zero mean and a standard deviation of 25 units. Here is the code that generates the signal.

```python
import numpy as np
import numpy.fft as FFT
import matplotlib.pyplot as plt
nu = [25, 300] # Frequencies of signals Hz

A = [2.5, 4]   # Amplitudes of signals
N = 10000       # Number of data points
dt = 1e-3   # data interval in seconds

t = np.arange(0, 10, 1e-3)  # Array for time (seconds)

# Clean signal
u = A[0]*np.cos(2*np.pi*nu[0]*t) +
    A[1]*np.sin(2*np.pi*nu[1]*t)

# Add noise to signal
sigma_noise = 25
u += np.random.normal(0, sigma_noise, len(u))  # Noisy
    signal
```

The resulting signal is depicted in Fig. 20.3.

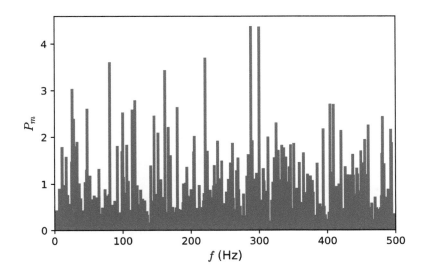

Fig. 20.4: Power spectrum calculated from first 1-second of the signal shown in Fig. 20.3

We will compute the power spectrum from the first 1 second (1000 data points) of the time series. The following code achieves this.

```
Nslice = 1000  #  Number of data points in sample
freqs = FFT.rfftfreq(Nslice, dt)  # + Frequencies
U = FFT.rfft(u[0:Nslice])/Nslice  # coefficients
P = np.abs(U)**2  #  Power spectrum
```

The resulting power spectrum is plotted in Fig. 20.4. Note that although the signals of interest are at 25 and 300 Hz, they are swamped by the large noise values.

If we break the original time series into 10 segments of one second each, find the spectra of each segement, and then average the spectra, we obtain the power spectrum shown in Fig. 20.5. Now the two signals readily show up while the spectra from the noise is considerably reduced. The code to calculate the averaged spectrum is shown below.

```
Uavg = np.zeros_like(freqs, dtype=np.complex_)
count = 0

for i in range(0, len(t), Nslice):
    count += 1
    Uavg += FFT.rfft(u[i:i+Nslice])/Nslice

Uavg /= count
Pavg = np.abs(Uavg)**2
```

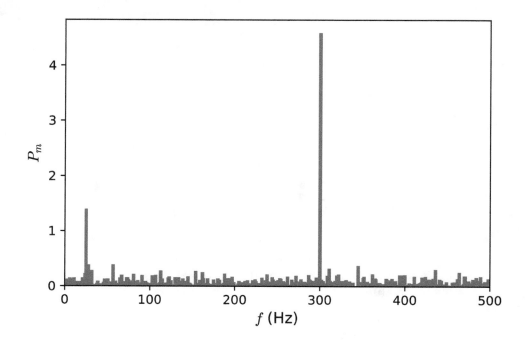

Fig. 20.5: Average of power spectra calculated from 10 one-second intervals of the signal shown in Fig. 20.3

TWENTYONE

MISCELLANY

21.1 Introduction

In this final chapter we briefly survey a few additional topics. We lump them together in a single chapter as our treatment is not so in-depth as to warrant separate chapters for each.

21.2 Interpolation and Resampling

21.2.1 Interpolation

The `scipy.interpolate` module contains functions for interpolating 1-D and 2-D data. For one-dimensional data the function is `interp1d(x, y)`, where x and y are 1-D arrays of equal length, containing the x and y values. By default, linear interpolation is used. The function returns another function that accepts a single x-value or an array of x-values as the argument and returns the corresponding interpolated y-values. For example, if the code

```
from scipy.interpolate import interp1d
import numpy as np
import matplotlib.pyplot as plt
x = np.arange(0, 10)
y = np.array([3.0, -4.0, -2.0, -1.0, 3.0,
              6.0, 10.0, 8.0, 12.0, 20.0])
f = interp1d(x, y)
```

is executed, the new function `f()` can then be used to find the interpolated y-values for any x-value, as shown here:

```
> f(0.2)   # Returns single y value
array(1.6)
> f([0.8, 1.8, 2.8])   # Returns multiple y-values
array([-2.6, -2.4, -1.2])
```

An interpolation using quadratic or cubic splines can be used by setting the keyword kind equal to either 'quadratic' or 'cubic'. For example, if the code in the previous example were run with

```
f = interp1d(x, y, kind='cubic')
```

then the values returned from f() would be interpolated using a cubic spline, and would be

```
> f(0.2)
array(0.18311783)
> f([0.8, 1.8, 2.8])
array([-3.78458811, -2.42311783, -1.36294057])
```

The code example shown below plots a cubic-spline interpolated curve through a series of points, the result being shown in Fig. 21.1.

```
from scipy.interpolate import interp1d
import numpy as np
import matplotlib.pyplot as plt
x = np.arange(0, 10)
y = np.array([3.0, -4.0, -2.0, -1.0, 3.0,
              6.0, 10.0, 8.0, 12.0, 20.0])
f = interp1d(x, y, kind='cubic')
xint = np.arange(0, 9.01, 0.01) # x values
yint = f(xint)  # interpolated y values
plt.plot(x, y, 's', c='k') # Plot data points
plt.plot(xint, yint, '-k')  # Plot interpolated line
plt.show()
```

There are also functions for interpolating in two dimensions. The interested reader should consult the scipy.interpolate documentation for details.

21.2.2 Resampling

The interp1d() function can be useful for resampling of data. For example, say that we have an array

```
> y = np.array([ -2.09304361,   4.56849882,   2.3124046,
                 10.11619563,   9.26474875,   8.89965967,
                  6.73885703,   6.32544084,   8.8194398,
                  5.09976788,   1.06934605,   1.22488735,
                -10.97521148,  -8.19781723,  -7.56523087,
                -11.52108314,  -8.40261767,  -6.53486933,
                 -9.69211778,  -5.53600703,  -0.5670341 ])
```

representing irregularly spaced measurements at locations

```
> x = np.array([0, 3, 8, 15, 17,
                22, 30, 33, 34, 40,
                45, 52, 60, 61, 63,
                70, 80, 85, 87, 95, 102])
```

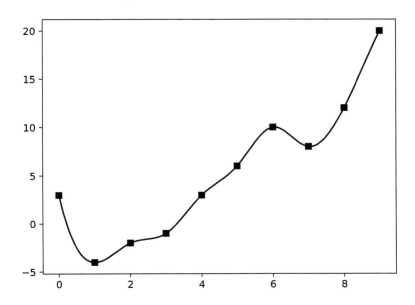

Fig. 21.1: A cubic-spline interpolated line through a series of points.

and we want to resample the data to a regular grid with a grid interval of 5. We first create the interpolation function

```
> f = interp1d(x, data, kind='quadratic')
```

and an array representing our new locations

```
> xnew = range(0, 105, 5)
```

and then create the resampled array

```
> ynew = f(xnew)
```

21.3 Linear Regression

The `scipy.stats` module contains a function titled `linregress(x, y)` which performs linear regression and finds the best-fit line through the data. The function returns a `LinregressResult` object that has five attributes, which are:

- `slope`, the slope m of the regression line.
- `intercept`, the y-intercept of the regression line.
- `rvalue`, the correlation coefficient between the two data sets.
- `pvalue`, the p-value for a two-sided hypothesis test, with a null hypothesis that $m = 0$.
- `stderr`, the standard error.

For example:

```
import numpy as np
from scipy.stats import linregress
x = np.arange(0, 20, 2)
y = np.array([0, 3, 5, 7, 8, 11, 10, 13, 15, 19],
             dtype=np.float_)
results = linregress(x, y)
results
```

returns the result

```
LinregressResult(slope=0.9303030303030304,
    intercept=0.7272727272727266,
    rvalue=0.9841108483092854,
    pvalue=2.735747508748771e-07,
    stderr=0.05934289705323078)
```

which is interpreted as telling us that the best-fit line through the data is given by the equation $y = 0.93x + 0.73$. The data are well-correlated with correlation coefficient of 0.98.

There are other modules that will also perform multivariate regressions. However, they are not simple extensions of the `scipy.stats.linregress()` function. If multivariate regression is needed the user can do a web search to find more information.

21.4   Numerical Differentiation and Integration

Differentiation and integration are fundamental mathematical operations on functions. There are two distinct contexts in which you might want to differentiate or integrate a function:

- Your starting point is a discretely sampled representation of $y = f(x)$ in the form of a 1-D Numpy array, where each element y_i corresponds to regularly spaced values of x_i with interval Δx.

- Your starting point is a Python function that returns a value $y = f(x)$ that is continuous with respect to x.

We will briefly outline approaches to each type of problem in turn.

21.4.1   Discretely sampled functions

Differentiation

When you have a vector of values y_i representing your function, then differentiation is as simple as taking differences between neighboring values and dividing by Δx. This is indeed nothing more than the finite-difference approximation to the derivative, and the assumption (or hope) is that Δx is small enough to capture the important features in the shape of $y(x)$. Mathematically,

$$\frac{dy(x_{i+\frac{1}{2}})}{dx} \approx \frac{y_{i+1} - y_i}{\Delta x}, \tag{21.1}$$

where $x_{i+\frac{1}{2}}$ is the midpoint between x_i and x_{i+1}. The following code illustrates the calculation:

```
import numpy as np
dx = 0.1                     # Interval in x
x = np.arange(0,4*np.pi,0.1) # Array of x-values
y = np.sin(x)                # Array of y-values
dydx = (y[1:] - y[:-1])/dx   # Differentiate y(x)
xp  = (x[1:] + x[:-1])/2     # Recentered x-values
```

Note that **dydx** has one fewer element than **y**, and **xp** has values of x centered between the original elements of **x**.

Simple integration

Likewise, integration can be as simple as taking a sum of the elements over the desired range and multiplying by Δx:

```
y_integral = np.sum(y)*dx
```

This is equivalent to the so-called rectangle rule for integration. Note that we are trading simplicity for a slight loss of precision. The more accurate trapezoidal rule, for example, is the same as the rectangle rule except that the endpoints are multiplied by ½. This difference is usually only important if **len(y)** is small.

More generally, we can take the antiderivative of $f(x)$ by calculating the *cumulative* sum, which returns a vector of the same length as the original y_i. In the code fragment below, we aim to recover the original function y (up to an unknown additive constant) from the derivative **dydx**:

```
yp = np.cumsum(dydx)*dx    # Integrate dy/dx
xpp = (xp[1:] + xp[:-1])/2 # Recentered x-values
yp = yp[:-1]               # Discard last value to
                           # match dimensions of xpp
```

Finally we can compare **y**, **dydx**, and **yp** using the following plotting code whose output appears in Fig. 21.2:

```
import matplotlib.pyplot as plt
plt.plot(x, y, 'y-', lw=5, label=r'$y(x)$')
plt.plot(xp, dydx, label=r"$\frac{dy}{dx}$")
plt.plot(xpp, yp,'k--',label=r"$\int\frac{dy}{dx}dx$")
plt.legend()
plt.show()
```

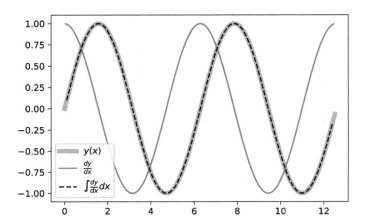

Fig. 21.2: Comparison of the computed derivative dydx of the discretely sampled function y and the antiderivative yp of dydx obtained using the code examples on p. 295.

Higher-order integration methods

More accurate integration of discretely sampled functions may be achieved using the the `scipy.integrate` module. Options include the composite trapezoidal rule (`trapz`), Simpson's rule (`simps`), and the Romberg method (`romb`). The arguments are arrays of the y and x values for the curve (note that the y values come before the x values in the arguments list). For example:

```
> import scipy.integrate as integrate
> import numpy as np
> x = np.arange(0, 20, 2)
> y = np.array([0, 3, 5, 2, 8, 9, 0, -3, 4, 9],
               dtype=np.float_)
> I = integrate.simps(y, x)
> print(I)
64.66666666666666
```

See the `scipy.integrate` documentation for additional integration tools for both sampled and continuous functions.

21.4.2   Differentiation of a continuous function

The `scipy.misc` module contains a function named `derivative()` that returns the derivative of a mathematical function. The derivative is approximated using centered differencing. The usage is

```
derivative(f, x, dx, n=order)
```

where the arguments are as follows:

- f, a Python function or lambda operator[1] that represents the mathematical function to be differentiated. The function or lambda operator takes a single argument or array representing the abscissa or x-values of the mathematical function. For example, if we wish to differentiate the mathematical function $f(x) = e^{-x}$, we would define f using the code

```
f = lambda x: np.exp(-x)
```

- x, either a single value, or a 1-D array of values representing the x coordinates at which the derivatives are to be evaluated.

- dx, an optional argument that specifies the spacing (distance) between data value. The default value is one. Note that if the argument x is an array of values, dx will still default to 1 even if the x values themselves have a spacing different than 1.

- n, the order of the derivative to be taken. For a first derivative $n = 1$, for a second derivative $n = 2$, etc.

The example code below plots the first and second derivatives for the function $f(x) = e^{-x} \sin x$. Note that we have used a spacing between x values of $dx = 0.1$. The results are shown in Fig. 21.3.

```
from scipy.misc import derivative
import numpy as np
import matplotlib.pyplot as plt
f = lambda x : np.exp(-x)*np.sin(x)  # f(x)
x = np.arange(0, 10.1, 0.1)              # x values
first = derivative(f, x, dx=0.1, n=1)   # f'
second = derivative(f, x, dx=0.1, n=2)  # f"
fig, ax = plt.subplots(3, 1, sharex=True)
ax[0].plot(x, f(x))
ax[0].set_yticks(np.arange(-0.05, .45, .1))
ax[0].set_ylabel(r'$f(x)$')
ax[0].set_xlim(0,)
ax[1].plot(x,first)
ax[1].set_yticks(np.arange(-0.4, 1.3, .4))
ax[1].set_ylabel(r'$f\/\prime(x)$')
ax[2].plot(x,second)
ax[2].set_ylabel(r'$f\/\prime\prime(x)$')
ax[2].set_xlabel(r'$x$', size='large')
plt.show()
```

---

[1]See Sec. 8.1.8 for discussion of lambda operators.

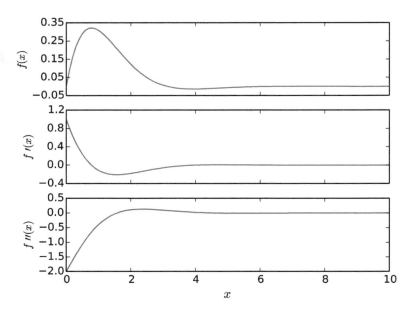

Fig. 21.3: The function $f(x) = e^{-x} \sin x$ and its first and second derivatives.

21.4.3   Integration of a continuous function

The `scipy.integrate` module already discussed in the context of sampled functions contains several functions for performing single, double, and triple definite integrals of known mathematical functions. We discuss only the `quad()` function here, which evaluates a single definite integral using Gaussian quadrature. The usage is

```
quad(f, lower, upper)
```

whose arguments are explained as follows:

- *f*, a Python function or lambda operator that represents the mathematical function to be integrated. The function or lambda operator takes a single argument or array representing the abscissa or *x*-values of the mathematical function. See the discussion of the arguments to the `scipi.misc.derivative()` function in Sec. 21.4.2 for further details.
- *lower*, the value of the lower bound for the definite integral.
- *upper*, the value for the upper bound for the definite integral.

The function returns a tuple of the form (*value, error*), where *value* is the value of the numerical integration and *error* is the estimated absolute error.

As an example, suppose we wanted to evaluate $\int_0^{2\pi} e^{-x} \sin x \, dx$. We could do this as follows:

```
> from scipy.integrate import quad
> import numpy as np
> f = lambda x : np.exp(-x)*np.sin(x)
> I = quad(f, 0, 2*np.pi)
> I
(0.49906627863414593, 6.023731631928322e-15)
```

which gives the value of the integral as approximately 0.499.[2]

21.5 Saving and Loading Arbitrary Python Objects

In Python, everything is an object. Objects can be as simple as single byte variables or as complex as an instance of a user-defined class with numerous attributes and methods. Python provides a convenient way to *pickle* most Python objects by serializing them and writing them to a disk file. They can then be loaded into the same or different program, recovering not only the structure itself but also the states of all attributes at the time the object was pickled.

While there are other ways to accomplish the same thing, the `pickle` module, which is part of the Python standard library, is notable for its ease of use, as illustrated by the following simple example, which saves the dictionary object data to a file *data.pkl*:

```
import pickle

data = {
    'a': "a random string",
    'b': np.array([1,2,3])
}

with open('data.pkl', 'wb') as f:
    pickle.dump(data, f)
```

The following then re-loads the pickled data:

```
import pickle

with open('data.pkl', 'rb') as f:
    data = pickle.load(f)
```

There are many options and variations, and if you decide to use `pickle` for more than simple storage and retrieval of objects for personal use, you should see the online documentation. In particular, note that pickled objects are not guaranteed to be portable between systems, and there are significant security concerns associated with loading pickled objects from untrusted sources.

---

[2]The actual error in this case is of the order of 10^{-17}, which is much smaller than the estimated error. The `quad()` function did a very good job of approximating this integral.

21.6 Physical Constants

The `scipy.constants` module contains a collection of physical constants. The constants are either directly defined within `scipy.contants`, or reside in the CODATA[3] database which can be accessed from the `scipy.constants` module.

In all of the examples in this section we assume the `scipy.constants` module has been imported and aliased as `sc`, using the command

```
> import scipy.constants as sc
```

21.6.1 Constants directly defined in `scipy.constants`

The values of the constants are accessed using their name. For example:

```
> sc.R    # Universal gas constant
8.3144598
> sc.c    # Speed of light in a vacuum
299792458.0
```

Table 21.1 lists the mathematical and physical constants directly defined in the `scipy.constants` module. Although the constants are defined using SI units, users should verify the values before relying on them in their code. Some of the constants can be accessed by alternate names. For instance, `Avogadro` and `N_A` both return Avogadro's number.

21.6.2 Constants in the CODATA database

The constants database contains the recommended values of physical constants from the CODATA database.[4] The values of the constants in the CODATA database are accessed via the `scipy.constants.value(`*name*`)` function, where *name* is the name of the constant. The units in which the constant is defined can be accessed via the `scipy.constants.unit(`*name*`)` function, and the precision via the `scipy.constants.precision(`*name*`)` function. For example:

```
> sc.value('Planck constant')
6.62606957e-34
> sc.unit('Planck constant')
'J s'
> sc.precision('Planck constant')
4.3766519040638443e-08
```

---

[3]National Institute of Standards and Technology Committee on Data for Science and Technology.

[4]When this book was being written the `scipy.constants` module contained the year 2014 recommended values.

Table 21.1: Constants directly defined within the `scipy.constants` module.

Constant	Access Name
π	`pi`
c, speed of light in a vacuum	`c`
μ_0, magnetic constant	`mu_0`
ϵ_0, vacuum permittivity	`epsilon_0`
h, Planck constant	`h`
$\hbar$, reduced Planck constant ($h/2\pi$)	`hbar`
G, universal constant of gravitation	`G`
g, standard gravity	`g`
e, elementary charge	`e`
R, universal gas constant	`R`
α, fine-structure constant	`alpha`
N_A, Avogadro's number	`N_A`
k, Boltzmann constant	`k`
σ, Stefan-Boltzmann constant	`sigma`
Wien displacement law constant	`Wien`
Rydberg constant	`Rydberg`
m_e, electron mass	`m_e`
m_p, proton mass	`m_p`
m_n, neutron mass	`m_n`
Golden ratio	`golden`

The CODATA database is extensive, and even contains constants in non-SI units. For example, to access the Planck constant in units of electronic-volts, we would use the name `'Planck constant in eV s'` as the argument as shown here:

```
> sc.value('Planck constant in eV s')
4.135667516e-15
```

A partial listing of constants contained in the CODATA database is shown in Table 21.2. The complete list can be found at *http://physics.nist.gov/cuu/Constants/index.html*.

21.7 Physical Dimensions and Units

Most scientific computations do not involve pure numbers but rather physical quantities such as lengths, masses, energies, velocities, etc. These quantities cannot be expressed purely numerically without some assumption about the units used. For example, saying that an object has a mass of 1.25 is meaningless unless it is also understood whether kilograms, grams, slugs, or some other

Table 21.2: Selected constants within the CODATA database. Constants are accessed using the constant name as a string for the argument to `scipy.constants.value(`*name*`)`, `scipy.constants.unit(`*name*`)`, and `scipy.constants.precision(`*name*`)`. The complete list of constants can be found at *http://physics.nist.gov/cuu/Constants/index.html*.

Constant name
`'alpha particle mass'`
`'Avogadro constant'`
`'Boltzmann constant in eV/K'`
`'Boltzmann constant in Hz/K'`
`'Boltzmann constant in inverse meters per kelvin'`
`'characteristic impedance of vacuum'`
`'electric constant'`
`'electron charge to mass quotient'`
`'electron mass'`
`'electron mass energy equivalent'`
`'electron molar mass'`
`'elementary charge'`
`'Faraday constant'`
`'Faraday constant for conventional electric current'`
`'fine-structure constant'`
`'Loschmidt constant (273.15 K, 100 kPa)'`
`'Loschmidt constant (273.15 K, 101.325 kPa)'`
`'magnetic constant'`
`'molar gas constant'`
`'molar mass constant'`
`'molar mass of carbon-12'`
`'Newtonian constant of gravitation'`
`'Planck constant'`
`'Planck constant in eV s'`
`'Planck constant over 2 pi'`
`'Planck constant over 2 pi in eV s'`
`'Planck length'`
`'Planck mass'`
`'Planck mass energy equivalent in GeV'`
`'Planck temperature'`
`'proton charge to mass quotient'`
`'proton mass'`
`'proton molar mass'`
`'Rydberg constant'`
`'Rydberg constant times c in Hz'`
`'Rydberg constant times hc in eV'`
`'Rydberg constant times hc in J'`
`'speed of light in vacuum'`
`'standard acceleration of gravity'`
`'standard atmosphere'`
`'standard-state pressure'`
`'Stefan-Boltzmann constant'`
`'Wien frequency displacement law constant'`
`'Wien wavelength displacement law constant'`

Table 21.3: SI Base Units

Physical quantity	Dimension Symbol	Unit name	Unit Symbol
Mass	M	Kilogram	kg
Length	L	Metre	m
Time	T	Second	s
Temperature	°	Kelvin	K
Amount of substance	N	Mole	mol
Current	I	Ampere	A
Luminous intensity	J	Candela	cd

mass unit is intended. Historically, it has been left to the programmer to keep track of which variables have which units and to manually convert between units where necessary. Failures to either track or correctly communicate assumed units have led to disasters, the most expensive and embarrassing of which was the $125 million Mars Climate Orbiter that burned up in the Martian atmosphere following a 10 month journey to the red planet in 1999.

In addition to the potential ambiguity in unit choice, there is a deeper issue that bears on the fundamental correctness of scientific calculation: the absolute requirement for *dimensional consistency*. It is just as invalid to try to add a length to a mass as it is to try to take the logarithm of a negative value. A valid result simply cannot follow from such a calculation, and a violation of dimensional consistency guarantees that the program is incorrect.

Surprisingly, it is only fairly recently that some programming languages have made it possible to detect errors of dimensional consistency as well relieving the programmer of the burden of converting manually between different systems of units. It appears that Python now has the most extensive libraries of any language for managing physical dimensions and units in scientific programs.

There are seven base physical dimensions and associated base units defined in the System International (SI) unit system (Table 21.3). Virtually all derived physical units can be expressed in terms of a pure scale factor combined with appropriate powers of the seven base units.

For example, a velocity is a length divided by time (LT^{-1}), acceleration is a velocity divided by time (LT^{-2}), force is a mass times acceleration (MLT^{-2}), energy is a force times distance (ML^2T^{-2}), and power is energy per unit time (ML^2T^{-3}). From the last of these, we can conclude, for example, that the SI unit for power, or Watt (W) can be expressed in terms of base units as kg m^2 sec^{-3}. A non-SI unit is horsepower (hp), and is equal to 745.7 W or 745.7 kg m^2 sec^{-3}.

To incorporate dimension and unit awareness into a Python program, a module must define a new class of objects that combines the numerical scale factor with a representation of its dimensions. The methods for those objects must throw exceptions when inappropriate operations are attempted, such as adding or subtracting objects having different physical dimensions or passing a dimensioned object to a transcendental function, such as `exp()` or `log()`. When multiplying or dividing two objects, not only must the scale factors be operated on but also the dimensional attributes. Finally, the module should predefine a wide array of both SI and non-SI units and physical constants.

An important exception to the above simple approach is temperature expressed in degrees Celsius or Fahrenheit, as these units require not only a scale factor but also a constant offset from absolute zero. To avoid this significant complication, which requires an otherwise unnecessary extension to the class definition and its associated operators, it is often considered preferable to store all temperatures internally as absolute temperatures (Kelvin or Rankine) and to convert to/from other scales only on input or output.

As of this writing, there are approximately 18 Python libraries that provide some degree of support for physical dimensions and units. Here we highlight just three of the more popular modules: `pint`, `unyt`, and `astropy`. At least superficially, all three behave similarly. You may wish to read the documentation and experiment with these and others to find the module that is the best fit for your application.

The following three short programs perform the same simple calculations and produce essentially the same output. Differences lie mainly in the slightly different ways predefined units are accessed. Note that there is no fundamental difference between a unit and a physical variable, so where necessary, as in the `astropy` example, we can readily define a new unit on the fly.

```python
# pint example

import pint
u=pint.UnitRegistry()
distance1 = 10.5*u.cm
distance2 = 3.3*u.ft
speed = 42.0*u.km/u.hour
print(distance1 + distance2)
# print(distance1 + speed)
```

```python
# unyt example

from unyt import cm, ft, km, hr
distance1 = 10.5*cm
distance2 = 3.3*ft
speed = 42.0*km/hr
print(distance1 + distance2)
#print(distance1 + speed)
```

```
# astropy example

import astropy.units as u
ft = 30.48*u.cm        # no predefined 'foot' in astropy!
distance1 = 10.5*u.cm
distance2 = 3.3*ft
speed = 42.0*u.km/u.hour
print(distance1 + distance2)
# print(distance1 + speed)
```

In all three cases, the first print statement outputs 111.08399999999999 cm. Note, however, that if the final print statement of any of the above programs is uncommented, a runtime error occurs because of the invalid attempt to add a length to a speed.

21.8 Special Mathematical Functions

Finally, we note in passing that the `scipy.special` module contains functions for returning the values of many special mathematical functions, such as Bessel functions, Legendre polynomials, spherical harmonics, etc.[5] However, the documentation for this module is poor-to-nonexistent. Many special functions, such as spherical harmonics, can be defined with different normalizing factors, and it is unclear which form of the definitions are used within the `scipy.special` module. The reader is cautioned to verify the values from any functions from the `scipy.special` module before any serious use. Or better yet, find a newer, more robust and better-documented Python package for special functions.

21.9 Speed and Optimization of Code

Python is an amazingly flexible language with an almost limitless range of easy-to-use add-on modules for performing specialized operations. If there is one serious drawback of using Python, it is in its speed and performance. Since Python is an interpreted language, there is a lot of overhead and it is often too slow for high-end numerical computations such as operational weather prediction models or high-resolution 3-D computational fluid dynamics simulations.

Fortunately, Python also provides a number of ways to bypass the interpreter when necessary, permitting substantial increases in execution speed for certain types of operations, especially those involving arrays and/or nested loops.

---

[5]There are two separate usages for the word *functions* in this sentence. This is unavoidable.

Here we draw your attention to just a few of the most common ways of boosting Python's performance.[6]

21.9.1 Numpy

We have already devoted considerable space to Numpy. We mention it again here simply to reiterate the value of using Numpy whenever possible to *vectorize* operations on arrays. For example, multiplying two matrices in native Python requires element-by-element multiplications inside of two nested loops, with the interpreter painstakingly stepping through and processing each line during each pass through the loop. Using Numpy operators the entire operation is achieved in one line of Python code that passes the arrays to an efficient pre-compiled C-language routine, which is hundreds, or even thousands, of times faster than the the Python interpreter.

In short, when working with numerical data you should always pay heed as to whether the computational task at hand can be recast in terms of vectorized Numpy operations, focusing especially on eliminating explicit loops in the Python code whenever possible (see Sec. 7.8.2).

21.9.2 Numba

Numba is a just-in-time (JIT) compiler that optimizes Python functions at run time. It works on top of the existing Python interpreter, and can significantly speed up numerical calculations with Numpy arrays.

By importing the `jit()` function from Numba

```
from numba import jit
```

and then using the decorator `@jit` prior to defining a function, the first time that the function is called it will be compiled using optimized code. Subsequent calls to the function will then use this optimized compiled code.

As an illustration, let us define a function for calculating the first derivative of a large array,

```
def deriv(y, dx):
    nx = len(y)
    dydx = np.zeros_like(y)
    dydx[0:nx-1] = (y[1:nx]-y[0:nx-1])/dx
```

---

[6]For an excellent look at high-performance Python-centric computing techniques relevant to the physical sciences, see *Effective Computation in Physics* by A. Scopatz and K. D. Huff (published by O'Reilly, 2015).

The arguments are the large array, y, and the spacing of the data points, dx. Here we define some data to be used with our function, a Numpy array containing one million elements of random numbers between 0 and 1000.

```
d = 1000*np.random.random(1000000)
```

We can import the **time** module and then call our function ten thousand times with the code here, which times the execution.

```
start = time.process_time()
nt = 10000
for i in range(0, nt):
    der = deriv(d, 2.0)
stop = time.process_time()
print((stop-start)/nt)
```

Running this code on my system shows that the function executes on average in about 0.01698 seconds. If we place the @jit decorator above the function definition,

```
@jit
def deriv(y, dx):
    nx = len(y)
    dydx = np.zeros_like(y)
    dydx[0:nx-1] = (y[1:nx]-y[0:nx-1])/dx
```

and then run our timing code, it shows that the code is sped up by over 5 times, for an average execution time of 0.00310 seconds.

There is far more to Numba than this brief explanation. More information may be found at *http://numba.pydata.org*.

21.9.3 Cython

For more general operations that cannot be delegated to Numpy, there exists a software project called Cython[7] that, in effect, allows you to:

- Selectively compile portions of your existing Python code to achieve C-like speed,
- Write complete Python extension modules that run as fast as if they were written in C, and/or
- Interface Python with existing C/C++ libraries.

The use of Cython is not an all-or-nothing proposition. For example, you can start with very simple embellishments to your existing Python code to make loops run faster, typically focusing on the most obvious bottlenecks that dominate the overall runtime. With additional effort, entire modules can be optimized. Depending on your level of skill and programming effort,

---

[7]*http://cython.org/*

increases in speed ranging from modest (e.g., 50%) to phenomenal (up to 100x) may be achieved.

This is accomplished by first creating a *.pyx* file with your source code instead of the usual *.py* file. The contents *can* be pure Python, but the benefits come when you add C-like declarations and other Cython features. Cython translates the *.pyx* file into a *.c* file, which is in turn compiled by the system's C compiler (e.g., gcc) into a binary *.so* file that can be loaded into the Python runtime environment.

21.9.4   F2PY

Especially in engineering and the physical sciences, there exists enormous – and still heavily used – bodies of legacy Fortran code devoted to everything from solving large systems of linear equations to predicting the weather. While Fortran is often disparaged and dismissed by computer scientists as an archaic language, later versions incorporate many modern features, and Fortran remains the language of choice for high-performance numerical and scientific computing.

The F2PY project,[8] which recently became part of Numpy, provides a Fortran-to-Python interface generator to allow Python programs to seamlessly call Fortran functions and subroutines and to share module data and COMMON blocks between Fortran and Python. It also allows Fortran or C programs to call Python functions.

A common way to use F2PY is to write efficient Fortran subroutines to handle computationally intensive operations and to call these routines from a top-level Python program that includes I/O and graphic display functionality, basic pre- and post-processing, and other tasks for which Python is better suited.

21.9.5   Parallel processing

The multiprocessing module

Modern supercomputing is built on the concept of parallelism; that is, the ability to take a demanding task, divide it into pieces, and give each piece to a different CPU to operate on. This is only possible when the computations on one piece of the task can be undertaken before the computations on a different piece are finished. Fortunately, there are many classes of computational tasks for which this is true to varying degrees.

Not surprisingly, there are also several Python packages available to facilitate parallel processing from Python, allowing any Python program to take

---

[8]*https://sysbio.ioc.ee/projects/f2py2e/*

advantage of the availability of multiple processors. Since even most laptop computers today have between two and four processors, one does not need a supercomputer to begin experimenting with parallel processing.

In particular, Python comes with a `multiprocessing` module that makes it easy to parcel out multiple copies of a particular task to different subprocesses which are typically, though not necessarily, executing on different processors. For example, consider the following simple function:

```python
import os
def square(x):
    pid = os.getpid()
    print("PID =", pid, ": x =", x)
    return x**2


print(square(2.0))
```

For demonstration purposes we have included a line to print the process ID that the function is executing, as well as the value of the argument it received.

Executing the previous code yields

```
PID = 7450 :  x =   2.0
4.0
```

In this case the PID refers to the process that is running the Python interpreter itself, so there is no parallelism. But we can instead run multiple copies of the task in separate threads as follows:

```python
import multiprocessing
pool = multiprocessing.Pool(processes=2)
result = pool.map(square, [1., 2., 3., 4.])
```

The second line instructs the multiprocessing module to fork two new processes that will be used for subsequent processing (if we happen to have four processors on our computer, we might instead set `processes=4`). The third line sets up our function to be called four times, each time with one of the arguments supplied in the list. The output from our embedded `print()` function is

```
PID = 7453 :  x =   2.0
PID = 7452 :  x =   1.0
PID = 7453 :  x =   3.0
PID = 7452 :  x =   4.0
```

We see that two new processes (7452 and 7453) were created that are distinct from the parent process (7450) and that our function was executed twice, each time with different arguments, within each process. We can print the results of the computation as follows:

```
> print(result)
[1.0, 4.0, 9.0, 16.0]
```

Note that in the above example the four calculations were completely independent of one another – that is, no communication between them was required. We could take advantage of multiple processors simply by executing two copies on one processor and two more on a different processor at the same time.

MPI

Many parallel computations require *message passing* between different processes that are executing simultaneously so as to exchange intermediate results. The *Message-Passing Interface*, known as *MPI*, has become the dominant framework for doing this in the supercomputing world. Not surprisingly, there is an *MPI for Python* package, the mpi4py module. Readers are referred to *https://planet.scipy.org/docs/usrman/index.html* for details.

21.9.6   Timing and benchmarking code

Benchmarking code refers to evaluating how long it takes for a piece of code to execute. This can be accomplished in a couple of ways, using either features from the time module, or the timeit module.

Timing using time module functions

Two functions from the time module that are useful for timing code are perf_counter() and process_time(). By calling either function at both the beginning and ending of a process, and then finding the difference in the values, the elapsed time of the process can be determined.

The two functions differ in whether or not they include the time the system is sleeping, with process_time() not including sleep and perf_counter() including sleep.

The example below uses the process_time() function to compare the time it takes to calculate the differences between adjacent elements of a large Numpy array of one million elements using both explicit and implicit looping.[9]

```
import numpy as np
import time

n = 1000000   # number of data points
d = 1000*np.random.random(n) - 500 # Random data
diff = np.zeros(n-1)   # Array of differences
```

---

[9]Refer to Sec. 7.8.2 for a discussion of implied loops.

```python
# Explicit Loop
start_process = time.process_time()

for i in range(0, len(diff)):
    diff[i] = d[i+1]-d[i]

stop_process = time.process_time()
elapsed = stop_process - start_process

print('Explicit results:')
print('Elapsed time: {0:f} sec'.format(elapsed))

# Implicit Loop
start_process = time.process_time()

diff[0:n-1] = d[1:n]-d[0:n-1]

stop_process = time.process_time()
elapsed = stop_process - start_process

print('Implicit results')
print('Elapsed time: {0:f} sec'.format(elapsed))
```

This code yields the following results,[10]

```
Explicit results:
Elapsed time: 1.923526 sec
Implicit results
Elapsed time: 0.012260 sec
```

showing that implicit loops are much faster than explicit loops.

The timeit module

Another means of benchmarking simple Python expressions is using the `timeit()` function from the `timeit` module. This function accepts Python expressions written as strings and executes them one million times, returning the averaged elapsed time. The **number** keyword can be set to alter the number of executions. The **setup** keyword can be used to specify a Python statement that gets executed one time before benchmarking. This is useful for either importing libraries or setting initial values of variables.

As an example, imagine we are curious as to the relative performance of evaluating an expression such as $(a + b)/c$ versus $(a/c + b/c)$. We could do this with the following code:

---

[10]Results will vary.

```
from timeit import timeit
print(timeit('a/c + b/c',
             setup='a,b,c = 4.5, 6.4, 3.9'))
print(timeit('(a+b)/c',
             setup='a,b,c = 4.5, 6.4, 3.9'))
```

which prints

```
0.06081064100000333
0.0430306189999925
```

showing that the expression $(a + b)/c$ executes faster.

Multiple Python expressions may be used in the `timeit` function. Each separate expression is written as a string with a semicolon at the end. Note that the semicolon is part of the string, and so must be within the quotes. The final statement does not get a semicolon.

For example, the benchmark test described in Sec. 7.5.3, where we timed the creation of an empty array followed by setting all elements to a value of 1.0,

```
a = np.empty((100,100), dtype=np.float_)
a[:] = 1
```

was performed using

```
timeit('a = np.empty((100,100), dtype=np.float_);'
       'a[:] = 1',
       setup='import numpy as np')
```

Code blocks can also be included, and are best illustrated by example. For example, if we wanted to time the code snippet

```
start = 0
end = 10000
while start <= end:
    start +=2
    end += 1
    print(start, end)
```

using values of start = 0 and end = 10000, we could use `timeit()` as follows:

```
print(timeit('while start <= end:'
             'start +=2;'
             'end +=1;'
             'print(start, end)',
             setup='start, end = 0, 10000'))
```

Note there is not a semicolon after the colon indicating the beginning of the code block. Also, note that it is not possible to include multiple statements in the setup variable. Parallel assignment can be used, however, to initialize multiple variables.

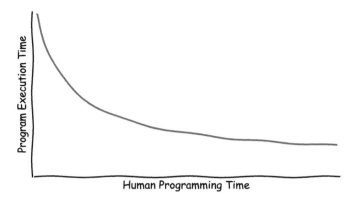

21.9.7   General comments on optimization

Notwithstanding the many tools and techniques available for improving the execution speed of Python programs, there is usually also a cost in terms of code complexity and time spent on learning how to effectively use the tools. Indeed, the human time invested in optimizing a particular program can easily exceed the CPU time saved as the result of that effort. Because CPU time is usually a much less expensive commodity than human time, it does not necessarily pay to obsess over squeezing every last bit of inefficiency out of your code unless the code will see enough repeated use to justify the effort. We schematically illustrate the above principle with one final program whose output appears above.[11].

```python
import matplotlib.pyplot as plt
import numpy as np
plt.xkcd() # emulate the hand-drawn look of XKCD comics
fig = plt.figure()
ax = fig.add_subplot(111)
ax.spines['right'].set_color('none')
ax.spines['top'].set_color('none')
plt.xticks([])
plt.yticks([])
xdata = np.arange(0., 10, 0.1)
ydata = 1. + 10./(xdata + 1.0)
plt.plot(xdata,ydata)
plt.ylim((0,10))
plt.xlim((0,10))
plt.xlabel('Human Programming Time')
plt.ylabel('Program Execution Time')
plt.show()
```

---

[11]See *http://matplotlib.org/xkcd/examples/showcase/xkcd.html* regarding the `pyplot.xkcd()` function.

JUPYTER NOTEBOOKS - A PRIMER

A.1   About Jupyter Notebooks

Jupyter notebooks are a way of running Python code[1] within a web-browser. The browser is opened on a local-host server, so it is not automatically publicly available. Running the code in a web browser has many advantages. The code can be split into *cells* which can be executed independently. The notebook can be saved and shared. And, in addition to running code within the notebook, the cells may also be configured to display text formatted in HTML, Markdown, LaTeX, and others forms. This makes it convenient for documenting code, and for use as a teaching tool.

A.2   Jupyter Lab or Juptyer Notebook?

Jupyter notebooks may be opened and run using the Jupyter Notebook application, which comes standard with Anaconda and Enthought's Canopy installations. A newer application called Jupyter Lab[2] is becoming more popular for opening and running Jupyter notebook files; however, as of this writing there were still some features that work fine in Jupyter Notebook but do not seem to work in Jupyter Lab out-of-the-box, without resorting to

---

[1]Jupyter notebooks can be used with other programming languages besides Python.

[2]Confusion alert! "Jupyter notebook" (lower case) refers to an actual notebook file, while "Jupyter Notebook" (upper case) refers to a specific software application for opening and running Jupyter notebook files. Jupyter Notebook (the application) is being replaced by Jupyter Lab (another application) which will continue to run Jupyter notebook files.

installing additional libraries or updating libraries from the command line.[3] For now, we encourage you to use Jupyter Lab, but if problems arise with your notebooks, try switching back to Jupyter Notebook.

A.3 Opening and Running a Notebook

How to open and run a Jupyter notebook depends on which Python distribution is being used, and how it is configured. It may be as simple as clicking on an existing Jupyter notebook file (file extension *.ipynb.*), which in many applications will automatically open the default web browser, start a localhost terminal, and open the notebook in the web browser. Jupyter Lab is a web-based interface for not only opening and running Jupyter notebooks, but also for opening an interactive console, viewing text files, and other operations, and comes preinstalled in Anaconda. You can also start Jupyter Lab from a terminal window by typing `jupyter lab`. If you do not have access to Jupyter Lab you may type `jupyter notebook` from the terminal window to open the notebook in the older Jupyter Notebook application.

A.3.1 The Jupyter Lab Launcher tab

Starting Jupyter Lab will open a 'Launcher' tab in the web browser. This screen will look something like that shown in Fig. A.1. The left side of the screen contains a pane for navigating through directories. Existing files may be opened by double-clicking them. Most file types may be opened for viewing, but only Jupyter notebook files may be executed.

From the Launcher tab you can also create and open new notebook files, open an interactive console window for running Python commands, open an external terminal, and even open a text file. Each new file is opened as another tab within the Jupyter Lab browser tab. New tabs and new Launchers may be opened from the 'File' menu.

If using Jupyter Notebook instead of Jupyter Lab, then the initial screen on opening will look similar to that in Fig. A.2. The layout of the older Jupyter Notebook application may be recreated in Jupyter Lab (for those suffering from nostalgia) by clicking the 'Help' menu and selecting 'Launch Classic Notebook'.

---

[3]As of November 7, 2019 the two issues we have had are: (1) Using widgets, although a fix is described in Sec. A.8.7; (2) Using `%matplotlib notebook` for Matplotlib plots, which gives a "Javascript Error: IPython is not defined". These issues may very well be fixed by the time you read this.

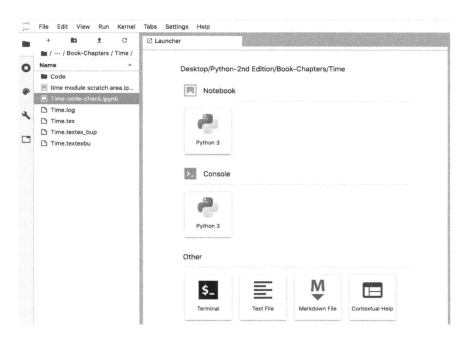

Fig. A.1: Example of Jupyter Lab Launcher tab.

Fig. A.2: Example of Jupyter Notebook navigation screen.

A.3.2   Moving, renaming, and deleting files

Files may be renamed, duplicated, or deleted from the file navigation pane, or using the menus. Moving a file to another directory is a bit more cumbersome, as it is not as simple as clicking and dragging the file to the new location. However, the file may be cut or copied from one directory and pasted into another.

A.4   Changing The Default Directory

This section mainly applies to those using Jupyter Notebook instead of Jupyter Lab. When using the Jupyter Notebook application the initial screen will open up in a preset default directory. This default directory may be changed as follows:

1. Open a terminal window.
2. Type `jupyter notebook --generate-config` which will create a configuration file titled 'jupyter_notebook_config.py'.
3. Navigate to the directory '*user*/.jupyter', where *user* is the user's home directory.
4. Open the 'jupyter_notebook_config.py' file in a text editor and find the line

    `# c.NotebookApp.notebook_dir = ' '`

5. Edit the line to set it to the directory to be used as the new default.

Jupyter Lab seems to remember the most recent directory, and therefore usually opens in a familiar location.

A.5   Working in a Notebook File

The notebook pane contains many menu items and icons which are best learned by exploring them. Many of the buttons and icons have keyboard shortcuts. Some of these keyboard shortcuts are consolidated in Table A.1.

A.6   Cells

There are three main types of cells in a notebook. These are code cells, markdown cells, and raw text cells.[4] The first two are of primary interest to us, and are discussed in more detail in subsequent sections.

The type of cell is set by clicking on the cell and then using the drop-down menu at the top of the notebook to select the cell type. Alternately, the keyboard shortcut ⌜control⌟ + M can be used to set command mode, followed by the additional typing of M for a markdown cell, Y for a code cell, or R for a raw cell.

Cells may be run either individually or collectively. The 'run' or 'arrow' icon will run the selected cell. The 'Run' menu also contains commands for running all cells, running highlighted cells, or running cells above or below a selected cell. Cells may also be run using keyboard shortcuts. Most useful are

---

[4]Older versions allowed a fourth type of cell labeled 'Heading', but these have been deprecated.

Table A.1: Jupyter notebook keyboard shortcuts. For Mac users note that ⟦enter⟧ is the same as return , but control is not the same as command .

Keystrokes + *Keys pressed together* , *Keys pressed in succession*	Result
control + M	Activate command mode
Setting cell type	
control + M , M	Set as markdown cell
control + M , R	Set as raw NBConvert cell
control + M , Y	Set as code cell
Insert, delete, copy and paste cells	
control + M , A	Insert cell above
control + M , B	Insert cell below
control + M , C	Copy selected cells
control + M , D , D	Delete selected cells
control + M , X	Cut selected cells
control + M , V	Paste selected cells below
Run or edit cells	
enter	Edit cell
control + enter	Run cell, move to next cell
control + shift	Run cell, stay in cell
Select multiple cells	
control + M , shift + J	Select cells scrolling down
control + M , shift + ↓	Select cells scrolling down
control + M , shift + K	Select cells scrolling up
control + M , shift + ↑	Select cells scrolling up
Other useful tasks	
control + M , L	Toggle line numbers
control + /	Toggle block comments of selected lines

shift + enter which runs a cell and moves to the next cell, or control + enter which runs the cell but keeps the focus on the cell.

A.6.1 Code cells

Code cells are used to run Python commands and code. Once a code cell is executed any output is displayed immediately below the cell. Although each code cell may be run independently of other cells, if there are variables defined or libraries loaded in previous cells and the current cell needs these variables or libraries, then the previous cell must be run first. Code blocks (such as loops, if-then-elif constructs, function definitions, etc.) may not be split between cells.

A very useful shortcuts for code cells is *block commenting*, in which multiple lines of code may be commented out at once. To do this, simply select the lines of code to be commented and then use the shortcut [control] + [/] . The same procedure may be used to uncomment the lines of code.

Another useful shortcut is [control] + [M] , [L] which displays or turns off the line numbers in the cell.

A.6.2   Markdown cells

Markdown cells allow use of the Markdown language, which is a streamlined markup language for text (full documentation can be found at *https://www.markdownguide.org*). Plain text can be typed directly into a Markdown cell. Markdown's usefulness, however, lies in its ability to format the text, use italics and bold fonts, and to change font sizes and colors. Markdown also allow the use of certain LaTeX and HTML commands. And, URLs and images may also be embedded within Markdown cells. These features are discussed as follows.

Text appearance

Headings: Headings are achieved by the # sign. The more # signs, the smaller the heading. Up to six may be used.

Line breaks and paragraphs: Line breaks are achieved by hitting [enter] . A new paragraph is formed by hitting [enter] twice.

Italics: Single asterisks (*) or underscores (_) indicate the beginning and ending of italicized text.

Boldface: Double asterisks (**) or underscores (__) indicate the beginning and end of boldface text.

Bullets: Bulleted lists are achieved by preceding each bullet point, on a new line, with an asterisk (*), plus sign (+) or a dash (-). There must be a space between the bullet indicator and the first character of the bullet. Nested bullets are achieved by indenting.

Numbered lists: Numbered (ordered) lists are achieved by preceding each item with any digit followed by a period and a space, such as

```
1. first bullet
2. second bullet
9. third bullet
2. fourth bullet
```

which produces the list

```
1.  first bullet
2.  second bullet
3.  third bullet
4.  fourth bullet
```

The example shows that the numbers are completely arbitrary, except that the first bullet must always be preceded by '1. '.

Text color

Text color is changed using HTML tags. For example, the code

```
<font color='blue'>This text is blue</font>, but this
    text isn't.
```

would render the words 'This text is blue' in the color blue.

Math and equations

Math symbols and equations are added using LaTeX-style commands. Dollar signs, $, are used at the beginning and end of inline math symbols and equations. For display-style equations, which are on their own line, double dollar signs, $$, are used at the beginning and ending. Appendix B describes some of the more commonly used LaTeX symbols.

Embedding images

Images are embedded in a Markdown cell by using a command of the form `![caption](path "title")` where

- *caption* is the image caption, and is text without quotes.
- *path* is the path to the image, without quotes.
- *"title"* is a string (with quotes) containing the image title (the title is optional).

The path may be either the path to a locally stored image, or it may be a URL to a remote image.

Embedding URLs

Hyperlinks to URLs are embedded by including the link between angle brackets, such as <http://www.sundogpublishing.com>.

A.7 Working with Matplotlib

Plots generated using the Matplotlib library can be displayed as output of code cells. When using Matplotlib for plotting in notebooks it must be specified whether the plots will open in an external window, or will be embedded within the notebook. Embedded plots also have the option of being static or interactive. The type of plot is set through the use of *magic commands* within a code, which are commands preceeded by a % sign. The magic commands for the three different types of plots are:

`%matplotlib` This specifies that the plots will be created in an external, interactive window. However, sometimes this does not work and the plot still appears in the notebook. If restarting the kernel doesn't fix the issue, try using `%matplotlib qt`, restart the kernel again, and rerun.

`%matolotlib inline` This specifies that the plots will be an embedded, static plots.

`%matplotlib notebook` This specifies that the plots will be embedded, interactive plots.[5] When changing the type of plot from one of these choices to another it is usually necessary to restart the Python kernel in order to get the change to take effect. Restarting the kernel is accomplished from the 'Kernel' menu of the notebook.

When using either external plots, or embedded static plots, each new plot will appear below the cell in which it was created. This is not the case when using embedded, interactive plots. Plotting commands in cells appearing below a plot will end up taking effect in the original plot. To achieve independent, embedded, interactive plots when using `%matplotlib notebook` it is necessary to create a new `Figure` object for each new plot. One easy way of doing this is to simply use the command `plt.figure()` at the beginning of the code cell in which the new plot is to be created. This will sever the tie with the old plot, and set the current figure to the new plot.

A.8   Widgets

Interactive widgets such as sliders, check boxes, and dropdown menus can be created within notebooks, and can be linked with Python code. We can even create plots that respond to sliders, check boxes, and dropdown menus.

In order to use widgets we need to import the `interact()` function from the `ipywidgets` library, using the command

```
from ipywidgets import interact
```

The `interact()` function allows us to interact with user-defined or built-in Python functions, and uses widgets such as sliders, check boxes, and dropdown menus to provide input to the functions.

Note: If you are using Jupyter Lab and experience problems with widgets either not rendering or not working, see Sec. A.8.7 for a possible solution.

---

[5]As of November 7, 2019 using `%matplotlib notebook` gives the following error when plotting: "Javascript Error: IPython is not defined"

A.8.1 Sliders

As a simple example using a slider we first define a function named `p_of_z()` which takes in an altitude in meters and returns the pressure at that height using the formula

$$p(z) = p_0 \exp\left(-\frac{z}{H}\right)$$

where $H = 8000$ meters and $p_0 = 1013.25$ hPa. The code for this function is

```
def p_of_z(z):
    H = 8000   # scale height (m)
    p0 = 1013.25   # surface pressure (hPa)
    return p0*np.exp(-z/H)
```

We link this function to a slider by calling `interact()` as follows:

```
p = interact(p_of_z, z=(0, 12000, 250))
```

This creates a slider in the output of the code cell.

```
1  p = interact(p_of_z, z=(0, 12000, 250))
```

z ⚬————— 8000

`372.75384376696394`

In the code the slider is defined by a tuple that gives the minimum and maximum values for the variable z, along with a striding index. As the slider is moved interactively, the value of z changes, and the returned value of pressure appearing below the slider changes commensurately.

In the example we saved the output of the function to the variable p, but we do not have to explicitly assign the output. The widget would still have worked if we had simply written

```
interact(p_of_z, z=(0, 12000, 250))
```

For functions requiring multiple inputs we could define multiple sliders. For instance, the code

```
def p_of_z(z, p0, H):
    return p0*np.exp(-z/H)

p = interact(p_of_z,
             z=(0, 12000, 250),
             p0=(950, 1050, 5),
             H=(7500, 8500, 5))
```

would create individual sliders for z, $p0$, and H.

A.8.2   Shorthand using a decorator

The decorator `@interact()` may be used as a shorthand for creating widgets. For example, we could create the slider from our first example using the code

```
@interact(z=(0, 12000, 250))
def p_of_z(z):
    H = 8000   # scale height (m)
    p0 = 1013.25   # surface pressure (hPa)
    return p0*np.exp(-z/H)
```

Whatever function is defined immediately after the decorator is passed automatically as the argument to the decorator. Any widgets must be defined within the arguments of the decorator. Decorators in general are discussed in Sec. 8.4 of Chapter 8.

One disadvantage to using the decorator is that we lose the ability to save the output of the function to a variable.

A.8.3   Check boxes

Check boxes are created from Boolean variables. As an example, consider this function

```
def circle_area(dis, radius=True):
    if not radius:
        dis /= 2
    return np.pi*dis**2
```

which calculates the area of a circle based on an input length that may be either a radius or a diameter. If the keyword `radius` is `True` then the input distance is a radius. Otherwise, it is a diameter. Running the code

```
a = interact(circle_area,
             dis=(0, 100), radius=True)
```

results in a slider and a checkbox for the radius. If the box is selected, then `radius=True`, and if the box is not selected then `radius=False`.

```
1  a = interact(circle_area,
2               dis=(0, 100), radius=True)
```

dis ⬤———— 50

☑ radius

7853.981633974483

A.8.4 Text boxes

Text boxes are created by using a string variable. For example, the code

```
@interact(string='')
def reverse(string):
    return string[::-1]
```

creates a text box, and displays the contents of the text box in reverse.

A.8.5 Dropdown menus

Dropdown menus are created from lists. For example, the code below creates a slider for lengths in meters, and a dropdown menu for selection of conversion units. The output of the function is the length in the new units.

```
@interact(units=['inches','feet', 'yards'],
        meters=(0.01, 50, 0.01))
def from_meters(meters, units):
    if units=='inches':
        return meters*39.701
    elif units=='feet':
        return meters*3.28084
    else:
        return meters*1.09361
```

A.8.6 Interactive plots

One very nice feature of using widgets is that we can change Matplotlib plots on the fly. The code below generates a plot of a sine or cosine wave, with the amplitude and wavelength set by sliders, and a check box for selecting sine or cosine.

```
x = np.linspace(0,20,100)
fig = plt.figure()
ax = plt.subplot(111)

@interact(A=(-10,10,0.5),
        wl=(2,20,0.5),
        sine=True)
def plot_wave(A=5, wl=10, sine=True):
    if sine:
        y = A*np.sin(2*np.pi*x/wl)
    else:
        y = A*np.cos(2*np.pi*x/wl)
    ax.clear()  # Clears axes before next plot
    ax.set_xlim(x[0],x[-1])
    ax.set_ylim(-12,12)
    ax.plot(x,y)
```

A few notes about this example:

- We set defaults for the slider values in the function arguments.
- We used the `clear()` method to clear the plot for each call to the function.

A.8.7   If widgets do not work in Jupyter Lab

There was a change in how `ipywidgets` are handled in Jupyter Lab vs. Jupyter Notebook. If widgets are not displaying in Jupyter Lab you can try the following, which comes from *https://ipywidgets.readthedocs.io/en/latest/user_install.html#installing-the-jupyterlab-extension*.

Close Jupyter Lab, and from a terminal window type

```
conda install -c conda-forge nodejs
```

and after it finishes processing, type

```
jupyter labextension install
    @jupyter-widgets/jupyterlab-manager
```

Reopen Jupyter Lab, and hopefully the widgets will work properly.

LATEX QUICK REFERENCE

B.1 Overview

This appendix is a quick reference to common LATEX commands and symbols. LATEX-like commands are used for text rendering of Greek and mathematical symbols in both Matplotlib (Sec. 10.9.7) and for Markup cells in Jupyter notebooks (Appendix A). Not all LATEX commands and symbols are available in both applications.

In Matplotlib the LATEX commands are inserted between dollar sign characters (\$). Raw strings (see Sec. 3.1.3) are used so that the special characters used in the LATEX-like markup language are not misinterpreted as special symbols.

In Jupyter notebook Markup cells, single dollar signs, \$, are used at the beginning and end of inline math symbols and equations. For display-style equations, which are on their own line, double dollar signs, \$\$, are used at the beginning and end.

A complete reference for all the math symbols and characters supported in Matplotlib can be found at *http://matplotlib.org/users/mathtext.html*. For LATEX in general, an outstanding reference is *More Math Into LATEX* by G. Grätzer.

B.2 Greek Letters

Greek letters are rendered by simply typing the name of the letter after a backslash \ character. For example, \alpha produces α, \beta produces β, etc. Uppercase letters are produced by capitalizing the first character of the letter's name. So, while \psi produces ψ, \Psi produces Ψ.

Some Greek letters (epsilon, theta, pi, rho, sigma, and phi) have variations. These are accessed by adding 'var' to the front of their names. For example, \phi and \varphi show as ϕ and φ respectively.

B.3   Operators

Some mathematical operators and examples are

Command	Purpose	Example	Result
\sqrt{ }	$\sqrt{\ }$	\sqrt{2 \pi}	$\sqrt{2\pi}$
\sqrt[]{}	Other roots	\sqrt[3]{2 \pi}	$\sqrt[3]{2\pi}$
\times	$\times$		
\nabla	∇		
\cdot	$\cdot$		

B.4   Fractions

Fractions are formed as shown by the example \frac{1}{2\pi}, which produces $\frac{1}{2\pi}$. This is called an *inline* fraction, because the result is sized to fit within a line of text. For larger-sized fractions use \dfrac. An example is \dfrac{1}{2\pi}, resulting in $\dfrac{1}{2\pi}$.

B.5   Superscripts and Subscripts

Superscripts are formed using the ∧ character, while subscripts are formed using the _ character. The single character immediately following will be the affected character. To superscript or subscript multiple characters, group them within braces. Here are some examples.

Example	Result
e^\pi x	$e^{\pi}x$
e^{\pi x}	$e^{\pi x}$
V_{i,j}	$V_{i,j}$

B.6   Escaping Special Characters

There are many special characters in LATEX. Among these are the carat ∧, the underbar _ , and braces { }. If you want to render a literal version of these characters, then they must be escaped. The underbar and braces are both escaped by putting a backslash \ before them, _, \{, and \}. The tilde character is more difficult to escape from, as the syntax \~ will place the tilde over the next character in some implementations, while in others it does nothing. If a literal tilde is needed you can try to use \textasciitilde. This works in newer versions of Matplotlib, but does not work for Markup cells on our current Jupyter Notebook implementation.

B.7   Integrals and Summations

Integrals and summations are formed as shown below. For definite integrals, and for showing the limits of summations, the subscript and superscript symbols are used. However, this may not place the limits in the desired location relative to the symbol. By using the `\limits_{}^{}` construct (not available in Matplotlib) the limits are placed above and below the symbol, instead of to the side. The functionality and final appearance may differ depending on your installation.

Command	Purpose	Example	Result
`\sum`	Sum, $\sum$		
`\int`	Integral, $\int$		
`\oint`	Path integral, $\oint$		
`\int_{}^{}`	Definite integral	`\int_{a}^{b}`	$\int_a^b$
`\sum_{}^{}`	Sum with limits	`\sum_{10}^{50}`	$\sum_{10}^{50}$
`\limits_{}^{}`	Limits (alternate)	`\int\limits_{10}^{50}`	$\int\limits_a^b$
		`\sum\limits_{10}^{50}`	$\sum\limits_{10}^{50}$

B.8   The Degree Symbol

Special mention is made of the degree symbol, $^\circ$, since it is accomplished differently in Matplotlib vs Markup. In Matplotlib you can simply use `\degree F` in order to render $^\circ F$. However, in Markup this is accomplished by `^\circ F`.

B.9   Other Symbols

A few more common symbols and operations are shown here.

Command	Purpose	Example	Result
`\partial`	Partial derivative	`\partial f`	∂f
`\vec{}`	Vector	`\vec{V}`	$\vec{V}$
`\overline{}`	Overbar	`\overline{u'v'}`	$\overline{u'v'}$
`\tilde{}`	Tilde	`\tilde{h}`	$\tilde{h}$
`\hat{}`	Hat	`\hat{k}`	$\hat{k}$
`\cdots`	Centered dots, $\cdots$	`1, 2, 3, \cdots`	$1, 2, 3, \cdots$

B.10   Mathematical Functions

Common mathematical functions in LaTeX are mostly self-explanatory.

- Trig functions: `\cos`, `\sin`, `\tan`, `\sec`, etc.

- Inverse trig functions: `\arccos`, `\arcsin`, `\arctan`, etc.

- Hyperbolic functions: `\cosh`, `\sinh`, `\tanh`.

- Logarithms: `\ln` and `\log`.

- Exponent: `\exp`.

B.11   Scalable Symbols

Sometimes parentheses, brackets, or braces are not large enough. For example, `(\dfrac{\partial T}{\partial V})_p` renders as $(\frac{\partial T}{\partial V})_p$, in which the parentheses look too small.

The commands `\left(` and `\right)` produce parentheses that scale to the equation. Using these, the code `\left(\dfrac{\partial T}{\partial V}\right)_p` produces $\left(\dfrac{\partial T}{\partial V}\right)_p$, which looks much better.

Brackets and braces may also be scaled in this manner, using `\left[` and `\right]` for brackets, and `\left\{` and `\right \}` for braces.

B.12   Forcing Whitespace

To force whitespace to be displayed, use a ~ character in Markdown, or a backslash followed by a slash, `\/`, in Matplotlib. Multiple characters may be used in succession to achieve the desired amount of whitespace.

B.13   Text Appearance

Strings of characters appearing in LATEX equations are rendered in italics with slightly odd spacing under the assumption that a string of letters is supposed to represent a product of individual variables and that whitespace should be ignored. As an example, the code
`$\sin\varphi over \cos\varphi is \tan\varphi.$`
renders as "sin $\varphi over$ cos φis tan φ."

If true text is desired in a mathematical expression we can either exit math mode for the text parts, and then reenter math mode as shown here
`$\sin\varphi$ over $\cos\varphi$ is $\tan\varphi$.`,
which results in "sin φ over cos φ is tan φ."

However, another way to do this is to use the `\text{}`, `\textit{}`, or `\textbf{}` functions within the math environment. These create plain text, italicized text, or boldface text, respectively. In our prior example we could have used
`$\sin\varphi \text{ over }`
`\cos\varphi \text{ is } \tan\varphi$.`
which prints as "sin φ over cos φ is tan φ."[1]

---

[1] As of the time this was written, the `\text`, `\textit`, and `\textbf` commands did not work in our version of Matplotlib.

The \mathbf{} function renders text in nonitalicized, bold font. This is useful for representing matrices. For example, \mathbf{M} produces **M**.

B.14 Final Note

The use and implementation of LaTeX formatting in Matplotlib and Markup is evolving. Depending on which versions of these packages you are using, some of the features described may or may not work. It is therefore always best to use the most up-to-date, stable versions of these packages.

Printed in the USA
CPSIA information can be obtained
at www.ICGtesting.com
LVHW071240101223
766124LV00008B/819

9 780972 903356